Introduction to Factor Analysis

Benjamin Fruchter

Associate Professor
Department of Educational Psychology
The University of Texas

D. VAN NOSTRAND COMPANY, INC.

Princeton, New Jersey

New York • Toronto • London

D. VAN NOSTRAND COMPANY, INC.
120 Alexander St., Princeton, New Jersey (*Principal office*)
24 West 40 Street, New York 18, New York

D. VAN NOSTRAND COMPANY, LTD.
358, Kensington High Street, London, W.14, England

D. VAN NOSTRAND COMPANY (Canada), LTD.
25 Hollinger Road, Toronto 16, Canada

————————

Library of Congress Catalog Card No. 54-6275
Printed in the United States of America

Preface

The increasingly widespread interest in, and application of, factor analysis in recent years has made it desirable that the method be introduced earlier in the student's statistical training than has usually been the case. There are a number of excellent advanced treatments of the subject such as Thurstone (1947c),[1] Holzinger and Harmon (1941), Thomson (1951), and Cattell (1952a). These treatments have been found difficult by many otherwise competent students because of the mathematics and notation involved. It is hoped that this book will serve as an introduction to the subject and as a steppingstone to these more advanced texts. An attempt has been made to introduce and develop the concepts of factor analysis in logical order.

In general, a background in high school mathematics only is called for, although a course in analytical geometry is helpful. The theory of matrices, the mathematical basis for factor analysis, is introduced in Chapter 3. The student should also have a background in statistics, through multiple correlation, and sufficient background in some content area to appreciate the need for the application of the factorial methods to that area.

A wide variety of methods and procedures is available in factor analysis. Only those methods which, in the author's experience, have been found to be the most generally useful and practical have been included in this introductory book. Possible exceptions are some of the methods in Chapter 8 (e.g., direct rotation) which are presented as much for their theoretical interest as for their practical value. Exercises and answers have

---

[1] See Bibliography at end of book for complete reference.

v

been provided so that the book can be used for self-instruction by those persons who do not have access to an organized class.

The writer has found it advisable to have his students obtain a broad background in the applications and methods pertinent to their fields of interest by having them read widely in the literature, and an extensive bibliography has been included to serve as a guide to recent contributions.

Acknowledgments to various authors and publishers have been made through the book. Special acknowledgments, however, are made to the University of Chicago Press, the American Psychological Association, and publishers of the following journals for permission to quote from their publications: *Journal of General Psychology, Journal of Genetic Psychology, Journal of Experimental Education, Journal of Personality, Psychometrika, Journal of Comparative Psychology, American Journal of Psychology.*

Many people have contributed to the development of this book. The writer is especially grateful to Professor J. P. Guilford for instruction, encouragement, and editorial guidance; to Professor L. G. Humphreys for first interesting him in factor analysis and for reading portions of the manuscript; to Professor L. L. Thurstone for his many original contributions to factorial methods; and to his students for constant stimulation. He owes a special debt of gratitude to his wife, Dorothy A. Fruchter, for continued interest and assistance in the preparation of the manuscript and drawing of the figures and to Annette Stewart for typing assistance.

Foreword

Since the time when that great innovator, Charles Spearman, presented to the world his theory and method of factor analysis, the use of factor-analytic procedures has increased at a rapid rate. This trend was given a sharp acceleration in the United States by Thurstone's generalization and extension of factor theory and methods with the publication of his important contribution, *Vectors of Mind,* in 1935.

More and more it is being realized that the end product of science is in the form of statements concerning the interrelationships between things. It is also realized that the most fruitful type of concept of the things related is in the form of variables or dimensions. The major problems are therefore correlation problems. Where the appropriate variables are readily observable or easily inferred from objective data, one may proceed to the discovery of the interrelationships. In psychology and the social sciences, where the number of potential variables is very large and the useful variables that we need for economical and dependable descriptive purposes are overlaid with multiplex manifestations, the demand for some method that will facilitate the discovery of those underlying variables is very great. It is in the fulfillment of this objective that we find factor-analysis methods to be of greatest value.

The factorial methods were instituted originally for the study of the basic or underlying variables needed to account for individual differences in measurements of abilities or aptitudes in terms of test scores. It was eventually realized that the methods could also be fruitfully used to discover underlying dimensions of temperament, interests, and attitudes—in fact, dimensions underlying any aspect of personality, including morphological and physiological traits. The extension of factorial methods to variations known as the Q-technique and the P-technique has offered promising tools for the understanding of personality structure in individuals. This has appealed to some clinical psychologists who seek a more rigorous way of approaching general principles of personality which keep close to the study of individuals. Factor theory is as yet the most promising source of a mathematical model for a comprehensive, rigorous theory of personality structure.

Problems in experimental psychology have also been attacked from the factor-analysis approach, including the problem of sensory attributes and problems of the variables of emotion, humor, and esthetic reactions. Problems of social behavior and of industrial morale have been approached through factorial methods. Outside the field of psychology there have been many applications; to problems of biological growth, to voting behavior of legislators and judges, to educational achievement, to criteria of job performance, and to allergy reactions.

As courses for the instruction of students in the ideas and ways of factor analysis have been introduced one by one, the need for a simple introduction has increased. In writing this volume Professor Fruchter has kept in mind the beginner in the study of factor analysis. Fruchter's extensive experiences in the methods have fitted him well for this assignment. The clear and succinct exposition of theory and methods will undoubtedly be welcomed especially by those who have not been favored by the opportunity to acquire the mathematical background necessary for the expert's grasp of the subject. The selection of techniques to be presented seems to include those that are most likely to be needed by the average investigator who utilizes factor analysis in his research. The step-by-step demonstrations should be relatively easy to follow. It is anticipated that this volume will be useful as a ready handbook for the investigator as well as a textbook for the beginner in factor analysis.

J. P. GUILFORD

Contents

Preface   v

Foreword   vii

1. INTRODUCTION   1
   The Nature of Factor Analysis   1
   Preliminary Concepts   4
   Spearman's Two-factor Theory   6
   Holzinger's Bi-factor Theory   10

2. CLUSTER ANALYSIS   12
   Cluster Analysis with Fictitious Data   13
   Problems   17

3. MATHEMATICS ESSENTIAL FOR FACTOR ANALYSIS   18
   Matrix Algebra   18
      Definition of a Matrix   18
      Transpose of a Matrix   19
      Determinants   21
      Determinant of a Matrix   21
      Minors of a Determinant   21
      Rank of a Matrix   22
      Some Common Types of Matrices   23
      Matrix Multiplication   24
      Inverse Matrix   26
   Matrix Geometry   31
      Geometric Representation of a Correlation
       Coefficient   31
      Graphical Representation of a Table of
       Intercorrelations   32
      Graphical Representation of a Table of
       Correlations in Two Dimensions   33

Reproducing the Table of Correlations from the
   Factor Matrix   35
Graphical Representation of a Correlation Matrix
   in Three Dimensions   35
Rotation of Reference Axes   38
Summary of Vector Representation of the
   Correlation Matrix   41
Problems   43

4. BASIC ASSUMPTIONS OF FACTOR ANALYSIS   44
First Assumption   44
   Types of Variance   45
Second Assumption   47
Problems   50

5. DIAGONAL AND CENTROID METHODS OF FACTORING   51
The Diagonal Method   52
   Numerical Example   52
   Summary of Routine for Diagonal Method   57
The Centroid Method   59
   Computation of the First Centroid Loadings   61
   Computation of the Residual Correlation Matrix   62
   Reflection   64
   Minimum Number of Variables to Determine r
      Common Factors   68
Example of an Analysis of an Eleven-variable
   Problem by the Centroid Method   69
   Description of Tests   69
   First Centroid Factor Loadings   71
   Second Centroid Factor Loadings   73
   Third and Subsequent Centroid Factors   76
   Criteria for Sufficient Factors   77
   Application of the Criteria for Sufficient Factors   82
   Checking the Centroid Loadings   84
Problems   85

6. MULTIPLE-GROUP AND PRINCIPAL-AXES METHODS OF
   FACTORING   87
The Multiple-group Method   87

Numerical Example 88
Calculation of the Inverse of a Triangular Matrix 94
The Orthogonal Factor Loadings 98
Principal-axes Method 99
Numerical Example 99
Other Methods of Extraction of Factors 104
Problems 105

7. METHODS OF ROTATION: ORTHOGONAL AXES 106
Simple Structure and Positive Manifold 109
Graphical Rotation 114
Rotation of the Eleven-variable Example 115
Calculating the Transformation Matrix 121
Calculating the Rotated Values 127
Problems 131

8. METHODS OF ROTATION: OBLIQUE AXES 132
Single-plane Method Applied to the Eleven-variable
Example 133
Direct Rotation to Primary or Simple Structure 140
Eleven-variable Example 142
Problems 148

9. INTERPRETATION OF FACTORS 149
Eleven-variable Example 149
Reporting a Factorial Study 153
Problems 154

10. APPLICATIONS IN THE LITERATURE 155
Factor Analysis of Conditioned Response Indices 156
Is There a General-intellective Factor in
Performance Tests? 157
Learning Dynamics in Bright and Dull Rats 159
An Analysis of Criterion Measures 162
Direct Rotation to Primary Structure in the Study of
Personality Factors Related to Success in Student-
teaching 165
Relative Roles of Central and Peripheral Factors in
Pitch Discrimination 169
Second-order Analysis of Reasoning Tests 172

Obverse Analysis of Supreme Court Voting Records   176
Obverse Factor Analysis of Prepsychotic Personality
   Traits   179
P-technique in the Study of Personality   186

11. SOME GENERAL CONSIDERATIONS   192
   Simple Axes and Primary Axes   192
   Oblique vs. Orthogonal Solutions   194
   Frequently Identified Factors   196
   Influences on Factor Loadings   199
      Selection of the Sample   199
      Background, Training, Experience, and Set   200
      Type of Correlation Coefficient   201
      Experimental and Linear Dependence   201
      Time Limit and Scoring Formula   201
   Experimental Designs   202
   The Estimation of Factor Scores   204
   Mechanical Aids to Computation   205
   Next Steps in Factor Analysis   206

APPENDIX—CALCULATION OF THE ESTIMATED FACTOR
      LOADINGS OF A VARIABLE NOT INCLUDED IN THE
      ORIGINAL ANALYSIS   209

BIBLIOGRAPHY   221

ANSWERS TO PROBLEMS   267

INDEX   273

CHAPTER 1

Introduction

THE NATURE OF FACTOR ANALYSIS

IN THE continuing effort of science to establish theoretical systems which will account for observed phenomena, identification and measurement of basic variables are of paramount importance. Almost every field of science has set up a number of classificatory categories which can be described and measured. Factor analysis starts with a set of observations obtained from a given sample by means of such *a priori* measures. It is a method of analyzing this set of observations from their intercorrelations to determine whether the variations represented can be accounted for adequately by a number of basic categories smaller than that with which the investigation was started. Thus data obtained with a large number of *a priori* measures may be explained in terms of a smaller number of reference variables.

Psychologists and educators, for example, have tried to generalize concerning the supposed basic dimensions of human behavior and have adopted such well-known trait-concepts as memory, imagination, judgment, etc. In the field of mental testing there has been an outpouring of tests of general intelligence and of specialized abilities such as clerical, mechanical, or medical aptitude. With regard to intelligence, factor analysts might be interested in determining whether the individual differences represented by intelligence-test scores are attributable to a single source of variation or whether they represent the operation of a combination of several mental traits, such as reasoning, verbal, and numerical abilities which individuals may possess in varying combinations. They might also inquire whether the various types of specialized ability that have been distinguished are really different or whether they represent conglomerations of a set of basic factors which run through them, in terms of which they can all be described, and which would make their similarities and differences more apparent. Similarly, in the area of clinical psychology a large number of diagnostic categories have been adopted by psychiatrists, clinical psychologists, and others to classify neurotic and psychotic behavior disorders. The role of factor analysis here might be to determine whether these classification systems can be verified with empirical data for specific populations, or whether they overlap to such an extent as to call for a reordering and redefinition of the sets of diagnostic categories.

Factor analysis provides a mathematical model which can be used to describe certain areas of nature. A series of test scores or other measures are intercorrelated to determine the number of dimensions the test space occupies, and to identify these dimensions in terms of traits or other general concepts. The interpretations are done by observing which tests fall on a given dimension and inferring what these tests have in common that is absent from tests not falling on the dimension. Tests correlate to the extent that they measure common traits. By observing and analyzing the pattern of intercorrelations, the operation of one or more underlying traits or other sources of common variance is inferred.

It is thus by establishing the basic sources of variance in a field of investigation and determining the nature of each measure in terms of basic categories that we can know what types of variations the tests (or other variables) are measuring, the interrelationships of these measures, and what needs to be done to modify or improve them when they are not entirely satisfactory for our purposes.

It has been pointed out by Royce (1950c) that a proper order for research programs might be, first, to use a set of *a priori* measures in a field of investigation and factor analyze them to determine the basic traits or other sources of variance operating; second, to study these factors, one at a time, by the techniques of analysis of variance to determine how they are affected by different experimental conditions or how they vary among groups that differ with respect to age, sex, education, or other pertinent background variables; and lastly, to study them experimentally in the laboratory for specific groups under carefully controlled conditions. While this order need not be invariable it does help to point up the proper function of each type of approach. In factor analysis the "individual differences" represented by a large number of measures, that are given to a single population, usually at one time under a standard set of conditions, are studied to detect possible common sources of variation or variance. In analysis of variance a *single* measure is administered over a series of occasions and conditions to determine the significance of group differences. The individual differences by this latter approach are often used as an estimate of "error variance" against which to evaluate the group differences.

It is quite understandable that some psychologists have used the results of factor analysis in the area of cognitive tests as support or disproof of theories of intelligence. The results of factor analysis can serve only as indirect evidence for this purpose, however, since factor analysis attempts to account statistically for differences in traits among individuals rather than for the mental organization within any one individual.[1] The fact that the observed differences can be accounted for by weighted sums of measures of the reference variables obtained from a factor analysis should *not* be construed to mean that any one individual's behavior is a resultant of the additive combination of these hypothetical traits. They merely serve to account mathematically for observed or predicted individual differences. Moreover, as methods of measurement and prediction become more refined and exact, factorial methods based on multiplicative or more complicated relationships for combining variances undoubtedly will be developed. While nonlinear relationships may be more appealing logically,

---

[1] For a possible exception to this see the descriptions of O- and P-techniques in Chapters 10 and 11.

they have yet to prove their usefulness at our present stage of knowledge.

The interpretations of the results of factor analysis, as is true of all scientific interpretations, are tentative. Just as the theory of relativity has replaced Newtonian physics as an interpretation of observed facts, so may present theories based on factorial results be superseded by other interpretations, if they more adequately account for the data. Factors are not eternal verities; they merely serve to represent the fundamental underlying sources of variation operating in a given set of scores or other data observed under a specified set of conditions.

Factor analysis has many limitations, and those who apply it should have considerable skill in experimental design and theorizing to obtain meaningful results. Without such skill and insight the considerable effort involved will be wasted.

PRELIMINARY CONCEPTS

One of the major applications of factor analysis in psychology has been an attempt to identify the traits which tests measure in common and which result in their intercorrelations. Most of the examples in this book will be in terms of psychological tests and their correlations, although what is said about them applies equally well to other continuously measurable variables.

Let us suppose that two tests, one consisting of arithmetic-reasoning problems and the other of reading-comprehension items, are given to a class of 100 students, and a correlation coefficient of +.50 is obtained between the two sets of scores (see Figure 1.1a). How is this coefficient to be interpreted? The correlation coefficient indicates that there is some positive relation between the rank of individuals, relative to the class, on the arithmetic-reasoning test and on the reading-comprehension test. We can speculate as to what these tests have in common that results in their ranking individuals similarly, so that standing on one test may serve as a partial basis for prediction of relative standing on the other test. It may be because they both assess reading-comprehension ability, since this seems to be involved in both tests. It may be vocabulary, reasoning ability, test-wiseness, speed of working, or any one of several other possible hypothetical traits. This is, in simplest form, one of the kinds of problems which factor analysis frequently is called upon to help solve.

The correlation between two tests is not a sufficient datum on which to base a scientific inference. If the arithmetic-reasoning

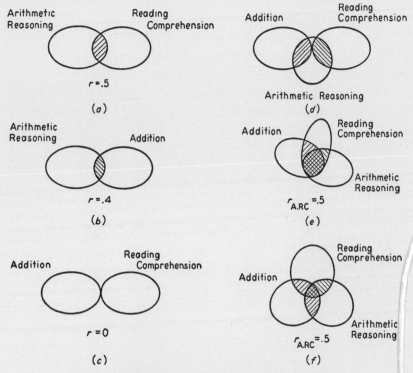

FIGURE 1.1 Schematic representation of test correlations.

test were also correlated with a test of simple addition, administered to the same group of students, it might yield a correlation coefficient of +.40 (Figure 1.1*b*). Here the overlap might be due to arithmetic-computation ability, numerical facility, or some other element common to the two tests. It is also of interest to observe the correlation of the reading-comprehension and addition tests. If this correlation were *not* significantly different from zero (Figure 1.1*c*), we could assume that the overlap of each of these tests with the arithmetic-reasoning test is due to separate, nonoverlapping traits (Figure 1.1*d*). If there were a significant correlation between the reading-comprehension and addition tests, there would be two alternative possibilities, and we would need the correlations with still another test to decide which is the more likely. The overlap could be either largely on the same trait as that between the arithmetic-reasoning and reading-comprehension tests (Figure 1.1*e*), or it could be wholly or in part on other factors (Figure 1.1*f*). In the former case, a single factor would account for most of the observed intercorrelations, whereas, in the latter instance, it would be necessary to assume more than one common factor.

In this way, if tests were added one at a time and the degree of their correlation with each previous test observed, the number of relationships to be held in mind with each added variable would increase rapidly, and more systematic ways of summarizing these relationships would be needed. The various methods of factor analysis have been devised for that purpose.

SPEARMAN'S TWO-FACTOR THEORY

Spearman was one of the first to attack the factor problem. At first he worked with groups of four tests. Observing that tests of abilities tend to have positive intercorrelations, he was able to show mathematically that the intercorrelations as represented in Table 1.1 could be, but were not necessarily, accounted

TABLE 1.1.   INTERCORRELATIONS OF FOUR TESTS

Test	1	2	3	4
1		r_{12}	r_{13}	r_{14}
2	r_{21}		r_{23}	r_{24}
3	r_{31}	r_{32}		r_{34}
4	r_{41}	r_{42}	r_{43}	

for by a single source of variation (or factor) if the coefficients in any combination of two columns (avoiding the cells in the principal diagonal, which are vacant) are proportional. Thus, for columns 1 and 2, to satisfy this "criterion of proportionality," we have the equation

$$\frac{r_{31}}{r_{32}} = \frac{r_{41}}{r_{42}} \quad \text{or} \quad r_{31}r_{42} = r_{32}r_{41} \tag{1.1}$$

For columns 1 and 3

$$\frac{r_{21}}{r_{23}} = \frac{r_{41}}{r_{43}} \quad \text{or} \quad r_{21}r_{43} = r_{23}r_{41} \tag{1.2}$$

For columns 1 and 4

$$\frac{r_{21}}{r_{24}} = \frac{r_{31}}{r_{34}} \quad \text{or} \quad r_{21}r_{34} = r_{24}r_{31} \tag{1.3}$$

Similar equations can be written for columns 2 and 3, 2 and 4, and 3 and 4. These would, however, merely duplicate the equations already written. When the equalities of equations 1, 2, and 3 exist, the criterion of proportionality is said to be satisfied, and the four tests are assumed to have one factor in common. Another way of expressing equations 1.1, 1.2, and 1.3 would be:

$$r_{31}r_{42} - r_{32}r_{41} = 0 \tag{1.1a}$$

$$r_{21}r_{43} - r_{23}r_{41} = 0 \tag{1.2a}$$

$$r_{21}r_{34} - r_{24}r_{31} = 0 \tag{1.3a}$$

These are Spearman's famous tetrad differences. Divergence of these differences from zero, within the limits of sampling error, are tolerated. If more than four tests are being investigated for this criterion, all combinations of four tests are examined, one at a time. This becomes quite laborious, of course, if there are many tests. Ten tests would yield 252 different tetrads, 20 tests would yield 2,907. Any one of n tests is involved in $\frac{1}{2}(n-1)(n-2)(n-3)$ different tetrad differences and any one correlation coefficient in $(n-2)(n-3)$ different tetrad differences.

Spearman and others found a considerable number of ability tests whose intercorrelations satisfied the proportionality criterion with sufficient closeness that their intercorrelations could be accounted for by a single factor. This factor was called g, the general-intellectual factor. Spearman's two-factor theory postulated that every test which satisfies the criterion of proportionality contains two factors, g and s. His g-factor is a general factor common to all intellectual tests. The s-factor is specific to each test and represents that portion of the reliable variance of a test that does *not* correlate with other tests. Spearman developed the hypothesis that *g* is a function of heredity, whereas *s*-factors represent the acquisition of specific learnings and experiences. Those tests that did not satisfy the proportionality criterion were discarded from the battery of tests of *g* or general intelligence.

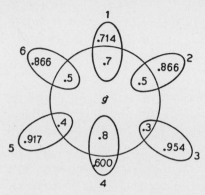

FIGURE 1.2 Schematic representation of Spearman's two-factor theory for six tests.

More efficient methods of examining tables of intercorrelations for proportionality or "hierarchy," as it is sometimes referred to, have been developed. However, it is now generally realized that examining a table of correlations to determine whether it can be accounted for by a single factor is a special case of the more general problem of determining the minimum number of common factors that are needed to account for all of the relationships. Spearman's technique is now largely of historical interest, but it should be added that Spearman has had a strong influence on British factor analysts, and they and their followers

TABLE 1.2. TABULAR REPRESENTATION OF SPEARMAN'S TWO-FACTOR THEORY

Test	Factor							h^2
	g	s_1	s_2	s_3	s_4	s_5	s_6	
1	.7	.714						.49
2	.5		.866					.25
3	.3			.954				.09
4	.8				.600			.64
5	.4					.917		.16
6	.5						.866	.25

usually look first for a general factor in any table of intercorrelations.

A schematic representation of Spearman's two-factor theory for six tests is shown in Figure 1.2. Table 1.2 presents the same information in tabular form. The numbers inside both the circle and ovals are the correlations (or loadings) of each test with g. The numbers in the portion of the ovals not included in the circle are the loadings of the tests on their specific factors, assuming perfectly reliable tests. Each of these loadings must be squared to determine the proportion of the total variance of the test represented on the general factor.[2] For a perfectly reliable test j, the total variance in standard scores can be represented by equation 4, where g stands for the loading on the general factor and s

$$g_j^2 + s_j^2 = 1.00 \qquad (1.4)$$

stands for the loading on the specific factor.[3] Thus, for test 4 in Table 1.2, $.8^2 + .6^2 = 1.00$.

Seven factors, one general and six specific, are represented in Table 1.2, but only one of them, g, is required to account for the correlations. The correlation between any two tests is dependent on the amount of g-factor they have in common and is obtained from the product of the two loadings. The correlation of tests 1 and 2 (in Table 1.2) is $.7 \times .5$ or $.35$, that between tests 1 and 3 is $.7 \times .3$ or $.21$, etc. In this way the entire table of correlations can be obtained and is shown in Table 1.3. The numbers in parentheses (in the diagonal cells) are obtained by multiplying the loading of each test on g by itself. This value is known as the *communality* of the test, represented by the symbol h^2, and indicates the proportion of the total variance of the test which is held in common with the general factor.

---

[2] As in all test theory, variance is equal to the square of the standard deviation. Factor loadings represent correlation and must be squared to be converted to variance.

[3] The g-loading of test j can be calculated from its correlations with 2 other tests k and l by the formula

$$g_j = \sqrt{\frac{r_{jk}r_{jl}}{r_{kl}}}$$

if the proportionality criterion is satisfied for these tests. In a matrix of correlations, the g-loading of variable j can be estimated by the formula

$$g = \sqrt{\frac{A_j^2 - A_j'}{T - 2A_j}}$$

where T = sum of all the correlations (where each occurs twice and the diagonal cells are empty); A_j = sum of all the correlations in row j; A'_j = sum of the squared correlations in row j; A_j^2 = the square of A_j. Cf. Spearman (1927), appendix.

TABLE 1.3. INTERCORRELATIONS OF SIX TESTS REPRE-
SENTED IN FIGURE 1.2 AND TABLE 1.2

Test	1	2	3	4	5	6
1	(.49)	.35	.21	.56	.28	.35
2	.35	(.25)	.15	.40	.20	.25
3	.21	.15	(.09)	.24	.12	.15
4	.56	.40	.24	(.64)	.32	.40
5	.28	.20	.12	.32	(.16)	.20
6	.35	.25	.15	.40	.20	(.25)

HOLZINGER'S BI-FACTOR THEORY

More recently Spearman and his adherents have realized that those tests which do not satisfy the criterion of proportionality and which Spearman has termed "disturbers" may be retained in the correlation matrix if it is recognized that some of the tests may have a factor in common, in addition to the general factor that is not common to all of the tests. These factors, common to groups of tests, are termed *group* factors. Holzinger's *bifactor* method, which is a variation of Spearman's *two-factor* method, obtains a general and one or more group factors.

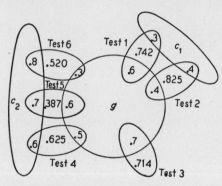

FIGURE 1.3   Schematic representation of Holzinger's bi-factor theory.

The bi-factor theory may be represented schematically, as in Figure 1.3. Table 1.4 gives the same information in tabular form. The variance for test j in standard scores, if it is assumed

TABLE 1.4. TABULAR REPRESENTATION OF HOLZINGER'S
BI-FACTOR THEORY

Test	Factor									h^2
	g	c_1	c_2	s_1	s_2	s_3	s_4	s_5	s_6	
1	.6	.3		.742						.45
2	.4	.4			.825					.32
3	.7					.714				.49
4	.5		.6				.625			.61
5	.6		.7					.387		.85
6	.3		.8						.520	.73

to be perfectly reliable, is given by equation 5, where c is its loading with a group factor.

$$g_j^2 + c_j^2 + s_j^2 = 1.00 \tag{1.5}$$

The correlation between two tests is determined by the extent to which they are loaded on the same factors and can be calculated from the cross-products of their loadings according to equation 6.

$$r_{jk} = g_j g_k + c_{j1} c_{k1} + c_{j2} c_{k2} + \cdots + c_{jr} c_{kr} \tag{1.6}$$

The correlation between tests 1 and 2 (in Table 1.4) is equal to $(.6 \times .4) + (.3 \times .4)$ or .36, and the correlation between tests 1 and 5 is equal to $(.6 \times .6) + (.3 \times .0) + (.0 \times .7)$ or .36. The correlations among all the other tests may be similarly computed. In this example nine factors are used, but only three of them, the general and two group factors, enter into the correlations among the six tests. An advantage of the bi-factor method over the two-factor approach is that it does not insist on a single common factor but allows tests which do not fit the proportionality criterion to be retained by placing part of their common variance under group factors.

If one were interested in attempting to infer the psychological nature of the general factor, he would try to determine what all the tests loaded on the factor had in common that was not shared by the tests which did not fit the proportionality criterion. In addition, he might also try to infer what the tests appearing on a group factor have in common which is not shared with tests that do not appear on the group factor. More confidence would be placed in the identification of the second group factor in the example of Figure 1.3, since there are three tests to examine for a common element, whereas for the first group factor there are only two tests to be considered. It might be possible to hypothesize two different traits that these two tests seem to measure in common. In the absence of a third test to support one hypothesis or the other, it would be difficult to decide which is more likely the common element. Among the group factors which have been identified by investigators using the bi-factor method are verbal ability, numerical ability, mechanical ability, attention, imagination, and such personality factors as perseveration, will, and oscillation.

CHAPTER 2

Cluster Analysis

CLUSTER analysis, a simple form of correlational analysis, is a useful technique in itself and can also be used to gain further understanding of the purposes and nature of factor analysis. There is one type of correlational matrix which would give the same results whether analyzed by cluster analysis or factor analysis. The case in which the variables are all "pure" (i.e., each would appear on only one common factor) gives similar results by the two methods. Cluster analysis is simpler to perform. One of the differences between cluster analysis and factor analysis is that in the former each variable as a unit is placed in a cluster, whereas in the latter, different portions of the variance of a variable may be assigned to different factors.

There are a number of other situations in which it would be appropriate to cluster analyze a matrix of intercorrelations. When dealing with a large unfamiliar table of correlations which is to be factor analyzed, it is sometimes helpful to do a preliminary cluster analysis to become familiar with the variables and the ways in which they are related. It would also be advisable to do a cluster analysis for tables of correlations on which, because of the small N, large number of variables, or desire to have each variable appear in only one category, the additional computational labor of a complete factor analysis is not justifiable. Cluster analysis may also be used as a preliminary step in some of the grouping methods of factor analysis, such as the multiple-group method (see Chapter 6).

Cluster Analysis with Fictitious Data

Several methods of cluster analysis have been suggested (Cattell, 1944a; Tryon, 1939; Holzinger and Harmon, 1941; and Peatman, 1947). The procedure presented here uses Tryon's modification of Holzinger and Harmon's B-coefficient (coefficient of belonging).

Given the intercorrelations of eight tests shown in Table 2.1, we may ask whether there are any clearly defined clusters of vari-

TABLE 2.1. TABLE OF INTERCORRELATIONS

Variable	1	2	3	4	5	6	7	8
1	( )	.48	.36	.40	.58	.38	.42	.50
2	.48	( )	.00	.16	.72	.08	.24	.56
3	.36	.00	( )	.63	.09	.72	.54	.18
4	.40	.16	.63	( )	.25	.58	.48	.28
5	.58	.72	.09	.25	( )	.17	.33	.65
6	.38	.08	.72	.58	.17	( )	.51	.23
7	.42	.24	.54	.48	.33	.51	( )	.33
8	.50	.56	.18	.28	.65	.23	.33	( )
Σ	3.12	2.24	2.52	2.78	2.79	2.67	2.85	2.73

ables which would indicate the operation of underlying factors. In order to study the interrelationships it is convenient, first, to list the correlations for each variable in order of size, as has been done in the rows of Table 2.2.   Thus, r_{12} is between .45 and .49, r_{13} is between .35 and .39, etc.   Examination of Table 2.2 indi-

TABLE 2.2. CORRELATION COEFFICIENTS FOR EACH VARIABLE LISTED IN ORDER OF SIZE

Variable	.00-.04	.05-.09	.10-.14	.15-.19	.20-.24	.25-.29	.30-.34	.35-.39	.40-.44	.45-.49	.50-.54	.55-.59	.60-.64	.65-.69	.70-.74
1								3,6	4,7	2	8	5			
2	3	6		4	7					1		8			5
3	2	5		8				1			7		4		6
4				2		5,8			1	7		6	3		
5			3	6		4	7					1		8	2
6		2		5	8			1			7	4			3
7					2		5,8		1	4	3,6				
8				3	6	4	7				1	2		5	

cates that the highest correlations are between variables 2 and 5 and variables 3 and 6. It would probably be well to start a cluster of variables with one of these correlations. The work of obtaining a B-coefficient [1] for a cluster is best done in a table like Table 2.3. The B-coefficient gives the ratio of the average intercorrelation of the variables in a cluster to their average correlation with the variables not included in the cluster. A B-coefficient of 1.00 would indicate that the variables in the cluster correlate no more highly among themselves than they do with the variables outside of the cluster.

It is customary to start a cluster with the two variables which correlate highest and to keep adding variables until the B-coefficient shows a marked drop.[2] In Table 2.3 let us start our cluster with variable 2 and add variable 5 to the cluster (the variable added to the cluster is given the general designation of variable i). The work is outlined in the following steps:

1. In column 1 of Table 2.3 list the variables in the cluster.

2. In column 2 indicate the sum of the correlations in column i in the table of intercorrelations (when starting a cluster with two tests this includes the sums of the columns of both variables).

3. In column 3 enter the sum of the correlations between the variable being added to the cluster and those already in the cluster.

4. In column 4 enter the sum of all the correlation coefficients in the cluster.

5. In column 5 enter the sum of the correlations of the variables in the cluster with the variables not in the cluster.

6. In column 6 enter the number of variables in the cluster.

7. In column 7 enter the number of the intercorrelations among the variables in the cluster.

8. In column 8 enter the number of remaining intercorrelations (i.e., between the variables in the cluster and those not in the cluster).

---

[1] See Holzinger and Harmon (1941, pp. 23-34).

[2] Holzinger and Harmon (1941, p. 27) have arbitrarily set the minimum significant value of a B-coefficient at 1.30, although, of course, the goal is to obtain the highest possible set of meaningful B-coefficients.

9. In column 9 enter the average of the correlation coefficients in the cluster.

10. In column 10 enter the average of the correlations between the variables in the cluster and the remaining variables.

11. In column 11 obtain the ratio of the average of the correlations in the cluster (column 9) to the average of the remaining correlations of the variables in the cluster (column 10). This is the B-coefficient.

For the cluster consisting of variables 2 and 5, the B-coefficient is equal to 2.40. Is there another variable which can be added to the cluster and not result in a greatly reduced B-coefficient?

TABLE 2.3. WORK SHEET AND SOLUTION FOR B-COEFFICIENTS IN CLUSTER ANALYSIS

(1) Preceding Cluster +i	(2) Sum of i with n Variables	(3) Sum of Correlations between i and Variables already in Cluster	(4) Sum of Correlations among Variables in cluster = (3)+(4) from Preceding Line	(5) Sum of Correlations of Variables in Cluster not in Cluster = (2)−2(3) +(5) from Preceding Line	(6) k=Number of Variables in the Cluster	(7) $\frac{k(k-1)}{2}$ = Number of Intercorrelations in Cluster	(8) $k(n-k)$ = Number of Remaining Intercorrelations	(9) Mean Intercorrelation in Cluster (4)÷(7)	(10) Mean of the Remaining Intercorrelations (5)÷(8)	(11) B-Coefficient (9)÷(10)
B(2,5)	2.24 + 2.79=5.03	.72	.72	3.59	2	1	12	.720	.299	2.40
B(2,5,8)	2.73	1.21	1.93	3.90	3	3	15	.643	.260	2.47
B(2,5,8,1)	3.12	1.56	3.49	3.90	4	6	16	.582	.244	2.39
B(3,6)	2.52 + 2.67=5.19	.72	.72	3.75	2	1	12	.720	.312	2.31
B(3,6,4)	2.78	1.21	1.93	4.11	3	3	15	.643	.274	2.35
B(3,6,4,7)	2.85	1.53	3.46	3.90	4	6	16	.577	.270	2.14

Looking along the row for variable 2 of Table 2.2 it may be observed that variable 8 has the next highest correlation. The same is true for variable 5. Adding variable 8 to the cluster gives the results shown in the next line of Table 2.3. The B-coefficient is slightly larger, and variable 8 is retained in the cluster.

Variable 1 is the next variable to be considered for inclusion in the cluster, since it has high correlations with all three variables already in the cluster. Adding variable 1 results in a B-coefficient of 2.39. This is still a satisfactorily large B-coefficient, and variable 1 is retained in the cluster.

None of the other variables seem to have higher correlations with the variables in the cluster than with the remaining variables, and the first cluster may be considered completed. To start the next cluster we search for the highest correlation coefficient not included in the first cluster. This is r_{36}, and the next cluster is started with variables 3 and 6. Their B-coefficient is 2.31.

Variable 4 has appreciable correlations with variables 3 and 6 and is added next. It raises the B-coefficient to 2.35. Variable

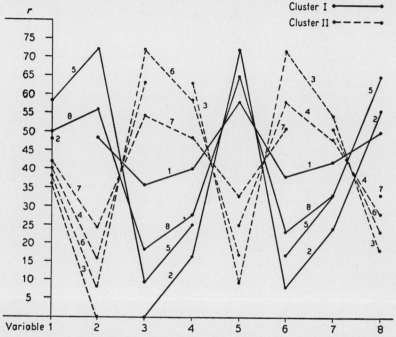

FIGURE 2.1   Correlational profiles of the variables in Table 2.1.

7 in considered next. It reduces the B-coefficient to 2.14 (see Table 2.3), but since this is a satisfactorily high coefficient, variable 7 is retained in the cluster. We have now assigned our eight variables to two clusters. Next, if desired, graphs may be drawn showing the profile of the correlations of each variable with the other variables. Variables which are similar should have similar profiles, and inspection of the graphs will exhibit the similarity. (See Figure 2.1.)

If it is desired to identify the nature of the clusters, the remaining step would be to infer what trait the variables in each cluster are measuring in common which is absent from or diminished in the tests not in the cluster. The process of describing or naming the clusters is one of logical inference and is in the nature of an interpretation or hypothesis which may be subjected to verification by further investigations.

PROBLEMS

CORRELATION MATRIX

$$N = 250$$

Variable	1	2	3	4	5	6	7	8
1		.63	.46	.51	.35	.18	.45	.24
2	.63		.36	.54	.45	.00	.27	.00
3	.46	.36		.42	.20	.36	.60	.48
4	.51	.54	.42		.30	.18	.42	.24
5	.35	.45	.20	.30		.00	.15	.00
6	.18	.00	.36	.18	.00		.48	.48
7	.45	.27	.60	.42	.15	.48		.64
8	.24	.00	.48	.24	.00	.48	.64	

1. Obtain the clusters for the above correlation matrix by the B-coefficient method.

2. Draw a correlational-profile graph of the 8 variables.

CHAPTER 3

Mathematics Essential for Factor Analysis

THE MATHEMATICAL operations of factor analysis are based upon matrix theory,[1] and in order to enable the student to follow them the fundamentals of matrix algebra and matrix geometry will be presented.

MATRIX ALGEBRA

Definition of a Matrix. A matrix is a rectangular or square arrangement of numbers in a table, regardless of what the numbers represent. A table of correlation coefficients may be considered a matrix. The numbers in a matrix do not have a predetermined arithmetical relationship to each other, and the matrix, considered as a whole, does not have a specific value attached to it. Table 3.1 shows a 4×4 square matrix. It is supposed to be written with double vertical lines on both sides to distinguish it from a determinant, but it is frequently written with single vertical lines. The letter a is used in this illustration to represent the numerical entry (called an element of the matrix) in

---

[1] The mathematics of matrices was developed primarily to solve systems of equations.

TABLE 3.1

$$
\begin{array}{c|cccc|}
 & 1 & 2 & 3 & 4 \\
\hline
1 & a_{11} & a_{12} & a_{13} & a_{14} \\
2 & a_{21} & a_{22} & a_{23} & a_{24} \\
3 & a_{31} & a_{32} & a_{33} & a_{34} \\
4 & a_{41} & a_{42} & a_{43} & a_{44} \\
\end{array} = A
$$

each cell. It is not necessary to number each row and column of a matrix, but, where it is desired to identify each element, it can be done by giving first the row in which it is located and then the column. Thus, the symbol a_{32} represents the numerical entry in the cell at the intersection of the third row and second column. An entire matrix may for convenience be represented by a letter, and the matrix in Table 3.1 is represented by the letter **A**.[2] A matrix with m rows and n columns is said to be of order $m \times n$. A square $n \times n$ is of order n.

Transpose of a Matrix. The transpose of a matrix is a second matrix whose *columns* are obtained from the *rows* of the first matrix. This relationship is represented schematically in Figure 3.1a.

The same result could have been obtained by using the columns of matrix **A** for the rows of its transpose, as indicated in Figure 3.1b. The transpose of a matrix is indicated by the addition of a prime (′) to the letter of the matrix.

Obtaining a transpose matrix is also illustrated by a numerical example in Table 3.2a and by a literal example in Table 3.2b.

A more generalized definition of the transpose of a matrix is that it is a matrix with the rows and columns of the original matrix interchanged. Thus reading down column 3 of matrix **B′** in Table 3.2a gives the same values as reading across row 3 of matrix **B**, and reading across row 3 of matrix **A′** gives the same values as reading down column 3 of matrix **A**.

---

[2] Representing a matrix by a letter is an example of matrix notation. The extensive use of matrix notation in most books on factor analysis puts them beyond the comprehension of many students who might otherwise understand the concepts. Limited use of matrix notation will be made in this book.

Matrix **A**

Matrix **A'**
(Transpose of Matrix **A**)

FIGURE 3.1*a*

Matrix **A**

Matrix **A'**

FIGURE 3.1*b*

TABLE 3.2

	1	2	3
1	.3	.2	.5
2	.7	.6	.3
3	.5	.4	.9
4	.1	.8	.6
5	.9	.3	.4
6	.6	.5	.8

Matrix **B**

	1	2	3	4	5	6
1	.3	.7	.5	.1	.9	.6
2	.2	.6	.4	.8	.3	.5
3	.5	.3	.9	.6	.4	.8

Matrix **B'**

(*a*)

	1	2	3
1	a_{11}	a_{12}	a_{13}
2	a_{21}	a_{22}	a_{23}
3	a_{31}	a_{32}	a_{33}
4	a_{41}	a_{42}	a_{43}
5	a_{51}	a_{52}	a_{53}
6	a_{61}	a_{62}	a_{63}

Matrix **C**

	1	2	3	4	5	6
1	a_{11}	a_{21}	a_{31}	a_{41}	a_{51}	a_{61}
2	a_{12}	a_{22}	a_{32}	a_{42}	a_{52}	a_{62}
3	a_{13}	a_{23}	a_{33}	a_{43}	a_{53}	a_{63}

Matrix **C'**

(*b*)

Determinants. A determinant is similar to a matrix in that it too is a table of numbers. It differs from a matrix in that it (1) is always square, and (2) has a definite numerical value associated with it. An $n \times n$ determinant is said to be of the order n. A determinant is written with single vertical lines on the sides to distinguish it from a matrix, which is written with double vertical lines. Table 3.3 illustrates two determinants, one of order 2 and one of order 4.

TABLE 3.3

$$
\begin{vmatrix} a_{11} & a_{12} \\ a_{21} & a_{22} \end{vmatrix}
\qquad
\begin{vmatrix} a_{11} & a_{12} & a_{13} & a_{14} \\ a_{21} & a_{22} & a_{23} & a_{24} \\ a_{31} & a_{32} & a_{33} & a_{34} \\ a_{41} & a_{42} & a_{43} & a_{44} \end{vmatrix}
$$

A Second-order   A Fourth-order
Determinant   Determinant

This is not the place to give the rules for numerically evaluating determinants. They can be found in any textbook of college algebra.[3] The numerical value of a second-order determinant is, however, easily obtained. It is given by the expression $a_{11}a_{22} - a_{21}a_{12}$, where the numerical values are arranged as in the 2×2 determinant in Table 3.3. Of course, if the product $a_{11}a_{22}$ is equal to the product $a_{21}a_{12}$, the determinant is equal to zero and is said to "vanish."

Determinant of a Matrix. Although matrices and determinants are different, it is desirable for some purposes to consider a square matrix as a determinant and to evaluate it according to the rules for evaluating determinants.

Minors of a Determinant. If one row and one column of a determinant of order n are eliminated, the remainder is a determinant of order $n - 1$. This determinant of order $n - 1$ is referred to as the *first minor* of the larger determinant. If a first minor were obtained, for example, from the 4×4 determinant in Table 3.3 by striking out the second row and third column, it would leave the third-order determinant shown (Table 3.4),

---

[3] See, for instance, W. B. Ford, *A Brief Course in College Algebra*, The Macmillan Co., New York, 1932, Chapter XIV.

TABLE 3.4

$$
\begin{vmatrix}
 & 1 & 2 & 3 & 4 \\
1 & a_{11} & a_{12} & a_{13} & a_{14} \\
2 & a_{21} & a_{22} & a_{23} & a_{24} \\
3 & a_{31} & a_{32} & a_{33} & a_{34} \\
4 & a_{41} & a_{42} & a_{43} & a_{44}
\end{vmatrix}
=
\begin{vmatrix}
 & 1 & 2 & 3 \\
1 & a_{11} & a_{12} & a_{14} \\
2 & a_{31} & a_{32} & a_{34} \\
3 & a_{41} & a_{42} & a_{44}
\end{vmatrix}
$$

which would be referred to as the first minor, a_{23} (the intersection of the row and column crossed out).

For a 4×4 determinant there are 16 possible first minors. For an $n \times n$ determinant there are n^2 first minors.

Similarly, if any two rows and any two columns of an $n \times n$ determinant are eliminated, we have remaining a determinant of order $n - 2$. Such determinants are known as the *second minors* of the $n \times n$ determinant. The 2×2 determinant in Table 3.3 is one of the second minors of the 4×4 determinant.

Rank of a Matrix. One type of problem approached by factor analysis may be stated as follows: given an $n \times n$ matrix of correlations, are n independent reference variables needed to account for the relationships represented by the correlation coefficients, or can the relationships be accounted for by a linear (i.e., additive, weighted) combination of fewer than n reference variables? The rank of the correlation matrix is the number of reference variables needed to account for the intercorrelations.

One way of determining the rank of a matrix is to find the order of its highest nonvanishing minors. For example, if the determinant of a 4×4 matrix when evaluated does not vanish, its rank is 4. If the determinant is equal to zero, the matrix is of rank 3 or less. If one or more of the first minors of this 4×4 matrix do not vanish, the rank of the matrix is 3. If all 16 first minors (which are of order 3) vanish, the rank of the matrix is less than 3. The mathematics of factor analysis is primarily adapted to testing the ranks of matrices.[4]

---

[4] It is of historical interest to note that Thurstone (1947c, p. vi) defined the multiple-factor analysis problem in these terms. He writes: "In 1931 I decided to investigate the relation between multiple-factor analysis and Spearman's tetrad differences. When I wrote the tetrad equation to begin this inquiry, I discovered

Some Common Types of Matrices.

A. Square Matrix
A square matrix is one having the same number of columns and rows.

$$\begin{Vmatrix} 2 & 7 & 1 \\ 3 & 9 & 2 \\ 4 & 8 & 5 \end{Vmatrix}$$

A Square Matrix

B. Symmetric Matrix
A symmetric matrix is a square matrix with equal values in corresponding positions relative to the principal diagonal (which extends from the upper left-hand corner to the lower right-hand corner and includes cells a_{11}, a_{22}, a_{33}, etc.). Thus matrix **A** is symmetric if $a_{12} = a_{21}$, $a_{23} = a_{32}$, and $a_{13} = a_{31}$.

$$\begin{Vmatrix} a_{11} & a_{12} & a_{13} \\ a_{21} & a_{22} & a_{23} \\ a_{31} & a_{32} & a_{33} \end{Vmatrix} = A$$

A Symmetric Matrix

Matrix **B** is also a symmetric matrix.

$$\begin{Vmatrix} .2 & .3 & .4 \\ .3 & .9 & .8 \\ .4 & .8 & .5 \end{Vmatrix} = B$$

A symmetric matrix and its transpose matrix are equal. (Two matrices are equal if their corresponding elements are equal.) A table of intercorrelations is, of course, a symmetric matrix, usually with no numerical entries in the principal diagonal.

---

that the tetrad was merely the expansion of a second-order minor and the relation was then obvious. . . . If the second-order minors must vanish in order to establish a single common factor, then must the third-order minors vanish in order to establish two common factors, and so on?"

C. A Diagonal Matrix

A diagonal matrix is one which has values greater than zero in its principal diagonal while all other elements are zeros.

$$\left\|\begin{array}{ccc} a_{11} & 0 & 0 \\ 0 & a_{22} & 0 \\ 0 & 0 & a_{33} \end{array}\right\|$$

A Diagonal Matrix

D. The Identity Matrix

A diagonal matrix that has principal-diagonal values all equal to 1, while all other values are zeros, is called an identity matrix and is often represented by the letter **I**. Its role in matrix mathematics is somewhat analogous to the use of the number *1* in arithmetic.

$$\left\|\begin{array}{ccc} 1 & 0 & 0 \\ 0 & 1 & 0 \\ 0 & 0 & 1 \end{array}\right\| = I$$

The Identity Matrix

Matrix Multiplication. Matrices may be multiplied. The rules for matrix multiplication are more complicated than for

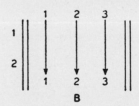

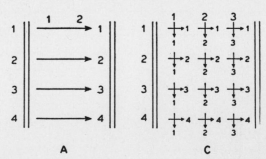

FIGURE 3.2 Illustration of the row-by-column rule of matrix multiplication.

arithmetic multiplication, but they can be mastered with a little application. The first respect in which matrix multiplication differs from arithmetic multiplication is that the *order* in which the multiplication is done must be specified. Thus, the product of matrices $\mathbf{A} \cdot \mathbf{B}$ is usually not equal to the product of matrices $\mathbf{B} \cdot \mathbf{A}$. In the former case matrix $\mathbf{A}$ is said to be post-multiplied by $\mathbf{B}$ and in the latter case matrix $\mathbf{A}$ is said to be pre-multiplied by $\mathbf{B}$.

In order for it to be possible to post-multiply matrix $\mathbf{A}$ by matrix $\mathbf{B}$, the number of *columns* of the former must be the same

TABLE 3.5.   MATRIX MULTIPLICATION

$$
\begin{array}{c}
\begin{array}{c|cc}
 & 1 & 2 \\
\hline
1 & a_{11} & a_{12} \\
2 & a_{21} & a_{22} \\
3 & a_{31} & a_{32} \\
4 & a_{41} & a_{42} \\
\end{array} \\
\mathbf{A}
\end{array}
\cdot
\begin{array}{c}
\begin{array}{c|ccc}
 & 1 & 2 & 3 \\
\hline
1 & b_{11} & b_{12} & b_{13} \\
2 & b_{21} & b_{22} & b_{23} \\
\end{array} \\
\mathbf{B}
\end{array}
=
$$

$$
\begin{array}{c}
\begin{Vmatrix}
(a_{11}b_{11} + a_{12}b_{21}) & (a_{11}b_{12} + a_{12}b_{22}) & (a_{11}b_{13} + a_{12}b_{23}) \\
(a_{21}b_{11} + a_{22}b_{21}) & (a_{21}b_{12} + a_{22}b_{22}) & (a_{21}b_{13} + a_{22}b_{23}) \\
(a_{31}b_{11} + a_{32}b_{21}) & (a_{31}b_{12} + a_{32}b_{22}) & (a_{31}b_{13} + a_{32}b_{23}) \\
(a_{41}b_{11} + a_{42}b_{21}) & (a_{41}b_{12} + a_{42}b_{22}) & (a_{41}b_{13} + a_{42}b_{23}) \\
\end{Vmatrix} \\
\mathbf{C}
\end{array}
$$

(*a*) Literal Example

$$
\begin{array}{c}
\begin{array}{c|cc}
 & 1 & 2 \\
\hline
1 & .1 & .7 \\
2 & .6 & .3 \\
3 & .4 & .8 \\
4 & .5 & .2 \\
\end{array} \\
\mathbf{A}
\end{array}
\cdot
\begin{array}{c}
\begin{array}{c|ccc}
 & 1 & 2 & 3 \\
\hline
1 & .9 & .4 & .3 \\
2 & .2 & .1 & .7 \\
\end{array} \\
\mathbf{B}
\end{array}
=
$$

$$
\begin{array}{c|ccc}
 & 1 & 2 & 3 \\
\hline
1 & .23 & .11 & .52 \\
2 & .60 & .27 & .39 \\
3 & .52 & .24 & .68 \\
4 & .49 & .22 & .29 \\
\end{array}
$$

C

(*b*) Numerical Example

as the number of *rows* of the latter. Matrix **A** in Figure 3.2 has two columns and can be post-multiplied by matrix **B** which has two rows.

The basic operation of matrix multiplication is the **row-by-column rule.** This rule is illustrated graphically in Figure 3.2. The value in each cell of the product matrix **C** is the sum of a series of individual products. Thus the element in the upper left-hand cell of matrix **C** is the sum of the product of each value in the first row of matrix **A** times the corresponding value of the first column of matrix **B**. This is also illustrated literally and numerically in Tables 3.5*a* and 3.5*b,* respectively.

The values in the other cells of matrix **C** are obtained similarly by **row-by-column** multiplication, as shown in Figure 3.2 and Tables 3.5*a* and 3.5*b*. The value at the intersection of the third row and second column of matrix **C**, for example, is obtained by multiplying the values in the third row of matrix **A** by the corresponding values of the second column of matrix **B**, and summing the products. In the example, each value in the product matrix is the sum of two products. If matrix **A** had 3 columns and matrix **B** 3 rows, each value in the cells of the product matrix would be the sum of 3 products, etc.

The product matrix has as many rows as the first matrix and as many columns as the second matrix. If a matrix of order $k \times n$ is multiplied by a matrix of order $n \times m$, the product matrix will be of order $k \times m$.[5]

Inverse Matrix. Not only may matrices be multiplied, but there is also a process in matrix algebra analogous to division. Just as in arithmetic we have the relationship that any number

---

[5] Since it is usually more convenient to multiply rows by rows or columns by columns, it should be observed that if the transpose of matrix **B** were written and the *rows* of matrix **A** were multiplied by the *rows* of matrix **B'**, the results would be the same as if the rows of matrix **A** had been multiplied by the columns of matrix **B**. Similarly if a column-by-column multiplication is the most convenient, the columns of matrix **A'** could be multiplied by the columns of matrix **B** to give the same results.

Any one of the following arrangements will result in the same product matrix **C** and whichever is most convenient may be used:

AB (rows-by-columns)
AB' (rows-by-rows)
A'B (columns-by-columns)

multiplied by its reciprocal is equal to 1, so in matrix algebra we have the relationship that any matrix multiplied by its inverse is equal to an identity matrix.[6] These relationships are illustrated by the following equations:

$$x \cdot 1/x = 1 \quad \text{(arithmetic)}$$

$$A \cdot A^{-1} = I \quad \text{(matrix algebra)}$$

A^{-1} indicates the inverse of matrix A and, as it has been pointed out, is analogous to a reciprocal in arithmetic. The analogy may be carried further. In arithmetic when a multiplier is transferred from one side of an algebraic equation to the other, it appears in reciprocal form on the second side. Similarly when a multiplying matrix is transferred, it appears in its inverse form on the other side of the equation. This is illustrated by the following equations:

$$\text{if } x \cdot y = a, \quad y = 1/x \cdot a = x^{-1}a \quad \text{(arithmetic)}$$

$$\text{if } A \cdot B = C, \quad B = A^{-1}C \quad \text{(matrix algebra)} \; [7]$$

Just as matrix multiplication is more complicated than arithmetic multiplication, so obtaining the inverse of a matrix is a

---

[6] An inverse exists for any square, non-singular matrix. A non-singular matrix is one whose determinant is *not* equal to zero.

[7] If matrix A appears to the left of matrix B, then matrix A^{-1} must appear to the left of matrix C. It would usually be incorrect to write $B = CA^{-1}$ in the example above.

The following is a brief summary of some basic relationships in matrix algebra:

$$A + B = B + A$$

$$A(B + C) = AB + AC$$

$$A + (B + C) = (A + B) + C$$

$$(B + C)A = BA + CA$$

$$(AB)C = A(BC)$$

$$AB \neq BA \text{ (in general)}$$

$$AI = IA = A$$

$$(AB)' = B'A'$$

$$AA^{-1} = I = A^{-1}A$$

$$(AB)^{-1} = B^{-1}A^{-1}$$

The process of addition is performed by adding the corresponding elements of matrices of the same order.

more complex process than division. Since, however, it is necessary to obtain the inverse of a matrix in several problems in factor
analysis, one method will be described.[8] This method is based
upon the following principles:

1. There are certain operations that can be performed on the
rows of a given matrix **A** by which it may be reduced to the identity matrix.[9]

2. These same operations applied in the same order to the
rows of an identity matrix will yield the inverse $(\mathbf{A}^{-1})$ of the given
matrix **A**.

Computation of the inverse of matrix **A** is illustrated in the
following steps:

TABLE 3.6

$$\left\| \begin{array}{ccc} .2 & .4 & .7 \\ .6 & .1 & .5 \\ .3 & .8 & .3 \end{array} \right\| \qquad \left\| \begin{array}{ccc} 1.0 & .0 & .0 \\ .0 & 1.0 & .0 \\ .0 & .0 & 1.0 \end{array} \right\|$$

$$\cdot \mathbf{A} \qquad\qquad\qquad \mathbf{I}$$

1. Divide each number in the first row of matrix **A** by the
value in the principal diagonal for that row (.2). Divide the numbers in the first row of matrix **I** by the same value (.2). This
gives the following values in the two matrices:

$$\left\| \begin{array}{ccc} 1.0 & 2.0 & 3.5 \\ .6 & .1 & .5 \\ .3 & .8 & .3 \end{array} \right\| \qquad \left\| \begin{array}{ccc} 5.0 & .0 & .0 \\ .0 & 1.0 & .0 \\ .0 & .0 & 1.0 \end{array} \right\|$$

2. Now that we have a 1.0 at the top of column 1 for the
matrix at the left, we wish to transform the remaining values in
the first *column* into zeros, in order to get it into the identity
matrix form. This can be done for the second row by subtracting
0.6 of each value in the first row from the corresponding value in

---

[8] Other methods are described in the following references: Thurstone (1947c),
Tucker (1938), Fruchter (1949d), Deemer (1947), Dwyer (1951), and Andree (1952).

[9] The permissible operations are as follows:

1. Dividing all of the elements in a row by a constant.

2. Adding or subtracting some fraction or multiple of the elements in one row
from the corresponding elements in another row of the matrix.

These operations may also be applied to the columns of matrices but we shall
not do so here.

the second row. (Whatever arithmetical operation is performed on one value in a row must also be performed on the other values in that row.) Likewise, for the matrix at the right, 0.6 of each value in the first row is subtracted from the corresponding value in the second row.

$$
\left\|
\begin{array}{rrr}
1.0 & 2.0 & 3.5 \\
.0 & -1.1 & -1.6 \\
.3 & .8 & .3
\end{array}
\right\|
\qquad
\left\|
\begin{array}{rrr}
5.0 & .0 & .0 \\
-3.0 & 1.0 & .0 \\
.0 & .0 & 1.0
\end{array}
\right\|
$$

3. Similarly, in order to obtain a zero for the value in column 1, row 3, we subtract .3 of each value in row 1 from the corresponding value in row 3 and perform a similar operation on the matrix at the right. For a matrix of more than 3 rows a similar process is continued until all the entries in the first column below the first row of the matrix on the left are zeros. It should be noted that while the operations are performed on the rows, it is the columns that are reduced to identity-matrix form one at a time.

$$
\left\|
\begin{array}{rrr}
1.0 & 2.0 & 3.5 \\
.0 & -1.1 & -1.6 \\
.0 & .2 & -.75
\end{array}
\right\|
\qquad
\left\|
\begin{array}{rrr}
5.0 & .0 & .0 \\
-3.0 & 1.0 & .0 \\
-1.5 & .0 & 1.0
\end{array}
\right\|
$$

4. Divide each number in the second row of the matrix on the left by the value in the principal diagonal of the second row (-1.1), giving 1.0 in that cell. Divide each number in the second row of the matrix on the right by the same value (-1.1).

$$
\left\|
\begin{array}{rrr}
1.00 & 2.00 & 3.50 \\
.00 & 1.00 & 1.45 \\
.00 & .20 & -.75
\end{array}
\right\|
\qquad
\left\|
\begin{array}{rrr}
5.00 & .00 & .00 \\
2.73 & -.91 & .00 \\
-1.50 & .00 & 1.00
\end{array}
\right\|
$$

5. In order to change the other values of the second column to zeros we go through a process similar to that applied in column 1. Subtract 2.0 times each value in the second row from the corresponding value in the first row. Subtract .2 of each value in the second row from the corresponding value in the third row. Do this for both matrices. If there are more than three rows, get the product of the second value in each row and each value in the second row and subtract it from the corresponding value in

the row being worked on. The first two columns of the matrix on the left have been reduced to identity form as indicated below.

$$\begin{Vmatrix} 1.00 & .00 & .60 \\ .00 & 1.00 & 1.45 \\ .00 & .00 & -1.04 \end{Vmatrix} \qquad \begin{Vmatrix} -.46 & 1.82 & .00 \\ 2.73 & -.91 & .00 \\ -2.05 & .18 & 1.00 \end{Vmatrix}$$

6. Divide each value in the third row of both matrices by the value in the principal diagonal of that row in the left-hand matrix (-1.04). Always start reducing a column by changing its value on the principal diagonal to 1.0.

$$\begin{Vmatrix} 1.00 & .00 & .60 \\ .00 & 1.00 & 1.45 \\ .00 & .00 & 1.00 \end{Vmatrix} \qquad \begin{Vmatrix} -.46 & 1.82 & .00 \\ 2.73 & -.91 & .00 \\ 1.97 & -.17 & -.96 \end{Vmatrix}$$

7. To change the values in the first two rows of the third column of the matrix on the left to zeros, subtract .6 of each value in the third row from the corresponding value in the first row, and 1.45 times each value in the third row from its corresponding value in the second row. Perform the same operations on the rows of the matrix on the right.

$$\begin{Vmatrix} 1.00 & .00 & .00 \\ .00 & 1.00 & .00 \\ .00 & .00 & 1.00 \end{Vmatrix} \qquad \begin{Vmatrix} -1.64 & 1.92 & .58 \\ -.13 & -.66 & 1.39 \\ 1.97 & -.17 & -.96 \end{Vmatrix}$$
$$\qquad\qquad \mathbf{I} \qquad\qquad\qquad\qquad \mathbf{A^{-1}}$$

The matrix on the left has now been reduced to the identity matrix, and the matrix on the right should be $\mathbf{A^{-1}}$ or the inverse of $\mathbf{A}$. The results may be checked by determining whether $\mathbf{A \cdot A^{-1}}$ gives the identity matrix. In order to do this we must, of course, apply the rules for multiplying matrices. Multiplying the two matrices we find that:

$$\begin{Vmatrix} .2 & .4 & .7 \\ .6 & .1 & .5 \\ .3 & .8 & .3 \end{Vmatrix} \cdot \begin{Vmatrix} -1.64 & 1.92 & .58 \\ -.13 & -.66 & 1.39 \\ 1.97 & -.17 & -.96 \end{Vmatrix} = \begin{Vmatrix} 1.00 & .00 & .00 \\ -.01 & 1.00 & .01 \\ .00 & .00 & 1.00 \end{Vmatrix}$$
$$\qquad \mathbf{A} \qquad\qquad\qquad \mathbf{A^{-1}} \qquad\qquad\qquad \mathbf{I}$$

The inverses of larger matrices can be found by the same routine operations.[10]

MATRIX GEOMETRY

Although it is not necessary to use graphical representation and geometrical concepts to work with factor-analysis problems, it is often helpful in order to visualize what is happening.

Geometric Representation of a Correlation Coefficient. If each test or variable being correlated is represented by a vector (V),[11] the correlation between two tests can be shown to be equal to the product of the length of the two vectors and the cosine of the angle (ϕ) between them, as is shown in the following formula: [12]

$$r_{12} = V_1 V_2 \cos \phi_{12} \tag{3.1}$$

If each test is represented by a vector of unit length, the correlation coefficient is equal to the cosine of the angle between them,

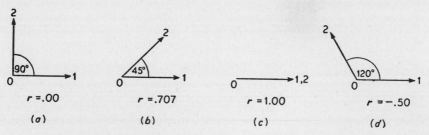

FIGURE 3.3 Vectorial representation of correlation coefficients.

as can be seen from the above formula. Since the cosine of an angle of 90° is 0.0, an r equal to zero can be represented by two unit-length vectors from a common origin at right angles (orthogonal) to each other as in Figure 3.3a. The cosine of 45° is equal to .707 (approximately), so an r of .707 can be represented by two unit-length vectors with an angle of 45° between them as in Figure 3.3b. The cosine of 0° is 1.0, and an r of 1.0 can be represented by two unit vectors with an angle of 0° between them or,

---

10 See p. 145 for a work sheet for this method.

11 A vector is a straight line with a given starting point, length, and direction.

12 This product is referred to as the scalar product. See Thurstone (1947c, p. 90) for a proof of this equation.

in other words, by one unit vector collinear with the other as in
Figure 3.3c. Any r between zero and +1.0 can be similarly represented by separating two unit vectors with the angle between 0°
and 90° whose cosine is equal to r. Negative correlations can be
represented similarly, but the angle between the vectors is obtuse
(between 90° and 180°). An r of −.50 can be represented by
two unit vectors separated by 120°, since the cosine of 120° is
−.50 as in Figure 3.3d. Any r between zero and −1.0 can be
represented by two unit vectors separated by the angle between
90° and 180° whose cosine is equal to r.[13]

Graphical Representation of a Table of Intercorrelations.
The diagram in Figure 3.4 is an attempt to represent all of the
intercorrelations in Table 3.7 geometrically
in two dimensions. The correlations between variables 1 and 2 and 1 and 3 are correctly represented. It will be observed, however, that the angles between vectors 1 and
2 and vectors 1 and 3 do not add up to the
angle between vectors 2 and 3. It would
therefore be necessary to resort to a three-
dimensional figure in order to represent the
three angles correctly. This may be re-
garded as a *geometrical* interpretation of the rank of a matrix.
The rank of a matrix is indicated by the number of dimensions

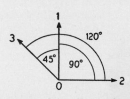

FIGURE 3.4   Illustration
to show that the correla-
tion matrix in Table 3.7
cannot be represented in
two dimensions.

TABLE 3.7.   CORRELATION MATRIX

	1	2	3
1	1.000	.000	.707
2	.000	1.000	-.500
3	.707	-.500	1.000

required correctly to represent the vectors and their angular separations. If they can be represented in one dimension (a straight

---

[13] In the examples given, a vector of unit length has been used. This would
be the correct representation of variables which could be measured with perfect
reliability and did not have any uncorrelated (specific) variance. If these conditions were not satisfied, the vectors would be of less than unit length and the correlation would be correspondingly reduced as indicated by formula 3.1.

line), the rank of the matrix is one, and only one reference vector (factor) is needed to represent the relationships. This would be true for four variables which satisfied Spearman's tetrad-difference criterion. If the vectors and their angular separations can be represented in two dimensions (a plane), the rank of the matrix is two, and only two factors are needed to account for the interrelationships. If the vectors and their relationships can be diagramed correctly only in three dimensions, the rank of the matrix, and hence the number of factors, would be three. Although we cannot visualize beyond three dimensions, the analogy holds. A matrix of rank n requires n dimensions to account for the interrelationships and has n factors.

TABLE 3.8.   INTERCORRELATIONS AMONG FOUR
VARIABLES

	1	2	3	4
1	(1.00)	.80	.96	.60
2	.80	(1.00)	.60	.00
3	.96	.60	(1.00)	.80
4	.60	.00	.80	(1.00)

Graphical Representation of a Table of Correlations in Two Dimensions. It will be recalled from plane geometry that two intersecting straight lines determine a plane. Any other line in the same plane can be expressed in terms of the first two lines and is said to be linearly dependent on them. The intercorrelations of 4 variables shown in Table 3.8 have been represented graphically in two dimensions in Figure 3.5. Since the relationships can be shown correctly in two dimensions, the rank of the 4×4 matrix is 2, and only 2 independent vectors are needed to account for all the interrelationships.

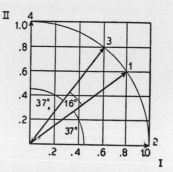

FIGURE 3.5   Vectorial representation of correlation coefficients in Table 3.8.

All four vectors can be expressed in terms of any two of the vectors. Vectors 2 and 4 are the most convenient, since they are at right angles (orthogonal) to each other, and the four vectors can be represented by the following equations: [14]

$$V_1 = .8V_2 + .6V_4$$
$$V_2 = 1.0V_2 + .0V_4$$
$$V_3 = .6V_2 + .8V_4$$
$$V_4 = .0V_2 + 1.0V_4$$

This is the equivalent of a factor analysis of the four variables in Table 3.8, although analyses usually are not done geometrically. Also practical problems are not so simple as this one and are done by other methods to be described later. It is seen that four variables can be accounted for in terms of two reference variables or factors, and a consequent parsimony is effected. When an analysis has been completed, resulting values are usually written in abbreviated matrix form as in Table 3.9. The values in columns

TABLE 3.9. FACTOR MATRIX

	Factor		
Variable	I	II	h^2
1	.8	.6	1.0
2	1.0	.0	1.0
3	.6	.8	1.0
4	.0	1.0	1.0

2 and 3 are referred to as factor loadings or saturations and may be used to interpret the hypothetical nature of the factors. A

---

[14] The equations are obtained by vector resolution. A vector may be resolved into component vectors by a number of vectors placed head to tail so that the tail of the first one coincides with the tail of the vector to be resolved and the head of the last one coincides with its head. Vector 1 in Figure 3.5 has been resolved into two such component vectors orthogonal to each other. Arithmetically this orthogonal case can be verified by the Pythagorean theorem that the square of the hypotenuse of a right triangle is equal to the sum of the squares of its sides. For some purposes it is preferable to have component vectors not orthogonal to each other. This is referred to as an oblique solution.

Vector　1

column labeled h^2 (communality) has been added. It is obtained by summing the squared factor loadings in each row and can be interpreted as that portion of the variance of each variable which is correlated with the other variables. (These values are also shown in the principal diagonal of Table 3.8.) The length of a test vector is equal to h (the square root of the communality). For the fictitious data presented above the communalities, and hence the test vector, are all equal to 1.0. For actual data the communality rarely attains a value of 1.0 due to unreliability and specific (uncorrelated) content of the variables. If the length of a vector is less than 1.0, the correlation with other variables is proportionately decreased since, it will be recalled, the correlation is equal to the scalar product of the length of the two vectors and the cosine of their angular separation (formula 3.1).

It may be observed from the example just presented that factor analysis is partly a method for determining (a) the number of dimensions needed to account for the interrelationships (correlations) of a set of variables, and (b) a set of arbitrary reference vectors (factors) in terms of which the vectors representing the variables can be expressed.

Reproducing the Table of Correlations from the Factor Matrix. Once the factor loadings have been obtained, it is possible to work back to obtain the correlations. The correlations may be computed by summing the cross-products of the rows of the factor matrix.[15] Thus to get r_{12} (.80), multiply the values in row 1 by the corresponding values in row 2 and summate (.6 $\times$ 0.0 + .8 $\times$ 1.0). For r_{24} (.00), summate the cross-products for rows 2 and 4 (.0 $\times$ 1.0 + 1.0 $\times$ .0). In this way an entire matrix of correlations can be "reproduced" from the factor loadings.

Graphical Representation of a Correlation Matrix in Three Dimensions. The correlation coefficients in Table 3.10 can be represented graphically in three dimensions. It will be observed in Table 3.10 that variable 3 has zero correlation coefficients with

---

[15] In matrix notation $\mathbf{R} = \mathbf{FF'}$, or the correlations matrix is equal to the product of the orthogonal factor matrix and its transpose. In the above example we can multiply rows by rows because we are multiplying not by $\mathbf{F'}$ but by its transpose. (See note 5 on p. 26.)

TABLE 3.10.   INTERCORRELATIONS OF TEN VARIABLES

	1	2	3	4	5	6	7	8	9	10
1	1.00	.96	.60	.48	.64	.80	.36	.48	.00	.70
2	.96	1.00	.80	.36	.48	.60	.48	.64	.00	.70
3	.60	.80	1.00	.00	.00	.00	.60	.80	.00	.50
4	.48	.36	.00	1.00	.96	.60	.64	.48	.80	.86
5	.64	.48	.00	.96	1.00	.80	.48	.36	.60	.82
6	.80	.60	.00	.60	.80	1.00	.00	.00	.00	.50
7	.36	.48	.60	.64	.48	.00	1.00	.96	.80	.86
8	.48	.64	.80	.48	.36	.00	.96	1.00	.60	.82
9	.00	.00	.00	.80	.60	.00	.80	.60	1.00	.70
10	.70	.70	.50	.86	.82	.50	.86	.82	.70	1.00

variables 6 and 9.   Variables 6 and 9 are also correlated zero with
each other.   The vectors for these three tests are at right angles

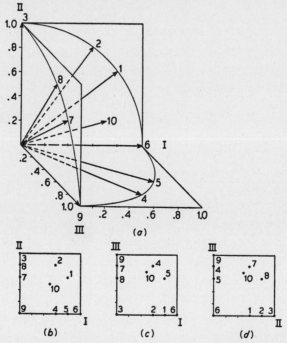

FIGURE 3.6 Graphical representation of correlation coefficients in Table 3.10.

to each other (cosine of $90° = .00$).   Unit-length vectors for the
ten variables in Table 3.10 are shown in their "correct" positions
in Figure 3.6a (i.e., all the unit length vectors are separated by

angles whose cosines are equal to the correlations between the variables). Vectors 1 and 2 are in the plane of vectors 3 and 6 and can be expressed as a linear combination of 3 and 6. Vectors 4 and 5 are in the plane formed by vectors 6 and 9 and can be expressed in terms of them. Similarly vectors 7 and 8 are in the plane formed by vectors 3 and 9. Vector 10 is not in any of these planes but is in the space bounded by vectors 3, 6, and 9 and can be expressed in terms of all three. If vectors 3, 6, and 9 are used as reference vectors (and called factors II, I, and III, respectively), we can read the loadings in the factor matrix in Table 3.11 from

TABLE 3.11. FACTOR LOADINGS

Variable	Factor I	Factor II	Factor III	h^2
1	.8	.6	.0	1.0
2	.6	.8	.0	1.0
3	.0	1.0	.0	1.0
4	.6	.0	.8	1.0
5	.8	.0	.6	1.0
6	1.0	.0	.0	1.0
7	.0	.6	.8	1.0
8	.0	.8	.6	1.0
9	.0	.0	1.0	1.0
10	.5	.5	.7	1.0

Figure 3.6a. Vector 1 can be expressed as .8 of factor I (vector 6), .6 of factor II (vector 3), and .0 of factor III (vector 9). The loadings for the other variables can be read similarly from the diagram. The reader can, if he desires, verify that the correlation coefficients can be "reproduced" from the summation of cross-products (e.g., $r_{12} = .6 \times .8 + .8 \times .6 + .0 \times .0 = .96$). Since the vectors representing the variables used in this example had unit length, the communality (h^2) of each variable is equal to 1.0.

The loadings of the variables on the factors can also be shown graphically in one plane at a time. This makes possible the graphical representation of any number of dimensions, two dimensions at a time. Figures 3.6b, c, and d show the three-dimensional example in Figure 3.6a in such two-dimensional graphs with the lower-numbered factor placed on the horizontal axis. To get a complete graphing for n factors requires $n(n - 1)/2$ graphs. These graphs can be made up by considering the factor loadings in each row of Table 3.11 as the coordinates of a test vector and plotting two columns at a time. It is customary in factor analysis to represent a vector by just a dot placed at its head, it being understood that the vector extends from the origin (intersection of the reference vectors) to the dot. .

Rotation of Reference Axes. A perennial criticism of factor analysis has been that there is no unique location for the frame

TABLE 3.12. FACTOR MATRIX

Variable	Factor I	II	h^2
1	.6	.4	.52
2	.6	.6	.72
3	.7	-.3	.58
4	.4	-.5	.41

of reference vectors. A given table of correlations has but a single configuration of vectors, but this configuration can be described with respect to an infinite number of locations of the frame of coordinate reference axes. Various locations of the reference frame can be obtained by rotating the reference axes about the origin.

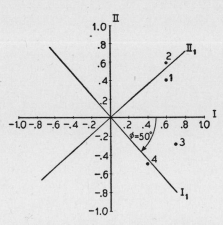

FIGURE 3.7 Graphical representation of Table 3.12 and rotation.

The four variables whose factor loadings are shown in Table 3.12 are represented graphically on two orthogonal reference axes (I and II) in Figure 3.7.

Any degree of rotation of the rotated reference axes (I and II) around the origin and in the plane could be used to represent the configuration of test vectors and hence the table of intercorrelations. However, with each new location of the axes the projections or *loadings* of the tests on the factors would be different. Axes may be rotated clockwise or counterclockwise any desired number of degrees without affecting the correlations among the variables. For a *clockwise* rotation of a pair of orthogonal axes I and II, the rotated factor loadings for a variable j may be calculated from the equations

$$a'_{j1} = a_{j1} \cos \phi - a_{j2} \sin \phi$$
$$a'_{j2} = a_{j1} \sin \phi + a_{j2} \cos \phi \qquad \text{(clockwise rotation)}$$

where ϕ represents the angle through which the axes are rotated, a'_{j1} represents the rotated loading of test j on factor I, a'_{j2} represents the rotated loading of test j on factor II, a_{j1} is the loading of test j on factor I prior to rotation, and a_{j2} is the loading of test j on factor II prior to rotation.

For rotation of a pair of orthogonal references axes in the *counterclockwise* direction the formulas are

$$a'_{j1} = a_{j1} \cos \phi + a_{j2} \sin \phi$$
$$a'_{j2} = -a_{j1} \sin \phi + a_{j2} \cos \phi \qquad \text{(counterclockwise rotation)}$$

The rotation can also be written in matrix form. For clockwise rotation the matrix, known as the transformation matrix and represented by the symbol Λ, is

$$\begin{vmatrix} \cos \phi & \sin \phi \\ -\sin \phi & \cos \phi \end{vmatrix}$$

(transformation matrix for 2 orthogonal axes rotated clockwise through an angle of ϕ degrees)

and for counterclockwise rotation

$$\begin{vmatrix} \cos \phi & -\sin \phi \\ \sin \phi & \cos \phi \end{vmatrix}$$

(transformation matrix for 2 orthogonal axes rotated counterclockwise through an angle of ϕ degrees)

The matrix multiplication of the factor matrix by the transformation matrix yields the rotated factor matrix:

Test	Factor	
	I	II
1	a_{11}	a_{12}
2	a_{21}	a_{22}
3	a_{31}	a_{32}
4	a_{41}	a_{42}
	F	

$$F \cdot \Lambda = F_1$$

$$\begin{vmatrix} \cos \phi & -\sin \phi \\ \sin \phi & \cos \phi \end{vmatrix} =$$

$$\Lambda$$

Test	Factor	
	I_1	II_1
1	a'_{11}	a'_{12}
2	a'_{21}	a'_{22}
3	a'_{31}	a'_{32}
4	a'_{41}	a'_{42}
	F_1	

in which $a'_{11} = a_{11} \cos \phi + a_{12} \sin \phi$, $a'_{12} = a_{11} (-\sin \phi) + a_{12} \cos \phi$, etc.

If factors I and II are rotated clockwise 50°, the rotated factor loadings can be read either directly from the graph or computed from the equations. The sine of 50° = .766, the cosine of 50° = .643.

The rotated loading of test 1 on factor I_1 is

$$(.6)(.643) - (.4)(.766) = (.3858) - (.3064) = .0794$$

The rotated loading of test 1 on factor II_1 is

$$(.6)(.766) + (.4)(.643) = (.4596) + (.2572) = .7168$$

The loadings of the other tests have been similarly computed in Table 3.13.

TABLE 3.13. COMPUTATION OF FACTOR LOADINGS FOR A CLOCKWISE ROTATION OF 50°

Test	1	2	3	4
$a_{j1} \cos \phi$	.3858	.3858	.4501	.2572
$-a_{j2} \sin \phi$	-.3064	-.4596	.2298	.3830
a'_{j1}	.0794	-.0738	.6799	.6402
$a_{j1} \sin \phi$	.4596	.4596	.5362	.3064
$a_{j2} \cos \phi$	.2572	.3858	-.1929	-.3215
a'_{j2}	.7168	.8454	.3433	-.0151

The rotated loadings to two decimal places are reported in Table 3.14. The communalities computed from the rotated loadings are a partial check on the accuracy of the calculations. Communalities should remain invariant within the margin of round-

TABLE 3.14. ROTATED FACTOR LOADINGS

Test	Factor I_1	II_2	h^2
1	.08	.72	.52
2	-.07	.85	.73
3	.68	.34	.58
4	.64	-.02	.41

ing error regardless of the amount of rotation or the number of factors.[16]

The rotated loadings can be obtained similarly either graphically or analytically for any degree of rotation of a pair of orthogonal axes clockwise or counterclockwise.

Considerations in determining the amount and direction of rotation will be presented in Chapters 7 and 8.

Summary of Vector Representation of the Correlation Matrix. The following summary of geometrical concepts which should serve as a useful review at this point has been adapted from Thurstone (1947c, pp. 98-100).

1. A frame of reference axes must be inserted into the test configuration before any factor matrix can be written.

2. Since the coordinate axes are not determined by the experimentally obtained correlation matrix, every factor matrix is in the nature of a factorial interpretation of the given correlations.

---

[16] The reason why the communality (h^2) remains invariant under rotation may be clearer from considering the accompanying diagram. From the Pythagorean theorem of geometry:

$$a_{j1}^2 + a_{j2}^2 = h_j^2 \quad \text{and} \quad a'^2_j + a'^2_j = h_j^2$$

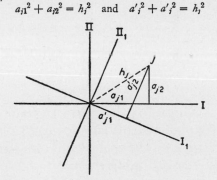

3. Each row of the orthogonal factor matrix can be interpreted as showing the rectangular components of a test vector.

4. Each column of a factor matrix identifies a factorial axis in the structure.

5. Each reference factor is represented by a unit-length reference vector (which can extend from $+1.0$ to -1.0).

6. The graphs on which are plotted pairs of columns of the factor matrix show the factorial structure which combines the test vectors and the reference frame.

7. If the entries in an orthogonal factor matrix are all positive or zero, all test vectors are in the first quadrant (or octant, etc.) and the structure has a positive manifold.

8. The correlation matrix can be interpreted as showing the scalar products of all pairs of test vectors.

9. The length of each test vector is equal to the positive square root of its communality.

10. The correlation matrix with known diagonal entries determines a unique configuration of test vectors that can be represented as a physical model if the rank of the matrix is less than 4.

11. The correlation matrix does not determine any reference frame.

12. No information is lost in representing the correlation matrix as a configuration or vice versa.

13. A positive correlation coefficient represents a pair of test vectors with acute angular separation. A negative correlation represents a pair of test vectors with obtuse angular separation.

14. A correlation matrix with coefficients that are all positive or zero determines a unique configuration of test vectors in which there are no obtuse angular separations.

15. The signs of all the entries in a column of the factor matrix may be reversed without altering the corresponding correlation matrix.

16. Reversing the signs in a column of the factor matrix reverses the direction of (i.e., reflects) the corresponding reference vector and reference factor.

17. If all of the signs are reversed in a row of the factor matrix, then all of the signs are reversed in the corresponding row and column of the correlation matrix.

18. To reverse the signs in a row of the factor matrix reverses the direction of the corresponding test vector.

19. The self-correlation of a test remains positive for all possible reversals of sign of tests and factors.

PROBLEMS

1. Post-multiply matrix **A** by matrix **B** and label the product matrix **C**.

$$
\left\|
\begin{array}{ccc}
.6 & .9 & .3 \\
.4 & .1 & .2 \\
.1 & .8 & .7
\end{array}
\right\|
\qquad
\left\|
\begin{array}{ccc}
.4 & .2 & .1 \\
.1 & .3 & .4 \\
.8 & .9 & .6
\end{array}
\right\|
$$

$$\qquad\qquad \mathbf{A} \qquad\qquad\qquad\qquad \mathbf{B}$$

2. Find the inverse of matrix **A**.

3. Check the calculation of the inverse matrix by the multiplication $\mathbf{A} \cdot \mathbf{A}^{-1} = \mathbf{I}$.

4. Check the multiplication in Problem 1, above, by the multiplication $\mathbf{B} = \mathbf{A}^{-1}\mathbf{C}$.

5. Post-multiply matrix **B** by matrix **A** and compare the results with the multiplication **AB** that you performed in Problem 1.

6. Rotate factors I and II in Table 3.12 counterclockwise 50°.

CHAPTER 4

Basic Assumptions of Factor Analysis

FIRST ASSUMPTION

A BASIC assumption of factor analysis is that a battery of intercorrelated variables has common factors running through it and that the scores of an individual can be represented more economically in terms of these reference factors. An individual's score on a test is dependent upon two things, the particular abilities assessed by the test and the amount of each of these abilities possessed by the examinee. This can be represented for r independent [1] factors by the equation:

$$s_{ji} = a_{j1}x_{1i} + a_{j2}x_{2i} + \cdots + a_{jr}x_{ri} \qquad (4.1)$$

where s_{ji} represents the standard score of individual i on test j, a_{jr} the factor loading of test j on factor r, and x_{ri} the amount, in standard scores of the uncorrelated trait measured by factor r which is possessed by individual i.

It is to be hoped, in the interests of parsimony, that the reference traits are fewer in number than the tests.

---

[1] The formula is more complex for correlated or "oblique" factors. For an advanced discussion of whether equations of the type of equation 4.1 can result in a unique set of loadings or weights, see Kestelman (1952).

It is of interest to note that even if all human behavior could be accounted for by a limited number of reference abilities, there would still be sufficient combinations of terms in equation 4.1 to insure each person in the world a unique pattern of abilities.

Types of Variance. The total variance [2] of a variable j may be subdivided into three general types—common, specific, and error variance. The common and specific variance combined make up the reliable variance and their combined value is usually indicated by the reliability coefficient.

Definition: **Common Variance** *is that portion of the total variance which correlates with other variables.*

Definition: **Specific Variance** *is that portion of the total variance which does not correlate with any other variable.*

Definition: **Error Variance** *is the chance variance due to errors of sampling, measurement, unstandardized conditions of testing, physiological and other changes within the individual, and the host of other influences which may contribute to unreliability. It is assumed to be uncorrelated with the reliable variance and other error variance.*

One function of factor analysis is to analyze the common variance to determine the number and types of common variances which result in the correlations between variables. The total variance of a variable j may be represented by the following equation: [3]

$$\sigma_j^2 = \underbrace{\sigma_{j1}^2 + \sigma_{j2}^2 + \cdots + \sigma_{jr}^2}_{\text{common variances}} + \underbrace{\sigma_{js}^2}_{\substack{\text{specific} \\ \text{variance}}} + \underbrace{\sigma_{je}^2}_{\substack{\text{error} \\ \text{variance}}} \quad (4.2)$$

Dividing both sides of equation 4.2 by σ_j^2.

$$\frac{\sigma_j^2}{\sigma_j^2} = 1.0 = \frac{\sigma_{j1}^2}{\sigma_j^2} + \frac{\sigma_{j2}^2}{\sigma_j^2} + \cdots + \frac{\sigma_{jr}^2}{\sigma_j^2} + \frac{\sigma_{js}^2}{\sigma_j^2} + \frac{\sigma_{je}^2}{\sigma_j^2} \quad (4.3)$$

The equation is now in standard-score form with the total variance of variable j equal to 1.0 and each type of variance expressed as a proportion of the total variance. For convenience we will repre-

---

[2] Variance (σ^2) is an index of the extent to which a test, or other variable, discriminates individual differences.

[3] There are assumed to be r contributors to *common* variances where the symbol r stands for the rank of the correlation matrix.

sent each type of variance by a letter symbol and equation 4.3 may be rewritten as follows:

$$1.0 = \underbrace{a_{j1}{}^2 + a_{j2}{}^2 + \cdots + a_{jr}{}^2}_{\text{common variances}} + \underbrace{s_j{}^2}_{\substack{\text{specific}\\\text{variance}}} + \underbrace{e_j{}^2}_{\substack{\text{error}\\\text{variance}}} \quad (4.4)$$

The values of the square roots of the common variances (a_{j1} through a_{jr}) are referred to as the factor loadings or saturations and (for independent factors) represent the amount of correlation

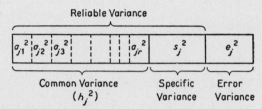

FIGURE 4.1   Diagrammatic representation of the total variance of a variable sub-divided into types of variance (in standard scores).

of test j with each factor.   The relationship may also be represented diagrammatically as in Figure 4.1.   This represents the **additive** assumption of factor analysis that the total variance of a test is the sum of its component variances.   The additive combination is a first approximation, appropriate to the present stage of accuracy of psychological measurements.   Later refinements may require ratios, products, or more complex types of combinations of factors.

It might be pointed out here that for purposes of prediction and the scientific identification of fundamental traits we are interested primarily in the common variances, since a variable will predict only to the extent to which it correlates with some criterion or other variable.   The specific variance, although it may be reliably measured, is of little scientific interest since it is not related to anything but itself.[4]

From equation 4.4 we can deduce some further relations and definitions.

---

[4] Specific variance, however, may serve to indicate areas which need further investigation, since it is potentially common-factor variance.

Definition: *The* **communality** *of variable* j *is the sum of its independent common variances and is represented by the symbol* h_j^2.

$$a_{j1}^2 + a_{j2}^2 + \cdots + a_{jr}^2 = h_j^2 \tag{4.5}$$

The total variance of variable j may now be represented by

$$h_j^2 + s_j^2 + e_j^2 = 1.0 \tag{4.6}$$

Since, as has been previously noted, the reliable variance of a test is the sum of its common and specific variances, it may be represented by the equation [5]

$$r_{jj} = h_j^2 + s_j^2 = 1 - e_j^2 \tag{4.7}$$

The communality of a variable is less than its reliability except for the limiting case in which the specific variance is equal to zero. Other relationships derivable from equation 4.7 which it may be of interest to observe are as follows:

$$h_j^2 = r_{jj} - s_j^2 \tag{4.8}$$

$$s_j^2 = r_{jj} - h_j^2 \tag{4.9}$$

Definition: *The* **uniqueness** *of variable* j *is that portion of the total variance which it does not have in common with any other variable and is represented by the symbol* u^2.

$$u_j^2 = s_j^2 + e_j^2 = 1 - h_j^2 \tag{4.10}$$

From equations 4.6 and 4.7 we also have

$$e_j^2 = 1 - (h_j^2 + s_j^2) = 1 - r_{jj} \tag{4.11}$$

SECOND ASSUMPTION

A second assumption of factor analysis is that the correlation between two variables j and k can be accounted for by

---

[5] r_{jj}, the *reliability* coefficient (not to be confused with r_{jk}, the *correlation* coefficient) represents a proportion of variance and does not need to be squared as do the other symbols in the formulas.

the nature and extent of their common factor loadings. For orthogonal factors this can be represented by the equation: [6]

$$r_{jk} = a_{j1}a_{k1} + a_{j2}a_{k2} + \cdots + a_{jr}a_{kr} \qquad (4.12)$$

This is the summation of cross-products referred to in Chapter 3, page 35, in reproducing correlation coefficients.

A number of interesting relationships among tests can be illustrated by the application of equation 4.12. Let us assume a matrix of factor loadings for three tests and a criterion on four factors as shown in Table 4.1. This can also be represented

TABLE 4.1

Test	Factor				h^2	s^2	r_{jj}
	I	II	III	IV			
1	.7	.0	.4	.3	.74	.12	.86
2	.0	.6	.0	.2	.40	.10	.50
3	.8	.1	.5	.0	.90	.05	.95
C	.3	.5	.6	.0	.70	.10	.80

schematically as in Figure 4.2, where the component variances are shown.

The correlation between tests 1 and 2 can be computed as follows:

$$r_{12} = (.7)(.0) + (.0)(.6) + (.4)(.0) + (.3)(.2) = .06$$

The correlation between tests 1 and 2 is seen to be due to their common loadings on factor IV alone.

The correlation between tests 1 and 3 is equal to

$$r_{13} = (.7)(.8) + (.0)(.1) + (.4)(.5) + (.3)(.0) = .76$$

The correlation between these two tests is due, in large part, to their common loadings on factor I and to a lesser extent to their loadings on factor III.

---

[6] This equation is derived from the basic equation of factor analysis for independent (orthogonal) factors, which in terms of matrix notation is

$$\mathbf{R = FF'} \qquad (4.13)$$

The equation indicates that the product of the factor matrix and its transpose is equal to the correlation matrix.

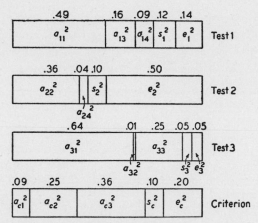

FIGURE 4.2 Digrammatic representation of the variances of the tests and criterion shown in Table 4.1.

The correlation between test 1 and the criterion is

$$r_{1C} = (.7)(.3) + (.0)(.5) + (.4)(.6) + (.3)(.0) = .45$$

This commonly is referred to as the validity coefficient for test 1. It will be observed that the validity of test 1 for this criterion is due to its having variance on factors I and III in common with the criterion variable.

The validity coefficients for tests 2 and 3 are

$$r_{2C} = (.0)(.3) + (.6)(.5) + (.0)(.6) + (.2)(.0) = .30$$
$$r_{3C} = (.8)(.3) + (.1)(.5) + (.5)(.6) + (.0)(.0) = .59$$

The validity of test 2 is due entirely to factor II, whereas the validity of test 3 seems to be a function of its complexity, since it measures three of the four factors.

Similarly, the other correlation and validity coefficients could be computed from Table 4.1.

From the equations for reproducing the validity coefficients of the tests some of the reasons why tests are valid, and what must be done to increase the validity of a test or a battery of tests, become apparent. This criterion is weighted in factors *A*, *B*, and *C*. Tests which are heavily weighted in these factors will have maximum validity for this criterion. To insure maximum validity for predicting a criterion all factors present in the criterion should

be represented in the test by a loading of like sign. The higher
the loading, the higher will be the validity. If a criterion has
considerable specific variance, tests should be sought which correlate with the specific variance and consequently transform it
into common-factor variance.[7]

PROBLEMS

Given the following data:

Variable	Factor					r_{jj}
	I	II	III	IV	V	
Test 1	.4	.4	.3	.5	.0	.74
Test 2	.6	.2	.0	.4	.0	.66
Test 3	.3	.6	.0	.2	.6	.90
Criterion	.1	.7	.3	.0	.5	.87

1. Compute the h^2 of test 1.
2. Which test has the largest specific variance?
3. Compute the uniqueness of test 2.
4. Compute the table of correlations for the four variables.
5. Which test is most valid for the criterion?
6. If test 1 were to be altered to increase its validity for the criterion, on which factor would it be most important to increase its
loading, and on which factor might it be most desirable to reduce its
loading?

---

[7] See Guilford (1948b).

CHAPTER 5

Diagonal and Centroid Methods of Factoring

THE FACTOR problem usually starts with a table of intercorrelations which is to be analyzed into factors. The principal diagonal of the correlation matrix, which should contain the correlation of a test with itself, is usually vacant. The various purposes of factoring call for different values to be inserted in the principal diagonal. Most commonly inserted is one of the following three values:

1. The communality (h_j^2) of variable j, which is that proportion of the total variance of a variable which is correlated with other variables.

2. The reliability (r_{jj}) of variable j, which is that proportion of the total variance of variable j, which can be correlated with itself.

3. Unity (1.0) which represents the self-correlation of variable j due to all of its variance including common, specific, and error variances.

For the scientific problem of studying the nature of the fundamental factors resulting in correlations, the communalities are usually inserted in the principal diagonal, since they will minimize the rank of the matrix, and the factors extracted will best reproduce the correlations. If it is desired to obtain factors which best account for that portion of the individual scores that is due to reliable variance, the reliabilities should be inserted in the principal diagonal since specific as well as common factors can then be obtained.

If it is desired to obtain factors which best reproduce the actual original individual scores with which the factor problem was started, unity should be inserted in the principal diagonal cells since the factors extracted will account for the error variance as well as the common and specific variances.

The communalities are inserted in the principal diagonal in most studies, and, since they usually are not known in advance, they must be estimated. In those relatively rare cases where they are known in advance or can be very accurately estimated, the diagonal method of factoring can be applied. The diagonal method is also used as one of the steps in the multiple-group method to be presented in the next chapter.

THE DIAGONAL METHOD

The diagonal method of extracting factors from a correlation matrix is one of the most simple and direct. Its usefulness in most problems, however, is limited by the fact that it requires very accurate estimates of the communalities. 'The method can be applied to tables of correlations of any size.

Numerical Example. By way of illustration, the correlation matrix in Table 5.1 will be factored by the diagonal method. The communalities of the variables in this fictitious problem are

TABLE 5.1. CORRELATION MATRIX WITH KNOWN COM-
MUNALITIES INSERTED IN THE PRINCIPAL DIAGONAL

Variable	1	2	3	4	5
1	(.52)	.48	.36	.40	.58
2	.48	(.64)	.00	.16	.72
3	.36	.00	(.81)	.63	.09
4	.40	.16	.63	(.53)	.25
5	.58	.72	.09	.25	(.82)

known in advance and have been inserted in the principal diagonal.

The general form of the table of *factor loadings* is shown in literal form in Table 5.2. It will be observed that all the entries

TABLE 5.2. GENERAL FORM OF THE FACTOR MATRIX OBTAINED BY THE DIAGONAL METHOD

Variable	Factor					h^2
	I	II	III	IV	V	
1	a_{11}	0	0	0	0	$h_1{}^2$
2	a_{21}	a_{22}	0	0	0	$h_2{}^2$
3	a_{31}	a_{32}	a_{33}	0	0	$h_3{}^2$
4	a_{41}	a_{42}	a_{43}	a_{44}	0	$h_4{}^2$
5	a_{51}	a_{52}	a_{53}	a_{54}	a_{55}	$h_5{}^2$

to the right of the principal diagonal are zeros. The number of factors is unknown at this point in the analysis. Room has been left for as many factors as there are variables, although, it is to be hoped that fewer factors than tests will be needed. The value of $a_{11}{}^2$ is equal to $h_1{}^2$, since it will be recalled that the communality of a test variable is the sum of the squares of its common factor loadings and the loadings for variable 1 on factors other than I are zeros. Hence,

$$a_{11} = \sqrt{h_1{}^2} = \sqrt{.52} = .7211 \quad (5.1)$$

Geometrically, this is the equivalent of passing factor I through test 1. The loading of test 1 on other factors will then be zeros if the other factors are placed orthogonal to factor I.

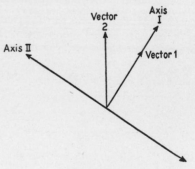

FIGURE 5.1 Illustration of the location of the first diagonal-method axis collinear with test-vector 1, and the second axis orthogonal to the first and in the plane determined by vectors 1 and 2.

The loading of the other variables on factor I may then be obtained if it is recalled that the correlation between two variables is equal to the cross-products of the common-factor loadings.

Thus

$$r_{12} = a_{11}a_{21} + a_{12}a_{22} + a_{13}a_{23} + a_{14}a_{24} + a_{15}a_{25}$$

Since each product after the first involves a zero, the formula reduces to

$$r_{12} = a_{11}a_{21} \text{ or } a_{21} = \frac{r_{12}}{a_{11}}$$

Substituting the known values for r_{12} and a_{11}

$$a_{21} = \frac{r_{12}}{a_{11}} = \frac{.48}{.7211} = .6656$$

Similarly,

$$a_{31} = \frac{r_{13}}{a_{11}} = \frac{.36}{.7211} = .4992$$

$$a_{41} = \frac{r_{14}}{a_{11}} = \frac{.40}{.7211} = .5547$$

$$a_{51} = \frac{r_{15}}{a_{11}} = \frac{.58}{.7211} = .8043$$

These values have been placed in the first column of the factor matrix in Table 5.3. The general formula for obtaining the

TABLE 5.3.   FACTOR LOADINGS DERIVED BY THE DIAGONAL METHOD OF FACTORING

Test	Factor					h^2
	I	II	III	IV	V	
1	.7211	0	0	0	0	.52
2	.6656	.4438	0	0	0	.64
3	.4992	-.7489	.000	0	0	.81
4	.5547	-.4714	.000	.000	0	.53
5	.8043	.4161	.000	.000	.000	.82

loading for the jth variable of the first column after the value for a_{11} has been determined is

$$a_{j1} = \frac{r_{1j}}{a_{11}} \tag{5.2}$$

It will be observed in Table 5.2 that all the common-factor variance of test 2 is accounted for on the first two factors, or

$$a_{21}{}^2 + a_{22}{}^2 = h_2{}^2$$

This is equivalent, geometrically, to putting the second factor orthogonal to the first in the plane determined by the first two test vectors. The loading of test 2 on all factors orthogonal to the first two will then be zero. Since the values of a_{21} and $h_2{}^2$ are known or have been determined, we can solve for a_{22}.

$$a_{22} = \sqrt{h_2{}^2 - a_{21}{}^2} = \sqrt{.64 - (.6656)^2} = .4438 \qquad (5.3)$$

By using the formula for reproducing the correlation coefficients from the cross-products, the remaining loadings on factor II may be obtained.

$$r_{23} = a_{21}a_{31} + a_{22}a_{32} + a_{23}a_{33} + a_{24}a_{34} + a_{25}a_{35}$$

Since each product after the second involves a zero, the formula reduces to

$$r_{23} = a_{21}a_{31} + a_{22}a_{32} \text{ and } a_{32} = \frac{r_{23} - a_{21}a_{31}}{a_{22}}$$

Substituting the known values,

$$a_{32} = \frac{r_{23} - a_{21}a_{31}}{a_{22}} = \frac{.00 - (.6656)(.4992)}{.4438} = -.7489$$

Similarly,

$$a_{42} = \frac{r_{24} - a_{21}a_{41}}{a_{22}} = \frac{.16 - (.6656)(.5547)}{.4438} = -.4714$$

$$a_{52} = \frac{r_{25} - a_{21}a_{51}}{a_{22}} = \frac{.72 - (.6656)(.8043)}{.4438} = .4161$$

The general formula for obtaining the loading of test j on the second factor after loading a_{22} and the loadings on the first factor have been determined is

$$a_{j2} = \frac{r_{2j} - a_{21}a_{j1}}{a_{22}} \qquad (5.4)$$

The values for the second factor have been entered in column II of Table 5.3.

When starting on a new factor, the first step is always to find the loading in the principal diagonal cell for that column. For factor III

$$a_{31}^2 + a_{32}^2 + a_{33}^2 = h_3^2$$

and   (5.5)

$$a_{33} = \sqrt{h_3^2 - (a_{31}^2 + a_{32}^2)}$$

Substituting the known values

$$a_{33} = \sqrt{.81 - (.4992^2 + .7489^2)} = .0072$$

This value is within rounding error of .00. Each successive test should, in turn, be interchanged with test 3. If loading a_{33} is within rounding error of zero, regardless of which test is put third, there are only two common factors and the analysis is completed. If loading a_{jj} is zero regardless of which test is placed in the jth position, there are $j - 1$ factors. In our example, a_{33} is within rounding error of zero regardless of which of the remaining tests is placed third. The rank of the correlation matrix is therefore two, and only two factors are needed to account for the correlation.

If the value of a_{33} had been significantly greater than zero, the remaining values in the column would have been obtained by means of the formula for reproducing correlation coefficients, just as they were in columns 1 and 2 of Table 5.3. The general formula for loading a_{kj} (i.e., the loading of test k on factor j) when it is a loading to the left of the principal diagonal can be obtained from the following formulas:

$$r_{jk} = a_{j1}a_{k1} + a_{j2}a_{k2} + \cdots + a_{jj}a_{kj} + \cdots + a_{jr}a_{kr}$$

All products after the jth contain a zero term and vanish and the formula reduces to

$$r_{jk} = a_{j1}a_{k1} + a_{j2}a_{k2} + \cdots + a_{jj-1}a_{kj-1} + a_{jj}a_{kj}$$

and

$$a_{kj} = \frac{r_{jk} - (a_{j1}a_{k1} + a_{j2}a_{k2} + \cdots + a_{jj-1}a_{kj-1})}{a_{jj}}$$ (5.6)

The general formula for finding loading a_{jj} (i.e., the loading of test j in principal diagonal cell of factor J) is obtained from the formulas

$$a_{j1}^2 + a_{j2}^2 + a_{j3}^2 + \cdots + a^2{}_{j,\,j-1} + a_{jj}^2 = h_j^2$$

and

$$a_{jj} = \sqrt{h_j^2 - (a_{j1}^2 + a_{j2}^2 + a_{j3}^2 + \cdots + a^2{}_{j,\,j-1})} \quad (5.7)$$

Summary of Routine for Diagonal Method. 1. Obtain the loading of test 1 on factor I by the formula

$$a_{11} = \sqrt{h_1^2} \quad (5.1)$$

2. Fill in zeros for the loadings of test 1 on the remaining factors.

3. Obtain the loadings of the other tests on factor I from the formulas

$$a_{21} = \frac{r_{12}}{a_{11}}$$

$$a_{31} = \frac{r_{13}}{a_{11}}$$

$$a_{j1} = \frac{r_{1j}}{a_{11}} \quad (5.2)$$

4. Obtain the loading of test 2 on factor II from the formula

$$a_{22} = \sqrt{h_2^2 - a_{21}^2} \quad (5.3)$$

5. Fill in zeros for the loadings of test 2 on the remaining factors.

6. Obtain the loadings of the other tests on factor II from the formulas

$$a_{32} = \frac{r_{23} - a_{21}a_{31}}{a_{22}}$$

$$a_{42} = \frac{r_{24} - a_{21}a_{41}}{a_{22}}$$

$$a_{j2} = \frac{r_{2j} - a_{21}a_{j1}}{a_{22}} \quad (5.4)$$

7. For each column first obtain the value in the principal diagonal cell. For test j use the formula

$$a_{jj} = \sqrt{h_j{}^2 - (a_{j1}{}^2 + a_{j2}{}^2 + \cdots + a^2{}_{j,\,j-1})} \qquad (5.7)$$

If the value of a_{jj} is within rounding-error of zero, try each subsequent test in place of test j. If they all give esentially zero values for a_{jj}, there are $j-1$ factors. If any gives a value greater than zero, interchange it with variable j and obtain the remaining loadings on factor J in the usual manner.

8. The loading of test k on factor J may be obtained from the general formula

$$a_{kj} = \frac{r_{jk} - (a_{j1}a_{k1} + a_{j2}a_{k2} + \cdots + a_{j,\,j-1}a_{k,\,j-1})}{a_{jj}} \qquad (5.6)$$

9. The accuracy of the computations may be checked by computing the communalities and intercorrelations from the factor loadings. They should agree with the original values within the margin of rounding error.

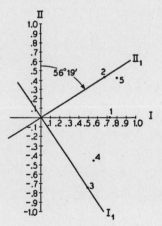

10. The factor loadings of each variable may be considered its coordinates on a system of orthogonal reference axes and the configuration of test vectors plotted. The factor loadings in Table 5.3 have been plotted in Figure 5.2. Since there are but two factors, only one 2-dimensional graph is needed to represent them. The reference axes may be rotated any number of degrees in the plane. A clockwise rotation of 56° 19′ would yield a convenient set of reference axes since all factor loadings would

FIGURE 5.2 Clockwise rotation of factors obtained by the diagonal method.

be positive and in a single quadrant. The rotated factor loadings are given in Table 5.4.

The diagonal method of factoring is theoretically correct and can be used with any size correlational matrix. It is very sensitive to the values of the communalities, however, and should be used only when very accurate estimates of them are available.

TABLE 5.4. ROTATED VALUES OF LOADINGS DERIVED BY THE DIAGONAL METHOD

Variable	Factor		h^2
	I_1	II_1	
1	.4	.6	.52
2	.0	.8	.64
3	.9	.0	.81
4	.7	.2	.53
5	.1	.9	.82

THE CENTROID METHOD

The method of factoring the correlational matrix which has probably been used the most frequently with experimental data is the complete centroid method developed by Thurstone (1947c, Chap. 8). Although it does not give a mathematically unique, least-squares solution, as does the principal-axes method to be described later (see p. 99), it is based on summations and is computationally less laborious.

In order to represent geometrically the steps involved in the extraction of centroid factors, let us consider a simple, two-dimensional example. The configuration of the five tests, whose intercorrelations are shown in Table 5.5, is represented in two dimensions in Figure 5.3. For the two-dimensional case, the first centroid axis is passed through the center (or centroid) of the configuration of test vectors in such a manner that the sum of the positive projections of the test vectors on the second centroid axis (which is in the plane and is orthogonal to the first centroid axis) are equal to the sum of the negative projections on that axis.[1] After the projections (or loadings) on the first centroid axis have been noted, the *residual* correlations among the tests in the second factor (and in the case of r factors in the $r - 1$ remaining dimensions) are obtained. In order to extract the loadings on the second centroid factor, the direction of some of the test vectors are re-

---

[1] This gives a null vector as the resultant for the configuration of residual test vectors in the dimensions remaining after the first centroid axis has been removed. The sum of the residual correlation coefficients in the remaining dimensions is zero. This could be verified for the example by obtaining the algebraic sum of the projections on axis II in Figure 5.3.

versed (reflected). The goal of this process of reflection is to make the resultant of the test vectors on the second factor (and remaining factors if more than two are involved) as large as possible. This will give a centroid point as distant from the origin as is

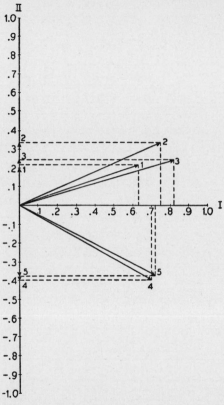

FIG. 5.3 Location of the first and second centroid factors and residual vectors for a configuration of five tests in two dimensions.

possible and permit the extraction of a maximum amount of variance with the second and succeeding centroid factors. For the example in Figure 5.3 this could be accomplished by reflecting the residual vectors for variables 4 and 5 on axis II. This would result in all of the residual vectors on axis II going in the same direction and would maximize their resultant vector. The computation of centroid loadings is a relatively straightforward mathematical procedure and does not necessarily require the understanding of the above geometrical considerations.

TABLE 5.5. CORRELATION MATRIX AND COMPUTATIONS
FOR THE FIRST CENTROID LOADINGS

Test	1	2	3	4	5	Σ_{j1}
1	(.54)	.50	.54	.33	.38	1.75
2	.50	(.71)	.71	.39	.41	2.01
3	.54	.71	(.71)	.49	.50	2.24
4	.33	.39	.49	(.65)	.65	1.86
5	.38	.41	.50	.65	(.65)	1.94
Σ_{j1}	1.75	2.01	2.24	1.86	1.94	$\Sigma\Sigma_{j1} = 9.80$
t_{j1}	2.29	2.72	2.95	2.51	2.59	$T_1 = 13.06$
a_{j1}	.634	.753	.816	.695	.717	$\sqrt{T_1} = 3.613862$
						$\dfrac{1}{\sqrt{T_1}} = .276712$
						$\Sigma a_{j1} = 3.615$ (Check)

Computation of the First Centroid Loadings. The correlation matrix in Table 5.5 will be used to illustrate the steps in the centroid method.

1. If, as is usually the case with experimental data, the communalities of the tests are not known, they may be estimated from the data at hand. One simple method of estimating the communality of a test is to guess it to be equal to the highest correlation of that test with any other variable in the correlation table.[2] The highest correlation in each column has been inserted in the principal diagonal cell of Table 5.5, in parentheses. This value is a first estimate of the communality of the test and is always positive regardless of the sign of the highest correlation coefficient in the column.

2. Add each column algebraically, omitting the diagonal values, and place the totals in the first row, below the matrix, labeled "Σ_{j1}."

---

[2] The justification for this method of estimating the communality is that the length of a test vector can be estimated by its projection on the vector closest to it. Other methods for estimating communalities will be referred to below.

3. Add each row algebraically, omitting the diagonal values, and place the totals in the first column to the right of the matrix, labeled "Σ_{j1}." The corresponding row and the column Σ's should check. *The importance of using checks for every step in the computations can hardly be overemphasized. They will save much time and effort in the long run.*

4. Usually the column totals of a table of intercorrelations are all positive. However, if any of the column totals are negative, it is necessary to go through a process of reflection at this point. In the example given in Table 5.5, all column totals are positive, and so reflection at this point is unnecessary. The reflection process will be explained in connection with the first table of residuals, Table 5.6, in which the column totals are negative.

5. Add the estimate of the communality of each variable to the column total of that variable. This row of totals is labeled t_{j1} (see Table 5.5).

6. Add the sums across in row t_{j1}. The sum of row t_{j1} gives the value T_1 which is the total sum of all of the values in the table.

7. Compute $\sqrt{T_1}$ and $1/\sqrt{T_1}$.

8. Multiply each entry in row t_{j1} by $1/\sqrt{T_1}$. The resulting values are the factor loadings on centroid factor I (a_{j1}) and are placed in the row directly below row t_{j1}.

$$a_{j1} = t_{j1} \left(\frac{1}{\sqrt{T_1}} \right) \tag{5.8}$$

9. A partial check on the computations is that $\Sigma a_{j1} = \sqrt{T_1}$.

10. Place the factor loadings vertically in the first column of a factor matrix. (See Table 5.8.)

11. For the first centroid factor, the loadings of variables which have been reflected are negative, and the loadings of variables which have *not* been reflected are positive. In the present example none of the variables have been reflected, and all of the loadings on the first factor are positive. They have been so entered in Table 5.8.

Computation of the Residual Correlation Matrix. 1. Prepare a tabular matrix form and number the columns and rows. (See Table 5.6.)

2. Place each of the first-factor loadings, without sign, above the corresponding column number for each variable. Also place the factor loadings in the cells to the left of the corresponding row numbers. (See Table 5.6.) When using factor loadings to compute residuals, *all factor loadings are considered to be positive*, regardless of their sign in the factor matrix.

3. Residual correlations are computed by subtracting the product of the factor loading of the column and the factor loading of the row, from the value in the corresponding cell of the preceding correlation or residual-correlation matrix. The result is placed in the corresponding cell of the new residual correlation matrix. The formula is

$$_1\rho_{jk} = r_{jk} - |a_{j1} \cdot a_{k1}| \tag{5.9}$$

where $_1\rho_{jk}$ is the first residual-correlation between variables j and k.

Example: To find the residual in cell$_{31}$ (Table 5.6), subtract from the value in cell$_{31}$ of the preceding matrix (Table 5.5) the absolute product of the factor loadings of row 3 and column 1:

$$_1\rho_{31} = .54 - (.816)(.634) = .023$$

4. Diagonal residual values are equal to the preceding *estimated* diagonal values minus the square of the factor loading of that variable.

5. The algebraic sum of each column (or row) of the new residual correlation matrix, Σ_0, should be equal to zero (within the margin of error due to rounding). This serves as a partial check on the accuracy of the computations.

6. From this point, the process of extracting loadings for the next factor is the same as the method described for the correlation matrix except that it is necessary to reflect some of the variables and to *re-estimate* the communality for each test in every residual correlation matrix. The communalities may be re-estimated by inserting the highest *residual* correlation of each column, regardless of sign, in the diagonal cell of that column immediately above the residual communality. The estimated communality

TABLE 5.6. FIRST RESIDUAL-CORRELATION MATRIX

a_{j1}		(.634)	(.753)	(.816)	*(.695)	*(.717)	
	Test	1	2	3	4	5	Σ_0
(.634)	1	.111 (.138)	.023	.023	±.111	±.075	−.002
(.753)	2	.023	.133 (.143)	.096	±.133	±.130	−.001
(.816)	3	.023	.096	.096 (.044)	±.077	±.085	.001
*(.695)	4	±.111	±.133	±.077	.152 (.167)	.152	−.002
*(.717)	5	±.075	±.130	±.085	.152	.152 (.136)	−.002
	Σ_0	−.002	−.001	.001	−.002	−.002	(Check)
	Σ_{j2}	−.140	−.144	−.043	−.169	−.138	$\Sigma\Sigma_{j2}=-.634$
Column 4		.082	.122	.111	.169	−.442	.042
	5	.232	.382	.281	.473	.442	1.810
	t_{j2}	.343	.515	.377	.625	.594	$T_2 = 2.454$
	a_{j2}	.219	.329	.241	.399	.379	$\sqrt{T_2} = 1.566524$
							$\dfrac{1}{\sqrt{T_2}} = .638356$
							$\Sigma a_{j2} = 1.567$

has a positive sign regardless of the sign of the correlation coefficient from which it is estimated. These re-estimated values will not be used, however, until step 11a in the next section.

Reflection. If any of the column sums (omitting diagonal values) Σ_{j2} of the table of residuals are negative, it is necessary to reflect certain of the rows and corresponding columns of the table of residuals. This will be the case for all residual tables of centroid factors. The goal of the process of reflection is to make the total algebraic sum of all the values in the table as highly pos-itive as is possible. This may be accomplished by the following steps:

1. Sum the column totals (Σ_{j2}) and place their total ($\Sigma\Sigma_{j2}$) at the right of the row of totals. (See Table 5.6.)

2. Select the column with the largest negative total (column 4 in Table 5.6). Copy the column total in the row immediately below, with the sign changed to positive. Label this row with the number of the variable being reflected.

3. Place an asterisk at the head of the reflected column and also in front of the number of the corresponding row, to indicate that the variable is reflected.

4. In each column, other than the one being reflected, *double* the value of the residual in the row being reflected, change its sign, and add that amount to the column total. Enter the new sum in the corresponding cell of the next row labeled column 4.

Example: To get the value in the first column for the row labeled "Col. 4," double the value in the fourth row, first column $(-.111)$, change its sign and add to the total for column 1.

$$-.140 + 2(.111) = .082$$

5. After all the values in the new row have been obtained in this way, they should be totaled. If the computations have been correct, the row total should be equal to the total of the previous row plus four times the total of the column which has just been reflected. This check should be satisfied for each row before proceeding to the next reflection.

Example: $-.634 + 4(.169) = .042.$

6. If any of the new column totals are negative, select the column with the highest negative total as the next column to be reflected.

7. Repeat the process in steps 1 to 4 above, using the adjusted column totals in the previous row in place of the original column totals. However, in columns which have been previously reflected once, the signs are *not* reversed before adding the doubled value (step 4).

Sometimes in carrying out the process of reflection it is necessary to reflect a given column (and corresponding row) more than once in the same table. For the first, third (or any odd) reflection, the sign of the doubled value should be changed before adding it to the adjusted column total as suggested in step 4. For the second (or any even-numbered) reflection, the sign of the doubled value is retained for the addition.

8. In order that previously reflected columns may be located easily, it is advisable to underline successive totals of reflected columns. (See Table 5.6.)

9. Continue this process of reflection until all column totals are zero or positive, applying for each row the check mentioned in step 5.[3]

10. Change the signs of the values in the correlation or residual matrix as follows:

    a. Reverse the signs of all reflected row values not in reflected columns.

    b. Reverse the signs of all reflected column values not in reflected rows.

11. The factor loadings for the next factor are then obtained by the steps mentioned previously and reviewed below:

    a. To the last row of adjusted column sums add the re-estimated communality for each column. These sums are the values in row t_{j2}.

    b. The sum of the values in row t_{j2} is Σt_{j2} or T_2.

    c. The factor loading for variable j on the second factor is

$$a_{j2} = t_{j2} \left(\frac{1}{\sqrt{T_2}} \right) \tag{5.10}$$

12. Place the loadings in the appropriate column of the matrix of centroid factor loadings (Table 5.8). The second centroid factor is placed in column II, etc.

13. The signs of the centroid loadings are determined as follows:

    a. The sign of a variable that has been reflected once (or one reflected an odd number of times) is the opposite of its sign on the preceding factor.

    b. The sign of a variable which has *not* been reflected (or one reflected an even number of times) is the same as its sign on the preceding factor. For example, if there are four centroid factors, a variable which has been reflected once in the first and second tables of *residuals* would have the following pattern of signs:

---

[3] Since the order of selecting variables for reflection is arbitrary, occasionally the table total can be made higher by continuing the process of reflection beyond this point on a trial-and-error basis (or see Holley (1947) for a criterion for reflection).

	Factor			
	I	II	III	IV
Variable	+	−	+	+

14. The second and subsequent tables of residuals are obtained by the same procedure as was used to obtain the first one. The product of the two loadings is subtracted from the corresponding residual correlation in the preceding table with its sign after reflection. The formula for the second residual is

$$_2\rho_{jk} = {}_1\rho_{jk} - a_{j2}a_{k2} \qquad (5.11)$$

where $_2\rho$ stands for the second residual, and the formula for the sth residual is

$$_s\rho_{jk} = {}_{s-1}\rho - a_{js}a_{ks} \qquad (5.12)$$

Table 5.7 presents the second residual correlations for the example.

TABLE 5.7. SECOND RESIDUAL-CORRELATION MATRIX

a_{j2}	Test	.219, 1	.329 2	.241 3	.399 4	.379 5	Σ_0
.219	1	.063	−.049	−.030	.024	−.008	.000
.329	2	−.049	.025	.017	.002	.005	.000
.241	3	−.030	.017	.038	−.019	−.006	.000
.399	4	.024	.002	−.019	−.007	.001	.001
.379	5	−.008	.005	−.006	.001	.008	.000
	Σ_0	.000	.000	.000	.001	.000	

15. For small batteries of fewer than 10 variables, the estimated communalities inserted in the diagonals of the correlation matrix should be compared with the communalities obtained from the factor loadings. If the discrepancies are large enough so that inserting the newly obtained communalities would affect the size of the first factor loadings appreciably, the entire analysis may be repeated as many times as may be necessary, using the obtained communalities in the diagonals, until the communality estimates are stabilized.

TABLE 5.8. CENTROID FACTOR MATRIX

	Factor	
Test	I	II
1	.63	.22
2	.75	.33
3	.82	.24
4	.70	−.40
5	.72	−.38

16. A check on the correctness of the factor loadings can be obtained by reproducing the correlations from the factor loadings. The discrepancy between a reproduced and original correlation should be equal to the corresponding residual correlation in the table of residuals computed subsequent to the last centroid factor extracted. This check is illustrated in connection with the eleven-variable centroid problem (see p. 84).

Minimum Number of Variables to Determine *r* Common Factors. The minimum number of variables needed to determine uniquely *r* factors is given mathematically by the formula: [4]

$$n = \frac{2r + 1 + \sqrt{8r + 1}}{2}$$

TABLE 5.9. MINIMUM NUMBER OF VARIABLES (*n*) NEEDED TO DETERMINE *r* FACTORS

r	n
1	3
2	5
3	6
4	8
5	9
6	10
7	12
8	13
9	14
10	15

Values for *n* corresponding to various numbers of factors are presented in Table 5.9.

---

[4] See Thurstone (1947c, 291-294).

By solving the above formula for r we can determine the maximum numbers of factors which can be uniquely determined by n variables.

$$r = \frac{2n + 1 - \sqrt{8n + 1}}{2}$$

In a factorial study, it is desirable to *overdetermine* the factors by having them represented by more than the minimum number of tests.

Although there are no exact methods for determining the number of factors contained in a matrix of empirical correlations, several approximate criteria have been suggested and will be presented in connection with the eleven-variable illustration in the next section.

EXAMPLE OF AN ANALYSIS OF AN ELEVEN-VARIABLE PROBLEM BY THE CENTROID METHOD

In Table 5.10 are presented the intercorrelations of eleven tests which were part of a battery of tests used by the U. S. Army Air Forces during World War II. The battery was used to classify aviation cadets into training assignments for aircrew positions such as pilot, bombardier, and navigator.

Description of Tests.[5] (1) *Dial and Table Reading.* The total scores for this test are composed of the scores from two separate parts, Dial Reading and Table Reading, which are contained in a single test booklet. Dial Reading measures how quickly and accurately the examinee can read the dials on an instrument panel. This part contains 57 items; the time limit is 9 minutes. Table Reading has two sub-parts. The first consists of a large bivariate table in which the examinee is given a pair of marginal values and is required to find the entry in the body of the table corresponding to these values. In the second sub-part the examinee must determine which one of four tables to enter to find the pair of numbers called for in the specific item. In Table

---

[5] For a complete description of these tests including directions, sample items, scoring formulas, distributions, reliability and validation statistics, see Guilford (1947b).

Reading, sub-part I has 43 problems with a time limit of 8 minutes, part II has 43 problems with a time limit of 7 minutes.

(2) *Spatial Orientation I.* This is a perceptual-speed test using aerial photographs as content. The examinee is required to locate small sections of an aerial photograph within a larger picture. The test contains 9 large photographs and 49 small cut-out photographs to be matched to the large photographs. The time limit is 5 minutes.

(3) *Reading Comprehension.* This reading-comprehension test was designed to measure understanding of paragraph material and ability to make inferences based on material read. An attempt was made to minimize mechanical and numerical content in the material presented. Material was included on navigation, physics, map reading, and astronomy. There are eight such paragraphs with 36 questions to be answered. The time allowed is 30 minutes.

(4) *Instrument Comprehension.* The original form of this test was the first of the tests used in the aviation psychology program which require the determination of the location of a plane from views of instruments or terrain as seen from the cockpit. Because of its validity, this area was explored intensively, and other factorially similar tests were constructed. In this test each item consists of pictures of two instruments, an artificial horizon and a compass, followed by pictures of a plane in five attitudes. The problem is to determine which of the five planes has a position and direction consistent with the instrument readings. There are 60 items in the test; the time allowed is 15 minutes.

(5) *Mechanical Principles.* The idea for this test was derived from existing tests such as Thurstone's Mechanical Movements test and Bennett and Fry's Mechanical Comprehension test. Each item consists of a pictured mechanical situation, with questions about it designed to test the examinee's ability to understand mechanical forces and movements. There are 40 items; the time allowed is 20 minutes.

(6) *Speed of Identification.* This is a perceptual-speed test similar to Thurstone's Identical Forms test; it requires the match-

ing of airplane silhouettes. The examinee must choose one of five silhouettes at the right which corresponds to the silhouette on the left. The test consists of 12 sets of planes with a total of 48 items. The time limit is 4 minutes.

(7 and 8) *Numerical Operations I and Numerical Operations II*. This is a simple numerical-computation test, scored in two parts for this analysis. The 100 problems printed on the front of the I.B.M. sheet (test 7) involve addition and multiplication. The 80 problems on the back (test 8) involve subtraction and division. The time limit for each test is 5 minutes.

(9) *Mechanical Information*. This is a verbally stated mechanical-knowledge test, relating particularly to the operation of parts of automobiles. Most of the items are quite brief, calling for only a limited amount of reading and requiring quite specific mechanical knowledge. There are 30 items; the time allowed is 12 minutes.

(10) *Practical Judgment*. This test requires the solving of verbally presented problem situations. A number of bits of factual information are presented; the examinee is required to determine the most practical course of action among the five proposed alternatives. There are 30 items; the time allowed is 30 minutes.

(11) *Complex Coordination*. This is an apparatus test of the speed and accuracy of hand and foot adjustment to a complex perceptual stimulus. The examinee operates controls similar to those used in an airplane in flight. The subject faces a stimulus panel on which there are three rows of red lights and three corresponding rows of green lights. A particular pattern of red lights, one light in each row, is presented to the subject. His task is to move his controls so as to turn on the green light corresponding to each of the red lights. As soon as each of the three red lights is matched by the corresponding green light, a new set of red lights is automatically presented. The total test time limit is 8 minutes.

First Centroid Factor Loadings. The centroid factor loadings of these tests are obtained from their intercorrelations as follows:

1. The highest correlation coefficient in each column is placed in the diagonal cell of that column as an estimate of the communality. (See Table 5.10.)

TABLE 5.10. CORRELATION MATRIX [1]

Test	1	2	3	4	5	6	7	8	9	10	11	Σ_{j1}	No.of Negatives
1 . Dial and Table Reading.....	(.55)	.40	.41	.37	.20	.32	.52	.55	.02	.27	.36	3.42	0
2 . Spatial Orientation I.......	.40	(.46)	.18	.28	.15	.46	.23	.23	.01	.14	.30	2.38	0
3 . Reading Comprehension	.41	.18	(.41)	.33	.32	.18	.29	.35	.18	.41	.20	2.85	0
4 . Instrument Comprehension..	.37	.28	.33	(.38)	.38	.28	.17	.22	.22	.26	.36	2.87	0
5 . Mechanical Principles	.20	.15	.32	.38	(.47)	.16	-.02	.08	.47	.33	.31	2.38	1
6 . Speed of Identification	.32	.46	.18	.28	.16	(.46)	.15	.18	.07	.14	.28	2.22	0
7 . Numerical Operations I....	.52	.23	.29	.17	-.02	.15	(.67)	.67	-.13	.13	.16	2.17	2
8 . Numerical Operations II...	.55	.23	.35	.22	.08	.18	.67	(.67)	-.06	.20	.12	2.54	1
9 . Mechanical Information...	.02	.01	.18	.22	.47	.07	-.13	-.06	(.47)	.25	.18	1.21	2
10 . Practical Judgment	.27	.14	.41	.26	.33	.14	.13	.20	.25	(.41)	.20	2.33	0
11 . Complex Coordination	.36	.30	.20	.36	.31	.28	.16	.12	.18	.20	(.36)	2.47	0
Σ_{j1}	3.42	2.38	2.85	2.87	2.38	2.22	2.17	2.54	1.21	2.33	2.47	26.84 $(\Sigma\Sigma_{j1})$	6=Total Negs. $\sqrt{T_1}$=5.670097
t_{j1}	3.97	2.84	3.26	3.25	2.85	2.68	2.84	3.21	1.68	2.74	2.83	32.15 = T_1,	$\frac{1}{\sqrt{T}}$=.176364
σ_{j1}	.700	.501	.575	.573	.503	.473	.501	.566	.296	.483	.499	5.670 = $\Sigma\,\sigma_{j1}$	
$|\Sigma_{j1}|$	3.42	2.38	2.85	2.87	2.42	2.22	2.47	2.66	1.59	2.33	2.47	27.68 = $\Sigma|\Sigma_{j1}|$	

$$\frac{+5.31}{32.99} = \Sigma\,h^2_{\text{Reest.}}$$

$$\phi_{\frac{1}{0}} = \frac{13.084}{32.99}$$

$$\phi_{\frac{1}{0}} = .397$$

[1] These are product-moment correlation coefficients computed from normalized distributions. They were obtained from Guilford (1947b, Appendix C), and they are based on a sample of 8,158 unclassified aviation students.

2. The sum of the correlation coefficients in each column (omitting the value in the diagonal cell) is entered below the column in the row labeled "Σ_{j1}." As a check each row is added across and the sum placed in the column to the right, also labeled "Σ_{j1}."

3. Since all column sums are positive, it is not necessary to reflect any of the variables at this point in the procedure.

4. To the total of the correlation coefficients in each column is added the estimated communality and the sum placed in the next row labeled "t_{j1}."

5. The column totals are summed across and the result is called "T_1." ($T_1 = \Sigma t_{j1}$.) This value is the sum of all the entries in the correlation matrix, including the diagonal values.

6. Calculate $\sqrt{T_1}$ and $1/\sqrt{T_1}$.

7. Obtain the loadings of the tests on the first centroid factor by multiplying each variable in row t_{j1}, in turn, by $1/\sqrt{T_1}$, $(a_{j1} = t_{j1} \cdot 1/\sqrt{T_1})$. If it is intended to calculate factor loadings to two decimal places, the calculations should be carried out to at least the third decimal place and preferably the fourth to minimize rounding errors.

8. Although, for convenience, the loadings have been obtained in a row, they are the first column of the matrix of centroid factor loadings and are entered as such to two decimal places in the first column of Table 5.18. Since there were no reflections of variables, the loadings on factor I are all positive.

Second Centroid Factor Loadings. The calculation of the second centroid factor loadings will be described under the following headings: residual correlation matrix, reflection, and calculation of loadings.

A. Residual Correlation Matrix. 1. The loadings on centroid factor I have accounted for a portion of each correlation. Now we wish to subtract the portion of each correlation which has been accounted for by the first centroid factor and determine the residual correlations. It will be recalled that, for orthogonal factors, $r_{jk} = a_{j1}a_{k1} + a_{j2}a_{k2} + \cdots + a_{jr}a_{kr}$. The first factor accounts for $(a_{j1}a_{k1})$ and the first residual correlation $({}_1\rho_{jk})$ is equal to ${}_1\rho_{jk} = r_{jk} - a_{j1}a_{k1} = a_{j2}a_{k2} + \cdots + a_{jr}a_{kr}$. Therefore, to determine the first residual correlation between variables j and k, the product of the loadings of the two variables on factor I is subtracted from the correlation between them. This is done systematically in Table 5.11 where all of the first residual-correlation coefficients are shown including the residual communalities in parentheses.

2. A partial check on the accuracy of the computation of the residuals is that the sum of each column (or row), including diagonal values, should be zero (or within a rounding-error margin). The sums are placed in a row (or column) labeled "Σ_0." [6]

---

[6] The reason for expecting this zero sum is that the first centroid-factor vector is located so that the sum of the residual correlations for each variable is zero.

TABLE 5.11.   FIRST RESIDUAL-CORRELATION MATRIX [1]

a_{j1}	Test No.	700 (1)	501 (2)	575 (3)	573 (4)	503 (5)	473 (6)	501 (7)	566 (8)	296 (9)	483 (10)	499 (11)	Σ_0	No. of Negatives
*700	1	187 (060)	049	-008	-031	-152	-011	169	154	-187	-068	011	002	3
*501	2	049	223 (209)	-108	-007	-102	223	-021	-054	-138	-102	050	-001	3
575	3	008	-108	132 (079)	001	031	-092	002	025	010	132	-087	001	4
573	4	-031	-007	001	117 (052)	092	009	-117	-104	050	-017	074	002	2
503	5	-152	-102	031	092	321 (217)	-078	-272	-205	321	087	059	-002	0
*473	6	-011	223	-092	009	-078	223 (236)	-087	-088	-070	-088	044	-002	5
*501	7	169	-021	002	-117	-272	-087	386 (419)	386	-278	-112	-090	-001	3
*566	8	154	-054	025	-104	-205	-088	386	386 (350)	-228	-073	-162	001	3
296	9	-187	-138	010	050	321	-070	-278	-228	321 (382)	107	032	001	0
483	10	-068	-102	132	-017	087	-088	-112	-073	107	132 (177)	-041	002	2
499	11	011	050	-087	074	059	044	-090	-162	032	-041	162 (111)	001	5
	Σ_0	002	-001	001	002	-002	-002	-001	001	001	002	001	$\Sigma\Sigma_{j2}$	30=Total Negs.
	Σ_{j2}	-058	-210	-078	-050	-219	-238	-420	-349	-381	-175	-110=	-2.288	
Column	7	-396	-168	-082	184	325	-064	420	-1.121	175	049	070	-608	
	8	-704	-060	-132	392	735	112	1.192	1.121	631	195	394	3.876	
	1	704	-158	-148	454	1.039	134	1.530	1.429	1.005	331	372	6.692	
	2	802	158	068	468	1.243	-312	1.488	1.321	1.281	535	272	7.324	
	6	780	604	252	450	1.399	312	1.314	1.145	1.421	711	184	8.572	
	t_{j2}	967	827	384	567	1.720	535	1.700	1.531	1.742	843	346	11.162=T_2	$\sqrt{T_2}$=3.340958
	a_{j2}	289	248	115	170	515	160	509	458	521	252	104	3.341=Σa_{j2}	$\frac{1}{\sqrt{T_2}}$ = .299315
	$|\Sigma_{j2}|$	840	854	496	502	1.399	790	1.534	1.479	1.421	827	650	10.792=$\Sigma|\Sigma_{j2}|$	

$$10.792=\Sigma|\Sigma_{j2}| \quad \phi_2 = \frac{7.076}{13.382}$$

$$+2.292=\Sigma h^2_{Resid.} \quad +2.590=\Sigma h^2_{Reest.}$$

$$13.084 \qquad 13.382 \qquad \phi_2=.529$$

[1] In this and in the succeeding residual-correlation matrices, all entries without decimal points are to three decimal places.

3. Next the sum of each column of the residual-correlation matrix, *without* the value in the diagonal cell, is obtained and placed in a column labeled "Σ_{j2}." These column totals are usually negative. The sum of these values $(\Sigma\Sigma_{j2})$ is placed to the right of the row and represents the total of the residual correlations in the table not including the residual communalities. If any or all of the column sums referred to are negative, a process of reflection of variables is begun to make the value of $(\Sigma\Sigma_{j2})$ as high positive as possible.

B. Reflection of Variables. 1. The order in which variables are reflected is arbitrary, the aim being merely to make the sum of the residual coefficients as high positive as possible in order to maximize the amount of variance which will be extracted in the next centroid factor. Although other criteria (e.g., column with largest number of negatives, highest communality, or highest absolute sum) for selecting the columns to be reflected could be used, we shall follow the principle of reflecting the column with the highest negative sum. In the first table of residuals, column 7 has the largest negative sum in row Σ_{j2} and variable 7 is reflected first.

2. Row 7 and column 7 are starred to indicate that they have been reflected. In the next row (labeled column 7 in Table 5.11), the sums of the columns, with the reflected values of column and row 7, are entered according to the procedure outlined in steps 4 through 9 in the previous section (see p. 65).

3. After these adjusted column totals have been obtained, they are summed and the total placed in the $\Sigma\Sigma_{j2}$ column to the right of the row. A check on the correctness of the computations may be obtained by adding four times the value of the adjusted sum of the reflected column to the preceding $\Sigma\Sigma_{j2}$ total. (In the example, $-2.288 + 4(.420) = -.608$, which is also the row total.) The total of the reflected column is changed from its minus value to the corresponding plus value and the same is true of the corresponding row total, hence the increase in the table total by four times the value of the reflected column sum.

4. The variable with the highest negative, adjusted column total (in the example column 8) is reflected next and so on until all the column totals are positive or zero.

C. Calculation of Loadings. 1. The re-estimated communality for each variable (equal to its highest residual correlation, but positive in sign), which has been placed above the residual communality, is added to the last adjusted column sum, and the total placed in row t_{j2}.

2. The factor loadings are then obtained by steps 11 and 12 of the preceding section (p. 66).

3. The signs of the reflected variables in the residual correlation matrix are changed according to the rules in step 10 (p. 66).

4. The second centroid factor loadings are entered in the second column of Table 5.18 with proper sign. Since none of the

TABLE 5.12. SECOND RESIDUAL-CORRELATION MATRIX

$q_{/2}$		289	248	115	170	515	160	509	458	521	252	104		
	Test No.	1	2	3	4	5	6	7	8	9	10	11	Σ_0	No. of Negatives
289	1	057/(103)	±023	±041	-018	003	±057	022	022	036	±005	-041	001	2
* 248	2	±023	183/(161)	079	±035	±026	183	±147	±168	⁻009	040	±076	-003	1
* 115	3	±041	079	103/(119)	±019	±028	074	±061	±078	±050	103	±099	-001	0
170	4	-018	±035	±019	060/(088)	004	±036	030	026	-039	±060	056	-003	2
515	5	003	±026	±028	004	053/(056)	±004	010	-031	053	±043	005	-001	1
* 160	6	±057	183	074	±036	±004	183/(197)	±168	±161	±013	048	±061	002	0
509	7	022	±147	±061	030	010	±168	168/(127)	153	013	±016	037	000	0
458	8	022	±168	±078	026	-031	±161	153	168/(176)	-011	±042	114	000	2
521	9	036	⁻009	±050	-039	053	±013	013	-011	053+/103/(050)	-024	-022	002	4
* 252	10	±005	040	103	±060	±043	048	±016	±042	-024	103+/(068)	±067	002	0
104	11	-041	±076	±099	056	005	±061	037	114	-022	±067	114/(151)	003	2
Σ_0		001	-003	-001	-003	-001	002	000	000	002	002	-003	$\Sigma\Sigma_{/3}=$	14 = Total Negs.
$\Sigma_{/3}$		-102	-164	-120	-091	-057	-195	-127	-176	-048	-066	-154	-1.300	
Column 6		012	-530	-268	-019	-049	_195_	209	146	-022	-162	-032	-520	
2		058	_530_	-426	051	003	_561_	503	482	-040	-242	120	1.600	
3		140	_688_	_426_	089	059	_709_	625	638	060	-448	318	3.304	
10		150	_768_	_632_	209	145	_805_	657	722	108	_448_	452	5.056	
$t_{/3}$		207	951	735	269	198	988	825	890	161	551	566	6.341 = T_3	
$a_{/3}$		082	378	292	107	079	392	328	353	064	219	225	2.519 = $\Sigma a_{/3}$	
$\lvert\Sigma_{/3}\rvert$		268	786	632	323	207	805	657	806	270	448	578	5.780 = $\Sigma\lvert\Sigma_{/3}\rvert$	

$\sqrt{T_3} = 2.518134$

$\dfrac{1}{\sqrt{T_3}} = .397119$

$5.780 = \Sigma\lvert\Sigma_{/3}\rvert$

$+\dfrac{1.296}{7.076} = \Sigma h^2_{Resid.}$ $\qquad +\dfrac{1.245}{7.025} = \Sigma h^2_{Reest.}$

$\phi_{\frac{3}{2}} = \dfrac{3.321}{7.025}$

$\phi_{\frac{3}{2}} = .473$

variables were reflected in the extraction of the first centroid factor, factor loadings for all variables reflected in the table of first residuals have negative signs. A new table of residuals is made up by subtracting the products of the factor loadings just obtained from the preceding residual matrix with changed signs for reflected variables.

Third and Subsequent Centroid Factors. The routine for extracting the third and each subsequent centroid factor is a repetition of that used to extract the second centroid factor. The major steps are as follows: first, obtain the residual correlation matrix as in Section A, above; second, reflect some of the variables so as to maximize the positive sum of the table of residual correlations (excluding the values in the principal

TABLE 5.13. THIRD RESIDUAL-CORRELATION MATRIX

$q_{/3}$	082 *	378	292	107 *	079 ·	392 *	328 *	353 *	064	219	225 *	Σ_0	No. of Negatives
Test No.	1	2	3	4	5	6	7	8	9	10	11		
082 1	059 (050)	±008	017	±027	-003	⁻025	±005	±007	031	-013	±059	001	3
*378 2	±008	043 (040)	±031	-005	±004	035	023	035	±033	±043	-009	000	2
292 3	017	±031	040 (018)	±012	005	±040	±035	±025	031	039	⁻033	000	1
*107 4	±027	-005	±012	046 (049)	±004	-006	-005	-012	±046	⁻037	032	001	5
079 5	-003	±004	005	±004	059 (047)	±027	±016	±059	048	026	±013	000	1
*392 6	⁻025	035	±040	-006	±027	040 (029)	039	023	±012	±038	-027	001	3
*328 7	±005	023	±035	-005	±016	039	056 (060)	037	±008	±056	-037	-003	2
*353 8	±007	035	±025	012	±059	023	037	059 (043)	±034	±035	035	001	1
064 9	031	±033	031	±046	048	±012	-008	±034	048 (049)	010	±036	000	0
219 10	-013	±043	039	⁻037	026	±038	±056	±035	010	056 (055)	⁻018	000	3
*225 11	±059	-009	⁻033	032	±013	-027	-037	035	±036	⁻018	059 (063)	000	5
Σ_0	001	000	000	001	000	001	-003	001	000	000	000	$\Sigma\Sigma_{j4}=$	26=Total Negs.
Σ_{j4}	-049	-040	-018	-048	-047	-028	-063	-042	-049	-055	-063	-502	
Column 11	069	-022	-084	-112	-021	026	011	-112	-023	-091	063	-250	
8	083	-092	-034	-088	097	-020	-063	112	091	-021	133	198	
2	099	092	028	-078	105	-090	-109	182	157	065	115	566	
7	109	138	098	-068	137	-168	109	256	173	177	041	1.002	
6	059	208	178	-056	191	168	187	302	197	253	-013	1.674	
4	113	198	202	056	199	156	177	278	289	179	051	1.898	
t_{j4}	172	241	242	102	258	196	233	337	337	235	110	2.463 $=T_4$	
a_{j4}	110	154	154	065	164	125	148	215	215	150	070	1.570 $=\Sigma a_{j4}$	
$\lvert\Sigma_{j4}\rvert$	195	226	268	186	205	272	261	302	289	315	299	2.818 $=\Sigma\lvert\Sigma_{j4}\rvert$ 2.818$=\Sigma\lvert\Sigma_{j4}\rvert$	

$\sqrt{T_4} = 1.569395$

$\dfrac{1}{\sqrt{T_4}} = .637188$

$\phi_4 = \dfrac{2.249}{3.383}$

$\dfrac{+.503}{3.321} = \Sigma h^2_{\text{Resid.}}$ $\dfrac{+.565}{3.383} = \Sigma h^2_{\text{Reest.}}$

$\phi_4 = .665$

diagonal), as in Section B above; and third, calculate the centroid loadings, following the steps in Section C. The computations are illustrated in Tables 5.12 to 5.17. The loadings for each factor are entered in the corresponding column of Table 5.18, and the communality (h_j^2) for each variable is computed.

Criteria for Sufficient Factors. There are no exact criteria for stopping extraction of factors. A number of empirical criteria, however, have been developed, several of which will be described.[7]

A. Tucker's Phi. This criterion uses the principle that if there is no significant decrease in the size of the residual values

---

[7] Twenty-five criteria are listed by Vernon *et al.* (1949). See also Burt (1952).

TABLE 5.14. FOURTH RESIDUAL-CORRELATION MATRIX

a_{j4}	110	154	154	065	164	125	148	215	215	150	070		
Test No.	1	2	3	4	5	6	7	8	9	10	11	Σ_0	No. of Negatives
* 110 — 1	051/(047)	±009	000	020	-021	±039	±011	±017	007	±030	051	-002	1
154 — 2	±009	021/(019)	007	±015	±021	016	000	002	000	020	±020	-001	0
154 — 3	000	007	044/(016)	̄002	±020	021	012	̄008	±002	016	±044	000	2
* 065 — 4	020	±015	̄002	047/(042)	-007	±014	±015	±026	032	±047	027	-001	2
* 164 — 5	-021	±021	±020	-007	024/(032)	̄007	±008	̄024	013	̄001	002	002	5
125 — 6	±039	016	021	±014	̄007	.039/(024)	021	-004	±015	019	-036	000	2
148 — 7	±011	000	012	±015	±008	021	047/(034)	005	±024	034	±047	001	0
215 — 8	±017	002	-008	±026	̄024	-004	005	026/(013)	±012	003	̄020	000	4
* 215 — 9	007	000	±002	032	013	±015	±024	±012	032/(002)	±022	021	000	0
150 — 10	±030	020	016	±047	̄001	019	034	003	±022	047/(034)	±029	-001	1
* 070 — 11	051	±020	±044	027	002	±036	±047	̄020	021	±029	051/(054)	-001	1
Σ_0	-002	-001	000	-001	002	000	001	000	000	-001	-001	$\Sigma\Sigma_{j5}=$	18 = Total Negs.
Σ_{j5}	-049	-020	-016	-043	-030	-024	-033	-013	-002	-035	-055	-.320	
Column 11	-151	020	072	-097	-034	048	061	-053	-044	023	055	-100	
1	151	038	072	-137	008	126	083	-019	-058	083	157	504	
4	191	068	068	137	022	154	113	033	-122	177	211	1.052	
9	205	068	072	201	-004	184	161	057	122	221	253	1.540	
5	163	110	112	187	004	170	177	009	148	219	257	1.556	
t_{j5}	214	131	156	234	028	209	224	035	180	266	308	1.985 = T_5	
a_{j5}	152	093	111	166	020	148	159	025	128	189	219	1.410 = Σa_{j5}	
$|\Sigma_{j5}|$	205	110	132	205	124	192	177	121	148	221	297	1.932 = $\Sigma|\Sigma_{j5}|$	

$\sqrt{T_5}$ = 1.408900

$\frac{1}{\sqrt{T_5}}$ = .709774

1.932 = $\Sigma|\Sigma_{j5}|$ $\phi_{\frac{4}{5}}$ = 1.268 / 2.361

+.317 = $\Sigma h^2_{Resid.}$ +.429 = $\Sigma h^2_{Reest.}$ $\phi_{\frac{5}{4}}$ = .537

2.249   2.361

from one matrix to the next, the significant common-factor variance has been extracted. The steps are as follows:

1. Add all of the values for a residual matrix (s), disregarding signs, and using the re-estimated values of the communality in the diagonal cells.

2. Add all of the values for the next residual matrix ($s + 1$), disregarding signs and using the residual communalities in the diagonal cells.

3. To obtain phi, divide the value obtained in step 2 by the value obtained in step 1 above. The formula for phi is:

$$\phi_{\frac{s+1}{s}} = \frac{\Sigma|\rho_{s+1}|}{\Sigma|\rho_s|} = \frac{\Sigma|\Sigma_{j,s+1}| + \Sigma h^2_{resid.}}{\Sigma|\Sigma_{js}| + \Sigma h^2_{re\text{-}est.}}$$

TABLE 5.15.   FIFTH RESIDUAL-CORRELATION MATRIX

$q_{/5}$		152	093	111	166	020	148	159	025	128	189	219		
	Test No.	1	2	3	4	5	6	7	8	9	10	11	Σ_0	No. of Negatives
152	1	024 (028) 019	±005	±017	-005	±024	⁻017	±013	013	-012	001	⁻018	001	4
*093	2	±005	019 (012) 020	-003	000	019	002	-015	000	±012	⁻003	000	001	3
*111	3	±017	-003	020 (032) 022	±020	018	004	-006	±011	±012	±005	020	000	2
166	4	-005	000	±020	022 (019) 025	±010	±011	±011	022	011	016	±009	002	1
*020	5	±024	019	018	±010	025 (024) 017	-009	005	±025	⁻010	±005	-003	000	3
*148	6	⁻017	002	004	±011	-009	017 (017) 015	-003	±008	±004	±009	004	000	3
*159	7	±013	-015	-006	±011	005	-003	022 (022) 025	⁻001	⁻004	⁻004	012	000	6
025	8	013	000	±011	022	±025	±008	⁻001	025 (025) 012	009	-002	±025	-001	2
128	9	-012	±012	±012	011	⁻010	±004	⁻004	009	012 (016) 016	-002	±007	001	4
189	10	001	⁻003	±005	016	±005	±009	⁻004	-002	-002	016 (012) 025	±013	000	4
*219	11	⁻018	000	020	±009	-003	004	012	±025	±007	±013	025 (003)	000	2
Σ_0		001	001	000	002	000	000	000	-001	001	000	000	$\Sigma\Sigma_{j6}=$	34 = Total Negs.
Σ_{j6}		-027	-011	-032	-017	-024	-017	-022	-026	-015	-012	-003	-206	
Column 3		007	-005	032	023	-060	-025	-010	-004	009	-002	-043	-078	
	5	055	-043	068	043	060	-007	-020	046	-011	008	-037	162	
	2	065	043	062	043	098	-011	010	046	013	002	-037	334	
	11	029	043	102	061	092	-019	-014	096	027	028	037	482	
	6	-005	047	110	083	074	019	-008	112	035	046	045	558	
	7	021	017	098	105	084	013	008	110	027	038	069	590	
t_{j6}		045	036	118	127	109	030	023	135	039	054	094	.810 $=T_6$	$\sqrt{T_6}=$ .900000
a_{j6}		050	040	131	141	121	033	026	150	043	060	104	.899 $=\Sigma a_{j6}$	$\frac{1}{\sqrt{T_6}}=$ 1.111111
$|\Sigma_{j6}|$		125	059	116	115	128	071	074	116	083	060	111	1.058 $=\Sigma|\Sigma_{j6}|$	1.058 $=\Sigma|\Sigma_{j6}|$ $\phi_6=$ .914

$+.210 = \Sigma h^2$ Resid. $+.220 = \Sigma h^2$ Reest. $\frac{\phi_6}{5}$ 1.278
1.268 1.278 $\frac{\phi_6}{5}=$ .715

4. Compute $(n-1)/(n+1)$ where n is the number of test variables in the matrix.

5. If ϕ exceeds $(n-1)/(n+1)$ in value, there are s significant factors. The adequacy of this criterion depends, in part, on the adequacy of the reflections. If the reflections for a matrix have not resulted in the highest positive sum, phi may exceed the value $(n-1)/(n+1)$ and then drop below it again on a succeeding factor. This criterion also involves considerable additional computation, since to show that there are s significant factors requires $s+1$ computed factors and $s+1$ tables of residuals. (See Thurstone 1938 and Blakey 1940.)

B. Humphrey's Rule. This criterion takes into account N, the size of the sample, and is dependent on the loadings of only

TABLE 5.16. SIXTH RESIDUAL-CORRELATION MATRIX

σ_{j6}		050*	040*	131	141	121*	033	026*	150*	043	060	104		
	Test No.	1	2	3	4	5	6	7	8	9	10	11	Σ_0	No. of Negatives
* 050	1	023 (022)	003	⁻010	±012	018	±019	012	005	±014	±002	±023	000	1
* 040	2	003	016 (017)	±008	±006	014	⁻001	-016	-006	⁻010	±005	±004	000	4
131	3	⁻010	±008	010 (003)	002	⁻002	000	±009	±009	006	-003	006	000	3
141	4	±012	⁻006	002	012 (002)	±007	006	⁻007	⁻001	005	008	-006	000	3
* 121	5	018	014	⁻002	±007	018 (010)	±013	002	007	±015	±002	±016	000	1
033	6	±019	⁻001	000	006	±013	019 (016)	±004	⁻003	003	007	001	001	2
* 026	7	012	-016	±009	⁻007	002	±004	016 (014)	-005	±005	±006	⁻009	-001	4
* 150	8	005	-006	±009	⁻001	007	⁻003	-005	011 (002)	⁻003	±011	⁻009	-001	6
043	9	±014	⁻010	006	005	±015	003	±005	⁻003	015 (010)	-005	003	001	3
060	10	±002	±005	-003	008	±002	007	±006	±011	-005	011 (012)	007	000	2
104	11	±023	⁻004	006	-006	±016	001	⁻009	⁻009	003	007	023 (014)	000	3
Σ_0		000	000	000	000	000	001	-001	-001	001	000	000	$\Sigma\Sigma_{j0}=$	32=Total Negs.
Σ_{j7}		-022	-017	-003	-002	-010	-015	-015	-003	-009	-012	014	-122	
Column 1		022	-023	-023	022	-046	023	-039	-013	019	-008	032	-034	
2		058	-051	-027	036	046	049	-043	-027	049	-004	064	150	
5		064	051	-011	048	074	047	-011	-015	029	006	072	354	
7		074	039	007	046	088	041	-001	015	023	028	054	414	
8		098	007	025	032	092	049	001	005	033	040	036	418	
t_{j7}		121	023	035	044	110	068	017	016	048	051	059	.592 $=T_7$	
σ_{j7}		157	030	045	057	143	088	022	021	062	066	077	.768 $=\Sigma\sigma_{j7}$	
$|\Sigma_{j7}|$		118	073	055	060	096	057	075	059	069	056	074	.792 $=\Sigma|\Sigma_{j7}|$	.792$=\Sigma|\Sigma_{j7}|$

$\sqrt{T_7}=$ .769415

$\dfrac{1}{\sqrt{T_7}}=$ 1.299688

$\dfrac{\phi_7}{6}=$ .727 ⁄ .966

+.122 $=\Sigma h^2$ Resid.   +.174 $=\Sigma h^2$ Reest.

.914   0.966

$\dfrac{\phi_7}{6}=$ .753

two variables (which should be sufficient to establish a factor) rather than on the entire matrix.

1. Find the product of the two highest loadings in a column of the centroid factor matrix.

2. Find the standard error of a correlation coefficient of zero, for the type of correlation and size of sample being used (e.g., $1/\sqrt{N}$ for the Pearson product-moment r).

3. If the product found in step 1 above does not exceed twice the standard error found in step 2, the factor is probably not significant. This rule works best for samples that are not too large.

C. Coombs' Criterion. This criterion is applicable only to analyses in which the table of correlations contains only positive

TABLE 5.17. SEVENTH RESIDUAL-CORRELATION MATRIX

a_{j7}		157	030	045	057	143	088	022	021	062	066	077	
	Test No.	1	2	3	4	5	6	7	8	9	10	11	Σ_0
157	1	(-002)	-002	-017	003	-005	005	009	002	004	-008	011	000
030	2	-002	(015)	007	004	010	-004	-017	-007	-012	003	002	-001
045	3	-017	007	(008)	-001	-009	-004	008	008	003	-006	003	000
057	4	003	004	-001	(009)	001	001	-008	-002	001	004	-010	000
143	5	-005	010	-009	-001	(-003)	000	-001	004	006	-008	005	-002
088	6	005	-004	-004	001	000	(011)	002	-005	-003	001	-006	-002
022	7	009	-017	008	-008	-001	002	(016)	-006	004	005	-011	001
021	8	002	-007	008	-002	004	-005	-006	(011)	-004	010	-011	000
062	9	004	-012	003	001	006	-003	004	-004	(011)	-009	-002	-001
066	10	-008	003	-006	004	-008	001	005	010	-009	(007)	002	001
077	11	011	002	003	-010	005	-006	-011	-011	-002	002	(017)	000
Σ_0		000	-001	000	000	-002	-002	001	000	-001	001	000	$\Sigma|\Sigma_{j8}|=$
$|\Sigma_{j8}|$		066	075	066	034	048	031	071	059	048	056	063	.617

$$+\frac{.110}{.727} = \Sigma h^2 \text{ Resid.}$$

or zero values. Small negatives, not significantly different from zero, are permissible. It depends on the patterning of residuals rather than on their size. It is assumed that, if there are significant factors, rather than merely error variance, remaining in the table of residuals, there should be no more negative values in the residual matrix, after reflection, than could be expected by chance from a residual table derived from a correlation matrix with positive manifold.

Count the number of negatives remaining in a table of residuals *after reflection*. If that number is not significantly different from the value of "C" obtained from Table 5.19, for the number of variables, sufficient factors have been extracted (Coombs, 1941b).

None of the criteria mentioned above are exact and, since they are based on different principles, they may give contrary indications. It is probably best, in practice, to get indications from several of them and to use that information to help make a judgment of the number of factors that will lead to meaningful results.

TABLE 5.18. CENTROID FACTOR MATRIX (F_c)

Test	Factor					h^2	No. of Reflections
	I	II	III	IV	V		
1 . Dial and Table Reading	.70	−.29	−.08	−.11	.15	.62	2
2 . Spatial Orientation I	.50	−.25	.38	−.15	−.09	.49	3
3 . Reading Comprehension . . .	.58	.12	−.29	−.15	−.11	.47	1
4 . Instrument Comprehension .	.57	.17	.11	−.06	.17	.40	2
5 . Mechanical Principles	.50	.52	.08	.16	−.02	.55	1
6 . Speed of Identification . . .	.47	−.16	.39	−.12	−.15	.44	3
7 . Numerical Operations I . . .	.50	−.51	−.33	.15	.16	.67	2
8 . Numerical Operations II. . .	.57	−.46	−.35	.21	.02	.70	2
9 . Mechanical Information. . .	.30	.52	.06	.21	−.13	.42	1
10. Practical Judgment	.48	.25	−.22	−.15	−.19	.40	1
11. Complex Coordination. . . .	.50	.10	.22	−.07	.22	.36	2

Check Values

Tests	Sum of Cross-Products	Resid. Corr. After Last Factor	Total Sign Changes for the Two Tests	Sum of Cross-Products + Resid. with Adjusted Sign	Correlation from Table 10
1 , 2	.3951	−.0050	odd	.4001	.40
2 , 3	.1822	−.0030	even	.1792	.18
3 , 4	.3094	−.0200	odd	.3294	.33
4 , 5	.3692	−.0100	odd	.3792	.38
5 , 6	.1668	−.0090	even	.1578	.16
6 , 7	.1459	−.0030	odd	.1489	.15
7 , 8	.6698	.0010	even	.6708	.67
8 , 9	−.0477	.0090	odd	−.0567	−.06
9 , 10	.2540	−.0020	even	.2520	.25
10 , 11	.1853	−.0130	odd	.1983	.20
11 , 1	.3441	.0180	even	.3621	.36

Application of the Criteria for Sufficient Factors. In order that the various criteria described above for determining when to stop extraction of factors may be applied, it is necessary to obtain the following sums for each correlation matrix:

1. Tucker's phi requires the absolute (non-algebraic) sum of all the entries in the matrix, *excluding* the diagonal cells. This is obtained first by columns and entered in row $|\Sigma_{jk}|$. (See Tables 5.10 through 5.17.) The sum of these values, $\Sigma|\Sigma_{jk}|$, is added first to the sum of the residual communalities and later the sum of the new (re-estimated) communalities. Tucker's phi is then calculated by the procedure described on pages 77-79.

TABLE 5.19. CRITICAL VALUES OF COOMBS' CRITERION
AND THEIR STANDARD ERRORS FOR BATTERIES OF FROM
TEN TO FIFTY VARIABLES [1]

n	%	C	σ_c	n	%	C	σ_c	n	%	C	σ_c
10	34.3	31	5	24	40.2	222	12	38	42.1	592	19
11	35.4	39	5	25	40.4	242	12	39	42.2	625	19
12	36.2	48	6	26	40.5	263	13	40	42.3	660	20
13	36.8	57	6	27	40.7	286	13	41	42.4	695	20
14	37.3	68	7	28	40.8	308	14	42	42.5	732	21
15	37.8	79	7	29	41.0	333	14	43	42.6	769	21
16	38.2	92	8	30	41.1	358	15	44	42.7	808	22
17	38.5	105	8	31	41.3	384	15	45	42.8	847	22
18	38.8	119	9	32	41.4	411	16	46	42.9	888	23
19	39.1	134	9	33	41.5	438	16	47	43.0	930	23
20	39.3	149	10	34	41.7	468	17	48	43.1	972	24
21	39.5	166	10	35	41.8	497	17	49	43.2	1016	24
22	39.8	184	11	36	41.9	528	18	50	43.3	1061	25
23	40.0	202	11	37	42.0	559	18				

[1] From Coombs (1941b)

n = Number of variables.
% = Percentage of negative entries in the residual matrix after sign change.
C = Number of negative entries in the residual matrix after sign change.
σ_c = Standard error of C.

2. The number of negative entries in each table of residuals, after the signs of reflected variables have been changed, should be obtained if it is desired to apply Coombs' criterion. The number of negatives in each row of the residual matrix is shown at the right, beginning with the first correlation matrix in the example. The number of negative entries in the entire table is shown in the sum at the bottom of the column. The application of this criterion is explained on pages 80-81.

Table 5.20 summarizes the data which have been obtained to help decide whether all of the common-factor variance has been extracted from the correlational matrix. Tucker's phi never does reach its criterion value in the example but does show a large increase for the sixth factor and maintains it for the seventh factor. This leveling off is often more indicative than the size of phi.

Although the number of negative signs comes within two standard errors of C for an eleven-variable matrix, at the second

TABLE 5.20. DATA FOR APPLYING THE CRITERIA FOR
SUFFICIENT COMMON FACTORS TO THE ELEVEN-VARI-
ABLE MATRIX CRITERION

Factor	Tucker's Phi	Humphrey's Rule	Coombs' Criterion
I	.397	.4025	6
II	.529	.2683	30
III	.473	.1482	14
IV	.665	.0462	26
V	.537	.0414	18
VI	.715	.0212	34
VII	.753	.0225	32
Criterion Value	.833	.0221	39 ± 5

factor, it drops again and does not reach the critical value again
until the sixth factor. All three of these approximate criteria
seem to signal that the sixth and seventh factors are not significant
and, hence only five factors should be retained for rotation and
interpretation.

Since the criteria are not exact, it is frequently necessary, in
practice, to extract more than the minimum number of factors
indicated by the criteria and determine by rotation how many
factors are needed to give a meaningful solution. If the rotations
are started with too many factors, some of them may be "resid-
ualized" (i.e., achieve small loadings only, usually between ±0.20)
during rotation.[8]

Checking the Centroid Loadings. The centroid loadings,
rounded to two decimal places, are recorded, with proper sign,
in Table 5.18. A partial check on the accuracy of the centroid
loadings may be had at this point, by reproducing the original
correlations, following the steps below. If reproducing the entire
matrix is considered too laborious, only the correlations in the

---

[8] A few of the other approximate criteria which have been used for significance
of factors are:

1. Obtain the absolute sum of the residuals, excluding the diagonal entries.
This value should level off abruptly after the significant factors have been extracted. (Mosier, 1939b.)

2. Make a frequency distribution of the coefficients in a table of residuals.
Compare the standard deviation of the distribution with the standard error of

diagonal above the principal diagonal need be reproduced ($cell_{1,2}$, $cell_{2,3}$, etc.) and the cell in the upper right-hand corner of the correlation matrix ($cell_{1,11}$) since that will use the loadings of each test twice.

1. Obtain the cross-products of the loadings of each variable with its neighboring variable [e.g., from Table 5.18, for variables 1×2: $(.70)(.50) + (-.29)(-.25) + (-.08)(.38) + (-.11)(-.15) + (.15)(-.09) = 0.3951$].

2. Determine the number of times each variable was reflected. (This can be done by counting the number of changes in the signs of the centroid loadings of a test. Thus, in Table 5.18, test 1 changes from positive to negative on factor II and continues negative until it changes back to positive on factor V, indicating 2 reflections for test 1 throughout the 5 factors.) If the combined sum of the number of reflections for the *two* variables whose correlation is being reproduced is an even number, the residual after the last factor (fifth residual matrix, with signs prior to reflection, see Table 5.15 in the example) is added algebraically to the sum of the cross-products. If the sum of the number of reflections of the two variables is an odd number, the sign of the residual is changed before adding it to the sum of the cross-products.

3. The resulting sum (rounded) should equal the correlation between the two variables. This work is carried out systematically for the example in the lower part of Table 5.18.

PROBLEMS

1. Factor the correlation matrix on page 17 by the diagonal method, using the following exact values for the communalities:

$$h_1^2 = .58 \qquad\qquad h_5^2 = .25$$
$$h_2^2 = .81 \qquad\qquad h_6^2 = .36$$
$$h_3^2 = .52 \qquad\qquad h_7^2 = .73$$
$$h_4^2 = .45 \qquad\qquad h_8^2 = .64$$

the mean r. An alternative is to compare the median residual, disregarding sign, with the probable error of the median r. (Thurstone, 1938.)

3. Obtain the standard deviation of the residuals for the sth factor. Obtain the average of communalities for all tests for the s factors extracted (h_s^2). Compute $\sigma_I = \sigma_s/(1 - h_s^2)$. The sth factor is significant if σ_I exceeds the standard error of a zero r. (McNemar, 1942a.)

2. Reproduce the correlation matrix including the communalities from the factor loadings. (FF′ = R.)

3. Plot the factor loadings and rotate the axes graphically to positive manifold. Obtain the rotated loadings from the plot. Check the h^2's of the rotated loadings against the h^2's of the diagonal loadings.

4. Rotate analytically the same number of degrees as was done graphically in Problem 3. Check the h^2's of the rotated loadings and compare the rotated loadings obtained graphically with those obtained analytically.

5. Factor the intercorrelation matrix on page 17 by the centroid method using the highest r in each column as an estimate of the h^2, and re-estimate the communality in each table of residual correlations. Repeat the entire process as many times as may be necessary to stabilize the communality estimates and apply the criteria for sufficient factors. Check the results by "reproducing" the correlation coefficients from the centroid loadings and then adding the coefficients in the final table of residuals as was illustrated at the bottom of Table 5.18.

6. Extract the factors from the correlation matrix below by the centroid method and apply the criteria for sufficient factors.

INTERCORRELATIONS OF SCORES OF ONE HUNDRED COLLEGE SOPHOMORES

Test	1	2	3	4	5	6	7	8	9	10
1. ACE [1] Arithmetic		.31	.52	.18	.21	.42	.10	.03	.24	.07
2. ACE Figure Analogies	.31		.59	.31	.27	.58	.11	−.10	.14	−.16
3. ACE Number Series	.52	.59		.21	.07	.33	.32	.01	.13	−.05
4. ACE Verbal Completion	.18	.31	.21		.71	.61	.19	−.04	.18	.04
5. ACE Same-Opposite	.21	.27	.07	.71		.68	.39	.19	.44	.24
6. ACE Verbal Analogies	.42	.58	.33	.61	.68		.21	.12	.33	.08
7. Educational Psychology—First Midterm	.10	.11	.32	.19	.39	.21		.62	.63	.47
8. Educational Psychology—Second Midterm	.03	−.10	.01	−.04	.19	.12	.62		.50	.72
9. Educational Psychology—Third Midterm	.24	.14	.13	.18	.44	.33	.63	.50		.60
10. Educational Psychology—Final Examination	.07	−.16	−.05	.04	.24	.08	.47	.72	.60	

[1] American Council on Education—Psychological Examination, 1941 Edition. (Data furnished by J. V. West.)

CHAPTER 6

Multiple-Group and Principal-Axes Methods of Factoring

THE MULTIPLE-GROUP METHOD

THE MULTIPLE-GROUP method is a variation of the centroid method. It is of interest because, instead of extracting one factor at a time, several factors may be extracted simultaneously. In this method some or all of the tests are placed in groups and the reference vectors are passed through the centroids of these groups instead of through the centroid of all the tests as is done in the complete centroid method. The only restriction on the groups is that they be linearly independent (see p. 201). Because of this restriction, the method is best used with variables about which sufficient is known so that independent groups can be selected. If the groups are not linearly independent, the method will yield imaginary numbers in one of the steps, and it will be necessary to start over with a new grouping of the tests. If groups of variables can be selected in advance that are similar in content to the factors to be obtained, the reference vectors obtained by the multiple-group method will be closer to their final rotated loadings and less rotation will be called for than in the centroid method. Thus, if one group were to consist of numerical tests, the vector passing through their centroid would be close to the final rotated position of the numerical factor.

After several factors have been extracted simultaneously, a table of residuals may be computed and examined to determine whether it contains additional common-factor variance. If it is decided that the table of residuals contains additional factors, they may be extracted by the multiple-group method, centroid method or any other suitable method from the table of residual-correlation coefficients.

Numerical Example. The correlations of the eleven variables in Table 6.2 which were factored previously by the centroid method will also be factored by the multiple-group method.

A. Estimation of Communalities. In this method there is not an opportunity to re-estimate the communalities after the extraction of each factor. Therefore, it is desirable to obtain an improved estimate of the communality of each test at the start. This may be done by the centroid method of estimating the communality according to the following steps: [1]

1. For each test, make a 4×4 correlation matrix containing the variable itself and the three variables with which it correlates highest. This has been done for tests 1 and 2 in Table 6.1. The highest correlations in each column of the 4×4 matrix are inserted in the diagonal cells. An estimate of the communality may be obtained from the formula

$$h^2 = \frac{[\Sigma r_1]^2}{\Sigma T} \tag{6.1}$$

where Σr_1 = sum of the values in the first column; ΣT = sum of the values in the entire 4×4 table. Do this, in turn, for each variable.

2. Enter the computed communality estimates in the diagonal cells of the correlation matrix. The estimates of the communali-

---

[1] For other methods of estimating the communalities, see Thurstone (1947c, Chapter 13).

TABLE 6.1. COMPUTATION OF COMMUNALITY ESTIMATES BY THE CENTROID FORMULA

Test 1

Test	1	8	7	3
1	.55	.55	.52	.41
8	.55	.67	.67	.35
7	.52	.67	.67	.29
3	.41	.35	.29	.41
Σr_1	2.03			

$\Sigma T = 7.88$

$$h_1^2 = \frac{(\Sigma r_1)^2}{\Sigma T} = \frac{(2.03)^2}{7.88} = .52$$

Test 2

Test	2	6	1	11
2	.46	.46	.40	.30
6	.46	.46	.32	.28
1	.40	.32	.40	.36
11	.30	.28	.36	.36
Σr_1	1.62			

$\Sigma T = 5.92$

$$h_2^2 = \frac{(1.62)^2}{5.92} = .44$$

ties obtained by formula 6.1 have been inserted in the diagonal cells of Table 6.2.

B. Grouping the Variables. 1. There are several methods by which the variables may be placed in groups for the extraction of factors. There should be, preferably, at least three or four variables in each group. One method of grouping might be to do a cluster analysis of correlations; or, if there is some *a priori* basis for groupings of variables, it can be employed. If the factor content of the tests is known from previous studies, this information can be used to guide the grouping. The method is not dependent on the grouping, however, except for the restriction, mentioned above, that the groups be linearly independent. Also, the groups need not contain the same number of variables.

In the example five groups were formed from the eleven tests and are indicated in Table 6.2. (In the example most groups consist of only two tests. It is not recommended that such small groups be used unless the tests and the way they can be grouped are well known to the investigator.)

C. Obtaining the Oblique Factor Loadings. After the groups have been formed the steps are as follows: 1. Sum each column of

TABLE 6.2. MULTIPLE-GROUP METHOD CALCULATIONS

Correlation Matrix

Test	1	2	3	4	5	6	7	8	9	10	11
1. Dial and Table Reading	(.52)	.40	.41	.37	.20	.32	.52	.55	.02	.27	.36
2. Spatial Orientation I	.40	(.44)	.18	.28	.15	.46	.23	.23	.01	.14	.30
3. Reading Comprehension	.41	.18	(.40)	.33	.32	.18	.29	.35	.18	.41	.20
4. Instrument Comprehension	.37	.28	.33	(.41)	.38	.28	.17	.22	.22	.26	.36
5. Mechanical Principles	.20	.15	.32	.38	(.50)	.16	-.02	.08	.47	.33	.31
6. Speed of Identification	.32	.46	.18	.28	.16	(.44)	.15	.18	.07	.14	.28
7. Numerical Operations I	.52	.23	.29	.17	-.02	.15	(.59)	.67	-.13	.13	.16
8. Numerical Operations II	.55	.23	.35	.22	.08	.18	.67	(.64)	-.06	.20	.12
9. Mechanical Information	.02	.01	.18	.22	.47	.07	-.13	-.06	(.36)	.25	.18
10. Practical Judgment	.27	.14	.41	.26	.33	.14	.13	.20	.25	(.37)	.20
11. Complex Coordination	.36	.30	.20	.36	.31	.28	.16	.12	.18	.20	(.35)

S

		1	2	3	4	5	6	7	8	9	10	11
Group 1 (1,7,8)	G1	1.59	.86	1.05	.76	.26	.65	1.78	1.86	-.17	.60	.64
2 (5,9)	G2	.22	.16	.50	.60	.97	.23	-.15	.02	.83	.58	.49
3 (2,6)	G3	.72	.90	.36	.56	.31	.90	.38	.41	.08	.28	.58
4 (3,10)	G4	.68	.32	.81	.59	.65	.32	.42	.55	.43	.78	.40
5 (4,11)	G5	.73	.58	.53	.77	.69	.56	.33	.34	.40	.46	.71

T

	1	2	3	4	5
1	5.23	.09	1.51	1.65	1.40
2	.09	1.80	.39	1.08	1.09
3	1.51	.39	1.80	.64	1.14
4	1.65	1.08	.64	1.59	.99
5	1.40	1.09	1.14	.99	1.48

Weights

$W_1 = .437269$
$W_2 = .745356$
$W_3 = .745356$
$W_4 = .793053$
$W_5 = .821997$

TABLE 6.2. MULTIPLE-GROUP METHOD CALCULATIONS (CONT.)

V' (Oblique Factor Loadings)

	1	2	3	4	5	6	7	8	9	10	11
P_1	.6953	.3761	.4591	.3323	.1137	.2842	.7783	.8133	.0743	.2624	.2799
P_2	.1640	.193	.3727	.4472	.7230	.1714	−.1118	.0149	.6186	.4323	.3652
P_3	.5367	.6708	.2683	.4174	.2311	.6708	−.2832	.3056	.0596	.2087	.4323
P_4	.5393	.2538	.6424	.4679	.5155	.2538	.3731	.4362	.3410	.6186	.3172
P_5	.6001	.4768	.4357	.6329	.5672	.4603	.2713	.2795	.3288	.3781	.5836

U

	1	2	3	4	5
P_1	2.2869	.0394	.6603	.7215	.6122
P_2	.0671	1.3416	.2907	.8050	.8124
P_3	1.1255	.2907	1.3416	.4770	.8497
P_4	1.3085	.8565	.5076	1.2610	.7851
P_5	1.1508	.8960	.9371	.8138	1.2166

R_{pq}

	1	2	3	4	5
1	.9999	.0294	.4922	.5722	.5032
2	.0294	1.0000	.2167	.6384	.6678
3	.4922	.2167	1.0000	.3783	.6985
4	.5722	.6384	.3783	1.0000	.6454
5	.5032	.6678	.6985	.6454	1.0000

$F_{pm} = \Lambda'_{mp}$

	1	2	3	4	5
1	1.0000	0	0	0	0
2	.0294	.9996	0	0	0
3	.4922	.2023	.8466	0	0
4	.5722	.6218	−.0344	.5336	0
5	.5032	.6533	.3764	−.0671	.4169

$(F'_{mp})^{-1} = (\Lambda_{pm})^{-1}$

	1	2	3	4	5
1	1.0000	−.0294	−.5744	−1.0751	−.8154
2	0	1.0004	−.2391	−1.1812	−1.5419
3	0	0	1.1812	.0761	−1.0542
4	0	0	0	1.8741	.3016
5	0	0	0	0	2.3987

the correlation matrix by groups. Each column will give as many sums as there are groups. Place the sum for each group in the appropriate row below the correlation matrix.

In the example, the first group consists of tests 1, 7, and 8. The sum of the correlations of these three variables with test 1 is 1.59. This is placed in row G_1 in the column for test 1 of matrix **S**.

The sum of variables 5 and 9 for group 2 is placed in line G_2 in the column for variable 1. The sums for the other groups in each column are placed correspondingly in the proper row and column. This table of group sums by columns is labeled matrix **S**.

2. Sum each row G_1, G_2, $\cdots$, etc., by *groups,* and place the results in an $n \times n$ matrix at the right (n represents the number of groups). This matrix is labeled "**T**."

In the example, the values for the first group (tests 1, 7, and 8) in row G_1 are summed $(1.59 + 1.78 + 1.86 = 5.23)$. This value is placed in the first cell of row G_1 of matrix **T**. The values for the second group are likewise summed $(.26 + -.17 = .09)$ and put in the second cell. The rest of the 5×5 matrix is obtained in a similar manner.

3. Obtain the reciprocal of the square root of each value in the diagonal cells of matrix **T**. These are the weights which are applied to the group sums in matrix **S** to obtain the *oblique* factor loadings. The formula for the weights is

$$W_j = \frac{1}{\sqrt{d_j}} \qquad (6.2)$$

where d_j is the value in the diagonal cell of matrix **T** in row j.

In the example the value in the diagonal cell of row 1 is 5.23 and its reciprocal, $W_1 = .437269$. The other weights are obtained similarly.

4. Multiply each value in each row of matrix **S** by the weight for that row. Enter the results in a matrix **V′** just below matrix **S**. In the example, the first value (.6953) is obtained by multiplying 1.59 by W_1.

The values in the **V′** matrix are the loadings of the variables on the reference vectors which were passed through centroids of the groups. These groups, except in rare instances, are not orthogonal to each other; in other words, the axes running through their centroids are oblique. The matrix V' is the transpose of the matrix V, the matrix of oblique factor loadings. If the groups have been chosen carefully to represent meaningful clusters of tests or other variables and it is not desired to rotate the factors or change the final groupings, the analysis may be terminated at this point, after a table of residuals has been calculated and it is determined that all the common-factor variance has been extracted. Or, the analysis may be continued through step 6, below, where the cosines of the angular separations of the oblique factor vectors are obtained. If, however, it is desired to rotate the factors they should be converted first to a reference frame of orthogonal factors by the following steps: [2]

5. Multiply the values in each row of matrix T by the weight for that row and enter the results in matrix U.

6. Multiply the values in each column of matrix U by the weight for the corresponding column (i.e., multiply the values in column 1 by W_1, in column 2 by W_2, etc.) and place the results in matrix R_{pq}. The values in the diagonal cells should be within rounding-error of unity and the other values in matrix R_{pq} are the correlations among the factors (i.e., the cosines of the angular separations of the unit-length reference vectors).

7. In order to obtain a transformation matrix by means of which the loadings on the oblique factors can be transformed to loadings on an orthogonal system, the matrix R_{pq} is factored by the diagonal method with unity in the diagonal cells. (See pp. 52-58.) The results are shown in matrix F_{pm}. (This is the point at which the method usually breaks down because of imaginary numbers if the groups are not linearly independent.)

8. The desired matrix which will transform the oblique to orthogonal reference axes is the transpose of the inverse of matrix F (i.e., the transpose of F_{pm}^{-1}).

9. A procedure for obtaining the inverse of a matrix is described in Chapter 3 and may be applied here. Since, however, the matrix whose inverse is desired is a triangular matrix (one

---

[2] For a method for going directly from the multiple-group loadings to the rotated oblique loadings (on the *primary* axes) see Harris and Schmid (1950).

which has zeros above the principal diagonal), its inverse may also be computed by a simpler method which will be described below.

Calculation of the Inverse of a Triangular Matrix. It will be recalled from formula 3.1 that $A \cdot A^{-1} = I$. If A is the triangular matrix with known values and A^{-1} is the inverse which we wish to find, the relationship for a 5×5 matrix can be written as follows:

$$
\begin{Vmatrix}
a_{11} & 0 & 0 & 0 & 0 \\
a_{21} & a_{22} & 0 & 0 & 0 \\
a_{31} & a_{32} & a_{33} & 0 & 0 \\
a_{41} & a_{42} & a_{43} & a_{44} & 0 \\
a_{51} & a_{52} & a_{53} & a_{54} & a_{55}
\end{Vmatrix}
\bullet
\begin{Vmatrix}
x_{11} & x_{12} & x_{13} & x_{14} & x_{15} \\
x_{21} & x_{22} & x_{23} & x_{24} & x_{25} \\
x_{31} & x_{32} & x_{33} & x_{34} & x_{35} \\
x_{41} & x_{42} & x_{43} & x_{44} & x_{45} \\
x_{51} & x_{52} & x_{53} & x_{54} & x_{55}
\end{Vmatrix}
=
\begin{Vmatrix}
1.0 & 0.0 & 0.0 & 0.0 & 0.0 \\
0.0 & 1.0 & 00 & 00 & 00 \\
0.0 & 0.0 & 1.0 & 0.0 & 0.0 \\
0.0 & 0.0\ 00. & & 1.0 & 0.0 \\
0.0 & 0.0 & 0.0 & 0.0 & 1.0
\end{Vmatrix}
$$

$$\quad\quad A \quad\quad\quad\quad\quad\quad\quad A^{-1} \quad\quad\quad\quad\quad\quad\quad I$$

$$
\begin{Vmatrix}
1.0000 & .0000 & .0000 & .0000 & .0000 \\
.0294 & .9996 & .0000 & .0000 & .0000 \\
.4922 & .2023 & .8466 & .0000 & .0000 \\
.5722 & .6218 & -.0344 & .5336 & .0000 \\
.5032 & .6533 & .3764 & -.0671 & .4619
\end{Vmatrix}
\bullet
\begin{Vmatrix}
x_{11} & x_{12} & x_{13} & x_{14} & x_{15} \\
x_{21} & x_{22} & x_{23} & x_{24} & x_{25} \\
x_{31} & x_{32} & x_{33} & x_{34} & x_{35} \\
x_{41} & x_{42} & x_{43} & x_{44} & x_{45} \\
x_{51} & x_{52} & x_{53} & x_{54} & x_{55}
\end{Vmatrix}
=
\begin{Vmatrix}
1.0 & 0.0 & 0.0 & 0.0 & 0.0 \\
0.0 & 1.0 & 0.0 & 0.0 & 0.0 \\
0.0 & 0.0 & 1.0 & 0.0 & 0.0 \\
0.0 & 0.0 & 0.0 & 1.0 & 0.0 \\
0.0 & 0.0 & 0.0 & 0.0 & 1.0
\end{Vmatrix}
$$

$$\quad\quad F_{pm} \quad\quad\quad\quad\quad\quad\quad F_{pm}^{-1} \quad\quad\quad\quad\quad\quad\quad I$$

By means of the row-by-column rule of matrix multiplication, simple equations can be set up for the solution of the unknown values in the inverse matrix as follows:

1. Row 1 × column 1

$$a_{11}x_{11} + 0.0x_{21} + 0.0x_{31} + 0.0x_{41} + 0.0x_{51} = 1.0$$

$$a_{11}x_{11} = 1.0$$

$$x_{11} = \frac{1.0}{a_{11}} = \frac{1.0}{1.0} = 1.0 \tag{6.3}$$

2. Row 1 × column 2

$$a_{11}x_{12} + 0.0x_{22} + 0.0x_{32} + 0.0x_{42} + 0.0x_{52} = 0.0$$

$$a_{11}x_{12} = 0.0$$

$$x_{12} = 0.0 \tag{6.4}$$

In the same way it can be shown that $x_{13} = 0 = x_{14} = x_{15}$ and that all other values x_{jk} (for $j > k$) to the right of the principal diagonal are equal to zero.

3. Row 2 × column 2

$$a_{21}x_{12} + a_{22}x_{22} + 0.0x_{32} + 0.0x_{42} + 0.0x_{52} = 1.0$$

$$a_{21}x_{12} + a_{22}x_{22} = 1.0$$

From equation 6.4 $x_{12} = 0.0$ and

$$a_{22}x_{22} = 1.0$$

or

$$x_{22} = \frac{1.0}{a_{22}} = \frac{1}{.9996} = 1.0004 \tag{6.5}$$

It can be shown in the same way that all other values in the principal diagonal of the inverse matrix (x_{kk}) are the reciprocal of the corresponding values in the given matrix, and hence

$$x_{33} = \frac{1}{a_{33}} = \frac{1}{.8466} = 1.1812 \tag{6.6}$$

$$x_{44} = \frac{1}{a_{44}} = \frac{1}{.5336} = 1.8741 \tag{6.7}$$

$$x_{55} = \frac{1}{a_{55}} = \frac{1}{.4169} = 2.3987 \tag{6.8}$$

and

$$x_{kk} = \frac{1}{a_{kk}} \tag{6.8a}$$

4. Row 2 × column 1

$$a_{21}x_{11} + a_{22}x_{21} + 0.0x_{31} + 0.0x_{41} + 0.0x_{51} = 0.0$$

$$a_{21}x_{11} + a_{22}x_{21} = 0.0$$

$$x_{21} = -\frac{a_{21}x_{11}}{a_{22}} = -\frac{(.0294)(1.0)}{.9996} = -.0294 \tag{6.9}$$

5. Row 3 × column 2

$$a_{31}x_{12} + a_{32}x_{22} + a_{33}x_{32} + 0.0x_{42} + 0.0x_{52} = 0.0$$

$$a_{31}x_{12} + a_{32}x_{22} + a_{33}x_{32} = 0.0$$

In equation 6.4 it was shown that $x_{12} = 0.0$, hence

$$a_{32}x_{22} + a_{33}x_{32} = 0.0$$

and

$$x_{32} = -\frac{a_{32}x_{22}}{a_{33}} = -\frac{(.2023)(1.0004)}{.8466} = -.2391 \quad (6.10)$$

Similarly, it can be shown that, for x_{21}, x_{32}, x_{43} and for all other values of x_{kj} (where $k = j + 1$), the value can be obtained by the equation

$$x_{kj} = -\frac{a_{kj}x_{jj}}{a_{kk}} \quad (6.11)$$

and hence

$$x_{43} = -\frac{a_{43}x_{33}}{a_{44}} = -\frac{(-.0344)(1.1812)}{.5336} = .0761 \quad (6.12)$$

$$x_{54} = -\frac{a_{54}x_{44}}{a_{55}} = -\frac{(-.0671)(1.8741)}{.4161} = .3016 \quad (6.13)$$

6. Row 3 × column 1

$$a_{31}x_{11} + a_{32}x_{21} + a_{33}x_{31} + 0.0x_{41} + 0.0x_{51} = 0.0$$

$$a_{31}x_{11} + a_{32}x_{21} + a_{33}x_{31} = 0.0$$

$$x_{31} = -\frac{a_{31}x_{11} + a_{32}x_{21}}{a_{33}}$$

$$= -\frac{(.4922)(1.0) + (.2023)(-.0294)}{.8466} = -.5744 \quad (6.14)$$

It can be shown that the general formula for getting the value in any cell a_{kj} (where $k > j$) of the inverse matrix is:

$$x_{kj} =$$
$$-\frac{a_{kj}x_{jj} + a_{k,\,j+1}x_{j+1,\,j} + a_{k,\,j+2}x_{j+2,\,j} + \cdots + a_{k,\,k-1}x_{k-1,\,j}}{a_{kk}} \quad (6.15)$$

Hence:

$$x_{42} = -\frac{a_{42}x_{22} + a_{43}x_{32}}{a_{44}}$$

$$= -\frac{(.6218)(1.0004) + (-.0344)(-.3391)}{.5336}$$

$$= -1.1812 \quad (6.16)$$

$$x_{53} = -\frac{a_{53}x_{33} + a_{54}x_{43}}{a_{55}}$$

$$= -\frac{(.3764)(1.1812)+(-.0671)(.0761)}{.4169} = -1.0542 \quad (6.17)$$

$$x_{41} = -\frac{a_{41}x_{11} + a_{42}x_{21} + a_{43}x_{31}}{a_{44}}$$

$$= -\frac{(.5722)(1.0)+(.6218)(-.0294)+(-.0344)(-.5744)}{.5336}$$

$$= -1.0751 \quad (6.18)$$

$$x_{52} = -\frac{a_{52}x_{22} + a_{53}x_{32} + a_{54}x_{42}}{a_{55}}$$

$$= -\frac{(.6533)(1.0004)+(.3764)(-.2391)+(-.0671)(-1.1812)}{.4169}$$

$$= -1.5419 \quad (6.19)$$

$$x_{51} = -\frac{a_{51}x_{11} + a_{52}x_{21} + a_{53}x_{31} + a_{54}x_{41}}{a_{55}}$$

$$= -\frac{\left\{\begin{matrix}(.5032)(1.0)+(.6533)(-.0294)\\ + (.3764)(-.5744)+(-.0671)(-1.1751)\end{matrix}\right\}}{.4169}$$

$$= -.8154 \quad (6.20)$$

In general, there are k minus j terms in the numerator of the equation for determining the value of x_{kj}, all values to the right of the principal diagonal are zero, the values in the principal diagonal of the inverse matrix are the reciprocals of the corresponding values in the principal diagonal cells of the given triangular matrix, and the other values are obtained by equations similar to equation 6.15. The inverse matrix $(\mathbf{F}_{pm}{}^{-1})$ is therefore [3]

$$\left\|\begin{matrix} 1.0000 & 0.0 & 0.0 & 0.0 & 0.0 \\ -.0294 & 1.0004 & 0.0 & 0.0 & 0.0 \\ -.5744 & -.23916 & 1.1812 & 0.0 & 0.0 \\ -1.0751 & -1.1812 & .0761 & 1.8741 & 0.0 \\ -.8154 & -1.5419 & -1.0542 & .3016 & 2.3987 \end{matrix}\right\|$$

$$(\mathbf{F}_{pm}{}^{-1})$$

[3] The accuracy of the calculations can be checked, of course, by the equation $\mathbf{F}_{pm}\mathbf{F}_{pm}{}^{-1} = \mathbf{I}$.

Since the matrix which will transform the oblique factors to orthogonal factors is the transpose of this matrix, it is written as follows:

$$
\begin{Vmatrix}
1.000 & -.0294 & -.5744 & -1.0751 & -.8154 \\
0.0 & 1.0004 & -.2391 & -1.1812 & -1.5419 \\
0.0 & 0.0 & 1.1812 & 0761 & -1.0542 \\
0.0 & 0.0 & 0.0 & 1.8741 & .3016 \\
0.0 & 0.0 & 0.0 & 0.0 & 2.3987
\end{Vmatrix}
$$

$$(F'_{mp})^{-1}$$

The Orthogonal Factor Loadings. 1. To obtain the orthogonal factor loading, multiply matrix V by matrix $(F'_{mp})^{-1}$ and enter the results in a matrix as in Table 6.3.[4]

TABLE 6.3. ORTHOGONAL FACTOR LOADINGS (F) EXTRACTED BY THE MULTIPLE-GROUP METHOD

	Test	Factor					h^2
		I	II	III	IV	V	
1	Dial and Table Reading	.70	.14	.20	.11	.21	.61
2	Spatial Orientation I	.38	.11	.55	-.02	.02	.46
3	Reading Comprehension	.46	.36	-.04	.29	.01	.43
4	Instrument Comprehension . .	.33	.44	.20	.02	.26	.41
5	Mechanical Principles	.11	.72	.03	.01	.06	.54
6	Speed of Identification	.28	.16	.59	.02	-.02	.45
7	Numerical Operations I	.78	-.13	-.09	-.06	-.01	.64
8	Numerical Operations II . . .	.81	-.01	-.11	-.05	-.21	.71
9	Mechanical Information	.07	.62	-.12	-.17	-.19	.47
10	Practical Judgment	.26	.42	-.01	.38	-.01	.39
11	Complex Coordination	.28	.36	.26	-.10	.25	.35

2. To obtain a table of residuals use the orthogonal loadings in the usual way:

$$\rho_{jk} = r_{jk} - (a_{j1}a_{k1} + a_{j2}a_{k2} \cdots a_{jr}a_{kr})$$

The residual correlations after the extraction of the 5 factors in the example are shown in Table 6.4. They are, by inspection, sufficiently small so that no further factors need be extracted.

---

[4] In matrix notation $F = V(F'_{mp})^{-1}$.

TABLE 6.4. RESIDUAL-CORRELATION MATRIX AFTER EXTRACTION OF FIVE MULTIPLE-GROUP FACTORS

	1	2	3	4	5	6	7	8	9	10	11
1	.09	.01	.01	.02	.00	-.01	.02	.06	-.03	-.01	.02
2	.01	.02	-.01	-.01	.01	.01	.00	-.01	-.02	.01	.00
3	.01	-.01	-.04	.02	.01	.01	-.01	-.01	-.03	.03	-.02
4	-.02	-.01	.02	.00	.01	.00	-.01	.03	.00	-.01	-.01
5	.00	.01	.01	.01	-.04	.00	-.01	.01	.03	.00	.00
6	.01	.01	.01	.00	.00	-.01	.01	.02	.02	.00	.00
7	.02	.00	.01	-.01	-.01	.01	-.05	.02	-.13	.00	.01
8	.06	-.01	-.01	.03	.01	.02	.02	-.08	-.17	.01	-.03
9	-.03	-.02	-.03	.00	.03	.02	-.13	-.17	-.04	.03	.00
10	-.01	.01	.03	-.01	.00	.00	.00	.01	.03	-.02	.02
11	.02	.00	-.02	-.01	.00	.00	.01	-.03	.00	.02	.00

If there is sufficient common-factor variance remaining in the residual correlations to justify the obtaining of additional factors, they may be extracted in the same way by the multiple-group method or by any other method appropriate for a table of residuals.

3. The orthogonal factor loadings may be rotated by the methods to be explained in the next chapter.

PRINCIPAL-AXES METHOD

The principal-axes method of factoring the correlation matrix is of interest for several reasons. Each factor extracts the maximum amount of variance (i.e., the sum of squares of factor loadings is maximized on each factor) and gives the smallest possible residuals. The correlation matrix is condensed into the smallest number of orthogonal factors by this method. The method also has the advantage of giving a mathematically unique (least squares) solution for a given table of correlations.

In practice this method has the limitation that the computations are laborious. Equivalent results can be obtained by the centroid method with less work if an additional factor or two is extracted so that the two solutions account for the same amount of variance.

Numerical Example. Hotelling (1935) has developed an iterative method of obtaining the loadings on the principal axes which can be carried to any desired degree of accuracy. As an example let us consider the fictitious 4×4 correlation matrix in Table 6.5 with known true *communalities* entered in the diagonal cells.

A. Iteration Procedure. 1. Enter the sum of each column of the correlation matrix ($\mathbf{R}$) in the row labeled "Σ_1."

2. Divide each value in the row labeled Σ_1 by the highest value in that row and enter the results in the next row, labeled "u_1."

3. Obtain the sum of the cross-products of row Σ_1 with each row of the correlation matrix. Enter the results in the next row, labeled "Σ_2." Thus the first entry of row Σ_2 is the *sum* of the cross-products of row 1 and row Σ_1, the second entry is the sum of the cross-products of row 2 and row Σ_1, etc.

4. Divide each value in row Σ_2 by the highest value in the row and enter the results in the next row labeled "u_2."

5. Compare the values in rows u_1 and u_2. If they agree to the desired degree of accuracy (in this example agreement to four decimal places will be required), the iteration is completed and the factor loadings may be computed. If the desired accuracy has not been obtained (as it has not in the example), the iteration is continued by the "squaring" process.

6. Multiply the correlation matrix by itself, using the *row-by-column* rule of matrix multiplication. The result is the product matrix $\mathbf{R}^2$ shown in Table 6.5.

7. Sum the columns of matrix $\mathbf{R}^2$ and enter the result in a row labeled Σ_2. As a check on the accuracy of the work to this point, the values in row Σ_2 in matrix $\mathbf{R}$ and in row Σ_2 in matrix $\mathbf{R}^2$ should be the same. If they check, copy the values from row u_2 in matrix $\mathbf{R}$ into the next row in matrix $\mathbf{R}^2$.

8. To obtain the expected values (Σ_3) for the columns of the next matrix ($\mathbf{R}^4$), sum the cross-products of row Σ_2 with each row of matrix $\mathbf{R}^2$ successively and enter the results in row Σ_3 of matrix $\mathbf{R}^2$.

9. Divide each value in row Σ_3 by the highest value in the row and enter the results in the next row, labeled u_3.

10. Compare the values in rows u_2 and u_3. If they agree to the desired degree of accuracy, the iteration is completed. If not,

TABLE 6.5. PRINCIPAL-AXES METHOD CALCULATIONS

Var.	Correlation Matrix (R) 1	2	3	4		Matrix R^2 1	2	3	4
1	(.90)	.60	.48	.69	1	1.8765	1.4445	1.2330	1.6515
2	.60	(.50)	.44	.57	2	1.4445	1.1285	.9690	1.2895
3	.48	.44	(.40)	.50	3	1.2330	.9690	.8340	1.1070
4	.69	.57	.50	(.65)	4	1.6515	1.2895	1.1070	1.4735
Σ_1	2.67	2.11	1.82	2.41	Σ_2	6.2055	4.8315	4.1430	5.5215
u_1	1.00	.79	.68	.90	u_2	1.0000	.7786	.6676	.8898
Σ_2	6.2055	4.8315	4.1430	5.5215	Σ_3	32.85079875	25.55073375	21.90066750	29.20083375
u_2	1.0000	.7786	.6676	.8898	u_3	1.00000000	.77778120	.66667078	.88889265

	Matrix R^4 1	2	3	4	
1	9.85557375	7.66510875	6.56997750	8.76013875	$v_{j1} = Ru$
2	7.66510875	5.96186375	5.11020750	6.81355375	
3	6.56997750	5.11020750	4.38025500	5.84022750	$a_{j1} = \dfrac{v_{j1}}{\sqrt{\Sigma u_4 v_{j1}}}$
4	8.76013875	6.81355375	5.84022750	7.78691375	
Σ_3	32.85079875	25.55073375	21.90066750	29.20083375	
u_3	1.00000000	.77778120	.66667078	.88889265	$\Sigma u_4 v = 6.53086411$
Σ_4	919.30287064	715.01334389	612.86858049	817.15810730	
u_4	1.00000000	.77777778	.66666667	.88888889	$\sqrt{\Sigma u_4 v} = 2.55555554$
v_{j1}	2.29999999	1.78888887	1.53333332	2.04444443	
a_{j1}	.90000000	.70000000	.60000000	.80000000	$1/\sqrt{\Sigma u_4 v} = .39130435$

	First Residual—Correlation Matrix 1	2	3	4				Factor Loadings Var.	I	II	h^2
1	(.09)	−.03	−.06	−.03				1	.90	.30	.90
2	−.03	(.01)	.02	.01				2	.70	−.10	.50
3	−.06	.02	(.04)	.02				3	.60	−.20	.40
4	−.03	.01	.02	(.01)				4	.80	−.10	.65
Σ_1	−.03	.01	.02	.01	$\Sigma u_2 v$	= .2500		Σa^2	2.30	.15	
u_1	1.00	−.33	−.67	−.33							
Σ_2	.1500	−.0500	−.1000	−.0500	$\sqrt{\Sigma u_2 v}$	= .50					
u_2	1.0000	−.3333	−.6667	−.3333							
v_{j2}	.1500	−.0500	−.1000	−.0500	$1/\sqrt{\Sigma u_2 v}$	= 2.00					
a_{j2}	.3000	−.1000	−.2000	−.1000							

the process must be continued with $\mathbf{R}^4$, $\mathbf{R}^8$, etc., until two successive rows of u agree to the specified number of decimal places.

In the example it was necessary to obtain matrix $\mathbf{R}^4$ and to obtain the expected values Σ_4 and u_4. The values in rows u_3 and u_4 agree to four decimal places and the iteration was, therefore, terminated.

B. Computation of the First Factor Loadings. 1. To compute the loadings on the first factor, it is necessary to obtain the sum of the cross-products of each row of the correlation matrix, $\mathbf{R}$, and the final row of u (u_4 in the example). The results are entered in the next row labeled v_{j1}.

$$v_{j1} = \mathbf{R}u \tag{6.21}$$

2. The formula for obtaining the loading for variable j on the first factor is

$$a_{j1} = \frac{v_{j1}}{\sqrt{\Sigma uv}} \tag{6.22}$$

The quantity Σuv is the sum of the cross-products of the final row u and row v_{j1}. In the example, $\Sigma u_4 v_{j1} = 6.53086411$; $\sqrt{u_4 v_{j1}} = 2.55555554$, and the reciprocal, $1/\sqrt{\Sigma u_4 v_{j1}} = .39130435$.

3. The factor loadings are obtained by multiplying the value of v_{j1} for variable j by $1/\sqrt{\Sigma u_4 v_{j1}}$.

C. Second and Succeeding Factors. 1. A table of residuals is obtained from the correlation matrix and first factor loadings by the same method as was used in the case of the correlation matrix and first centroid loadings (see p. 73). The formula is

$$_1\rho_{jk} = r_{jk} - a_{j1}a_{k1}$$

where $_1\rho$ denotes the first residuals. The table of first residuals for the example is shown in Table 6.5.

2. The communalities may be re-estimated at this point, and the process that was used for extracting factor I is repeated to obtain factor II from the first table of residuals.

3. In the example (Table 6.5) the values in row u_1 and row u_2 are identical, and so it is not necessary to apply the squaring process to obtain the second factor loadings.

4. Compute v_{j2} by the formula

$$v_{j2} = {}_1\rho u \tag{6.23}$$

In the example in Table 6.5, multiply each row of the first residual matrix by u_2 and enter the results in the next row, labeled v_{j2}.

5. To obtain the loadings on the second factor first compute

$$\Sigma u_2 v_{j2} = .2500$$

$$\sqrt{\Sigma u_2 v_{j2}} = .50$$

$$\frac{1}{\sqrt{\Sigma u_2 v_{j2}}} = 2.00$$

The formula for the second factor loadings is

$$a_{j2} = \frac{v_{j2}}{\sqrt{\Sigma u_2 v_{j2}}} \tag{6.24}$$

The values are entered in the last row of the first residual matrix and in the factor matrix in Table 6.5.

6. To compute the next and succeeding factors the second table of residuals is obtained, the communalities are re-estimated, and the process used in calculating the first factor is repeated. This is continued until the residuals are judged to be negligibly small. In the example the second table of residuals contains all zeros, and there are just two factors.

In the principal-axes solution the sum of the cross-products of any pair of columns in the unrotated factor matrix is equal to zero.

When the sums of the squares of loadings for different factor columns (Σa_{jr}^2) are unequal, successive values in the row u will converge to the desired degree of accuracy in relatively few trials. If, however, the sums of the squares for columns with the larger sums are nearly equal, convergence will be slow, and it may take many trial values of u. These values $(\Sigma a_{jr}{}^2)$, called the latent roots, are, of course, not known in advance, and in an actual problem, obtaining the principal axes may be laborious.

After the principal-axes factors have been determined with known or estimated communalities in the diagonal cells, they may be rotated to psychologically meaningful positions according to the principles described in the next chapter. Another use to which this method has been put is factoring the matrix with either unities or reliabilities in the principal diagonal. The resulting factors are called "principal components" and are used to reproduce the score matrix rather than the correlation matrix. The number of components extracted is equal to the number of tests in the battery (Hotelling, 1933b).

OTHER METHODS OF EXTRACTION OF FACTORS

The methods for extracting factors presented in this chapter are but a few of the many methods which have been developed. Several of the widely used or theoretically important methods not discussed in this introduction are group-centroid method (Thurstone, 1947c), the simple-summation method (Burt, 1917), the maximum-likelihood method (Lawley, 1951). The group-centroid method might be said to lie between the multiple-group and complete centroid methods described above, and, although it is computationally simpler than the latter, it is probably not as effective. Burt's simple summation method is very similar to the centroid method. Lawley's maximum-likelihood method which is seldom used because it is computationally laborious gives the most mathematically "efficient" estimates of the factor loadings and has the added considerable virtue of providing a chi-square test for the number of significant factors. As high-speed computing machines are more widely used, more exact methods such as the maximum-likelihood method are likely to gain wider usage.

It can be shown that the results from the different methods are mathematically equivalent and that the loadings derived by one method can be transformed into those derived by any other method (see Wolfle, 1940).

Problems

1. Factor the correlation matrix on page 17 by the multiple-group method. Use the results from the cluster analysis in Problem 1 of Chapter 2 to set up the groups. Estimate the communalities by the centroid-formula method.

2. Make up a 4 × 4 matrix consisting of the correlations of tests 3, 4, 7, and 8 in the correlation matrix on page 17. Factor the 4 × 4 matrix by the principal-axes method, using the communality estimates for these tests that were obtained in Problem 1 above.

CHAPTER 7

Methods of Rotation: Orthogonal Axes

OR A given matrix of correlations, each of the factoring methods presented in the preceding chapter will arbitrarily locate the reference axes in a different position. In order to move the axes from the arbitrary location determined by the method of extraction to some position useful for interpretation of the factors and for comparison with other studies, the axes are rotated. A major goal of rotation is to obtain meaningful factors that are as consistent (or invariant) as possible from analysis to analysis. The "proper" location of the reference frame depends upon the purposes and theoretical approach of the factor analyst.[1]

Rotation is the aspect of factor analysis which is the most difficult to teach and the most difficult to learn, because it requires considerable background, insight, and skill. Only after rotating in several problems in a given area can one expect to have confidence in his ability to find satisfactory rotational solutions. In other words, while the mechanics of rotation are mathematical and relatively straightforward, criteria for determining where to

---

[1] For a witty exposition of this point see Cureton (1939). Reprints of this humorous article are usually available, on request, from the World Book Co., Yonkers-on-the-Hudson, New York.

rotate are largely in the nature of interpretations of the data and are based on theoretical and conceptual considerations. The location of the reference vectors will vary, therefore, with the purposes of the investigation and the theoretical biases of the investigator, as indeed is true of the interpretations of most scientific investigations.

In some instances the configuration of the test vectors makes the location of the reference vectors, within certain limits, fairly obvious. Thus, Figure 7.1a presents a configuration of four test vectors in two dimensions. Where should the reference vector or vectors be placed? One possible solution might be to run a single reference vector through the configuration in such a location as to maximize the sum of the squares of the loadings as in Figure 7.1b. This would be the first principal axis and all four variables would have high loadings on it. If it were not rotated, it would be a general factor and would account for a great deal of the variance that the four variables have in common. If a second factor (II) were extracted, orthogonal to the first, we have the situation diagramed in Figure 7.1c. These two factors could be kept orthogonal to each other and rotated to the position shown in Figure 7.1d, or two planes, oblique to one another, could be passed through the centroids of clusters of highly correlated tests, so as to maximize the number of zero or near-zero loadings, and the factor axes (called normals to the planes) placed perpendicular to the planes at the origin as shown in Figure 7.1e. As can be seen from the diagram, the oblique solution is more complicated than the others. It will be discussed in more detail in the next chapter.

There are, of course, an infinite number of locations of orthogonal or oblique axes, but those mentioned above are some of the more common ones used to account for variance common to clusters of tests. Spearman's general factor, in the case where there is a unidimensional matrix (i.e., of rank 1) is represented by Figure 7.1f, where the departures of the variable vectors from the reference vector and from each other are no greater than can be attributed to random sampling fluctuation.

If the configuration of test vectors in Figure 7.1f represents a departure from a single dimension that is greater than chance, so that two dimensions are required to account for the interrela-

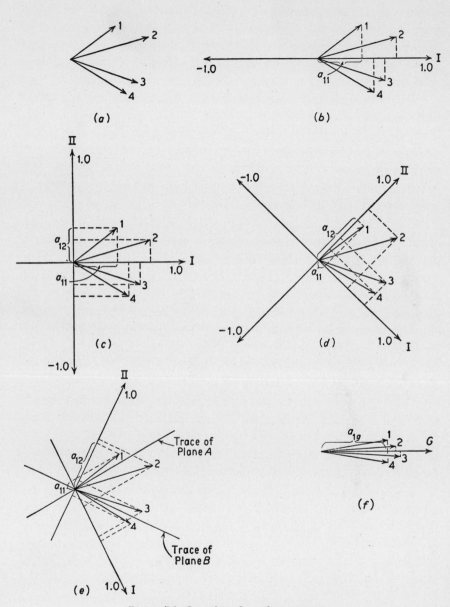

FIGURE 7.1 Locations for reference axes.

tionships, the G-vector might be passed through test 1 and a group-factor vector, orthogonal to G, might be used to represent that portion of the common variances of tests 3 and 4 not accounted for by G, as is done in the Holzinger bi-factor solution. Spearman's followers might also accept this type of location of the reference axes in configurations of two or more dimensions.

Thurstone and others who favor the multiple-factor approach find locations of axes such as in Figures 7.1d or 7.1e more useful. They use orthogonal or oblique reference axes, depending upon which seem to fit the configuration better. A number of factor analysts, however, prefer the orthogonal solution wherever it can be justified because of its greater simplicity and because it postulates independent reference variables.

Often in setting up a factorial study the variables can be chosen so that a given configuration is anticipated. When this is done, there is some basis for the location of the rotated reference axes. Thurstone has developed criteria for setting up a factorial investigation so that a relatively unique configuration may be expected and a relatively standard location for the reference frame can be established.[2] These are known as the criteria of "simple structure" and "positive manifold."

Simple Structure and Positive Manifold

These criteria will be illustrated with reference to a three-dimensional problem. Figure 7.2 shows 11 test vectors. All but test 11 have been selected so that their vectors lie in one of three planes (A, B, and C) which are orthogonal to one another. In this arrangement, if three orthogonal reference vectors (vector I, perpendicular to plane A, etc.) are placed at the intersections of these planes, no variable in a plane will be loaded on more than 2 factors. A vector which coincides with the intersection of two planes will have a loading on that reference vector only and is referred to as a "pure" measure of the factor. Variable 2, for instance, has loadings (projections) on reference vectors I and II but none on III. Vector 4 has a loading on II but none on I and III, since it is perpendicular to them. An eleventh variable

2 Thurstone (1947c, Chapter IX).

is shown in Figure 7.2 that is not in any of the planes but it is in the space bounded by them. It has loadings on all three of the factors, but it would not help to determine the positions of the planes and reference vectors.

Where several vectors lie in a plane (or for more than three dimensional configurations, a hyperplane) and determine its loca-

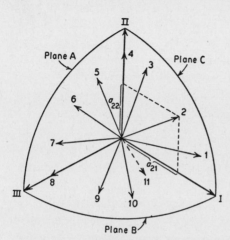

FIGURE 7.2 Illustration of simple structure and positive manifold in a three-dimensional configuration.

tion, there is a relatively unique location for the reference vectors at the intersections of these planes (or hyperplanes). Thurstone (1947c, p. 335) has set up specifications for simple structure, for the case where each variable is less complex than the battery as a whole. They can be stated as follows:

1. Each variable should have at least one loading close to zero.

2. There should be, for each factor column, at least as many tests with zero loadings as there are factors. (Thus in the three-dimensional, orthogonal illustration each reference vector should have at least three variable vectors orthogonal to it.)

3. For every pair of factors there should be several variables with projections on one factor vector but not on the other.

4. For problems having four or more factors, a large proportion of the variables should have negligible loadings on any pair of factors.

5. Only a small number of variables should have appreciable loadings on any pair of factors.

The essential aspects of simple structure are that each variable contains fewer factors than the configuration as a whole, that each variable contains a different combination of factors, and that the location of each plane (or hyperplane) is determined by several test vectors.

Positive manifold exists when the axes can be rotated so that

all loadings are positive or zero. In practice, small negative loadings are tolerated. This principle is especially useful in the area
of abilities, whose measures, generally speaking, are positively
correlated. In dealing with temperament traits, both positive
and negative loadings occur, and the restriction of positive manifold does not apply. In that case
bipolar factors frequently occur,
but the criteria for simple structure can still be applied.

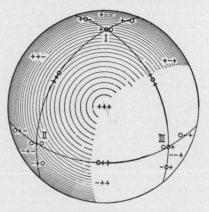

Thurstone (1947c, Chapter
IX) has distinguished a number
of configurations of variable vectors which, together with their
factor patterns, may be represented for the three-dimensional
orthogonal case by means of
spherical right triangles.

Figure 7.3 shows how such a
spherical right triangle is drawn
on the surface of a sphere. The
algebraic signs indicate the direction of the loadings on the

FIGURE 7.3 Showing the algebraic
signs of coordinates in the octants of
a sphere, which would also be the signs
of the three factor loadings of a variable whose vector is located in the
octant.

three factors. Thus a variable vector ending on the line between
the ends of axes I and III would have positive loadings on factors
I and III and a zero loading on factor II.

Below are some typical configurations.

1. *Isolated constellations.*

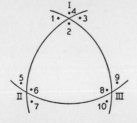

Factor Pattern			
Test	I	II	III
1	X		
2	X		
3	X		
4	X		
5		X	
6		X	
7		X	
8			X
9			X
10			X

This is the easiest type of simple structure to recognize. The
variables in each cluster are highly correlated and have very low
correlations with the variables in the other clusters. Each variable is a relatively pure measure of its factor.

Introduction to Factor Analysis

This same configuration of variables will yield different factor patterns if the reference axes are rotated to a position other than simple structure. These other patterns, such as would be obtained by putting axis I through the centroid of all of the vectors, although preferred by some investigators, are less simple and seem less useful.

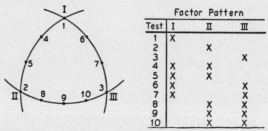

Test	I	II	III
1	X	X	
2	X	X	
3	X	X	
4	X	−	X
5	X	−	X
6	X	−	X
7	X	−	−
8	X	−	−
9	X	−	−
10	X	−	−

Factor Pattern

2. *Complete triangular configuration.*

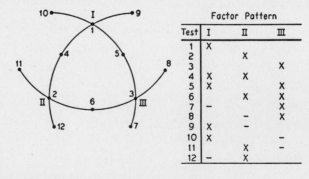

Test	I	II	III
1	X		
2		X	
3			X
4	X	X	
5	X	X	
6	X		X
7	X		X
8		X	X
9		X	X
10		X	X

Factor Pattern

This is similar to the configuration pictured in Figure 7.2. The tests in the corners at the intersections of the planes are of complexity one. All other tests are complexity two. This is an example of simple structure and positive manifold.

3. *Simple structure without positive manifold, due to the presence of bipolar factors.*

Test	I	II	III
1	X		
2		X	
3			X
4	X	X	
5	X		X
6		X	X
7	−		X
8		−	X
9	X	−	
10	X		−
11		X	−
12	−	X	

Factor Pattern

4. *Incomplete triangular configuration.* All tests have complexity of two except those that lie at the intersections.

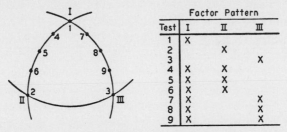

Test	I	II	III
1	X		
2		X	
3			X
4	X	X	
5	X	X	
6	X	X	
7	X		X
8	X		X
9	X		X

In this configuration there is one pure measure of each of the factors and other variables which are measures of combinations of factors I and II, and I and III, but none of the variables are measures of combinations of factors II and III. In such a situation it would be of interest to try to devise a measure which combined factors II and III. If the attempt were successful, it would be further confirmation that the factors had been meaningfully interpreted.

Other more complex configurations frequently occur in experimental data. If possible, the factorial experiment should be designed with some definite configuration in mind so that simple structure or other principles can be applied to guide the rotations. It should be noted, moreover, that alternative simple structures can sometimes be located in experimental data that do not have a clear-cut structure. Repeated studies in the area or theoretical considerations should help to determine which is the most useful or meaningful.

A number of other criteria for determining the rotated positions of factors have been discussed by Cattell (1944c). Briefly summarized they are as follows:

1. *Rotation to agree with clinical and general psychological findings.* Passing the axes through clusters of variables or syndromes known to exist from clinical or psychological theory and observation.

2. *Rotation to agree with factors from past factor analyses.* This principle would be especially applicable in fields and for populations with well-established factors and well-known measures of the factors.

3. *Rotation to put axes through the center of clusters.* The axes may be passed through either the outstanding correlation clusters in the correlation matrix or through the clusters which appear on the plots of factors represented two at a time.

4. *Rotation to agree with successively established orthogonal factors.* If there is only one new factor in a matrix of r factors, it can be placed orthogonal to the first $r - 1$ known factors. In this way starting with one factor of known position and successively adding one factor at a time, a large number of factors could be rotated into position. This principle, of course, has the limitation of applying to orthogonal factors only.

5. *Rotation to produce loading-profiles congruent with general psychological expectations.* Factors representing traits acquired by education or training might be expected to have either very high or very low loadings, while factors representing more basic, constitutional traits might be expected to have a more even distribution of loadings. If these two kinds of factors are present in a study, the rotations might be guided partly by this principle so as to bring about the maximum number of factors with the expected profiles of loadings.

6. *Rotation to produce parallel proportional profiles.* The purpose of this criterion is to extend the principle of parsimony over a wide range of studies rather than restricting it to one study at a time, as is true of the simple-structure principle. For this reason Cattell has given it the alternate title of "simultaneous simple structure." In considering a large number of studies, if there are fundamental, unitary factors common to them, the rotations should be done so as to get maximum agreement among all of the studies. If the studies differ in their experimental conditions or the populations to which they are applied, the agreement of the profiles of factor loadings would be expected to be proportional rather than absolute. In this way agreement could be obtained over a wide area of application and a wide variety of conditions.

GRAPHICAL ROTATION

One of the most convenient methods of rotation is to plot pairs of orthogonal axes and rotate them graphically. To get a complete picture of the structure at any point in the rotation process by this method requires the plotting of all combinations of pairs of axes. For r factors this would require $\frac{1}{2}r(r-1)$ plots.

After a pair of axes has been rotated, the rotated numerical values can be read from the graph and the new values plotted. If much rotation is to be done, it is advantageous to construct a simple apparatus designed by Zimmerman (1946) which requires

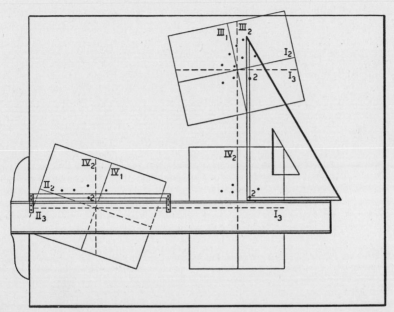

FIGURE 7.4 Graphical method for rotation of orthogonal axes, showing how point 2 can be plotted directly from rotated axes I_3 and IV_2. (See Zimmerman, 1946.)

a T-square with a special attachment and a triangle. This equipment eliminates the steps of converting the projections to numerical values after each rotation and the necessity of replotting the numerical values. Figure 7.4 shows how to set up and plot a point from a pair of rotated axes using this equipment.

Rotation of the Eleven-variable Example.[3] The first step is to plot the loadings of each centroid factor to some convenient

---

[3] If a positive manifold or something close to one is expected, because all of the correlations are positive, or if negatives are few and low, a first step might be to make a preliminary algebraic rotation by means of a Landahl transformation matrix. If all of the correlations are positive, this has the effect of inclining all of the rotated axes at 45° to the first centroid. This yields positive manifold with

scale on a separate piece of graph paper. If graph paper with 10 divisions to the inch is available, a scale of .10 to the half-inch (i.e., 10 inches for the range from +1.0 to −1.0) is usually convenient.

The next step is to plot the factors, two at a time, for rotation. It is customary to let the horizontal axis represent the factor with the lower number (e.g., if factors III and VII are being plotted together, factor III would be put on the horizontal axis and factor VII on the vertical axis). This arrangement gives a uniform meaning to clockwise and counterclockwise rotation.

Rotation 1. Figure 7.5 shows centroid factors I_c and II_c from Table 5.18 plotted together on a two-dimensional graph. These two axes were selected for rotation because the positive end of factor II_c contains two tests with mechanical content (Test 5, Mechanical Principles, and Test 9, Mechanical Information) and the negative end contains three "numerical" tests (Test 7, Numerical Operations I, Test 8, Numerical Operations II, and Test 1, Dial and Table Reading). Rotating axis II_c with axis I_c, which has high positive loadings for all the tests, in a counterclockwise direction, enables us to put these two groups of tests on orthogonal (independent) factors and thus come closer to one of the requirements of simple structure (i.e., having tests that have high loadings on one factor and near zero loadings on the other) and positive manifold. In labeling the rotated axes, what was formerly the negative end of axis II has been labeled as the positive end. This reflection of axis II is desirable because it results in most of the loadings on factor II being positive. In contrast to reflecting a test, reflecting a factor, it will be recalled, has no effect on the signs of the correlations.

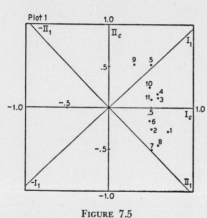

FIGURE 7.5

one rotation. Landahl (1938) gives the transformation matrices for three to nine factors and the simple rules for constructing these matrices of any rank. It is still necessary, of course, to rotate the factors to simple structure or any other position desired for interpretation.

Rotation 2. In looking for the next two factors to rotate together it was decided to pair centroid factor III (III_c) with rotated factor II (II_1),[4] as shown in Figure 7.6, because this would give a separation of the numerical tests (7, 8, and 1) from two tests which seem to involve perceptual tasks (2 and 6).

In general, for analyses in which positive manifold is expected (because the correlation matrix contains no significant negatives), an advantageous configuration for rotation exists when two groups

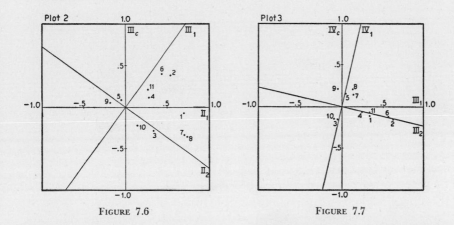

FIGURE 7.6   FIGURE 7.7

of tests, which are separated (i.e., one group positively loaded and the other group negatively loaded) on one factor, have positive loadings on the other. The group of tests which has positive saturations on both factors will be plotted in the $++$ quadrant of the graph and the other group in the $+-$ or $-+$ quadrant. (See Figures 7.6.) In the former case a clockwise rotation would be indicated and in the latter a counterclockwise rotation.

Rotation 3. Rotated factor III (III_1) and centroid factor IV (IV_c) were plotted together and rotated next as in Figure 7.7 for the following reasons:

1. The loadings of the perceptual tests (2 and 6) are increased on factor III.

2. The number of zero and near-zero loadings on factor IV is maximized.

3. The separation between the two groups of tests (group 1 consisting of 5, 7, 8, and 9 and group 2 consisting of 3 and 10) is increased so that these groups can be separated still better when paired with another factor in which both groups are positive in a future rotation to positive manifold.

Rotation 4. Figure 7.8a indicates how two previously rotated factors (I_1 and IV_1) are plotted. The purpose of this rotation is to split the mechanical tests (5 and 9) from Test 3, Reading Comprehension, and Test 10, Practical Judgment, both verbal in content, on factor IV. In this case it is seen that the two groups of tests are less than 90 degrees apart. This situation might call for oblique rather than orthogonal axes. Since, however, for the present solution orthogonal reference axes have been specified, we will rotate so that the axes are approximately equidistant from the two groups.[5]

Rotations 5 through 12 are also shown in Figure 7.8. Plot 5 (Figure 7.8b) was made to separate the verbal tests (3 and 10) from the spatial tests (11, 4, and 1). Plot 6 (Figure 7.8c) was made to improve the loadings of the verbal tests (3 and 10) on factor I, to split the mechanical tests (5 and 9) from the other tests on factor II, and to maximize the number of near-zero loadings.

Rotation 7 (Figure 7.8d) was made to maximize the number of zero and near-zero loadings and to increase the loadings of the numerical and mechanical tests on their respective factors by putting the axes more nearly through them. These two factors in an oblique representation would be slightly negatively related as might be expected, since numerical and mechanical tests tend to have low negative correlations (cf. Table 5.10; $r_{57} = -.02$, $r_{79} = -.13$, and $r_{89} = -.06$).

In rotation 8 (Figure 7.8e) slightly correlated axes are indicated. Since orthogonal axes are being used, however, the rotation indicated was made to improve the positive manifold. Like-

---

[5] See Chapter 8 for an oblique solution.

wise, in rotation 9 (Figure 7.8*f*), oblique axes are indicated. The rotation shown is a compromise to make the two clusters (spatial tests 4, 11, and 1, and perceptual tests 2 and 6) about equidistant from their respective axes.

The mechanical (tests 5 and 9) and verbal (tests 3 and 10) clusters in rotation 10 (Figure 7.8*g*) are also correlated, and the rotation was made for the same reasons as given for rotation 9.

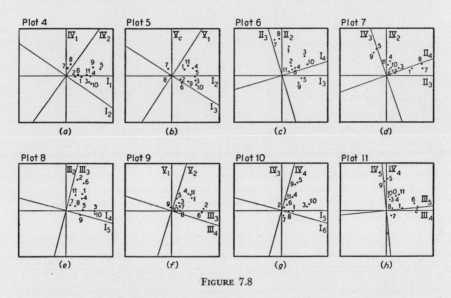

FIGURE 7.8

Rotation 11 (Figure 7.8*h*) is a slight adjustment to improve the positive manifold.

A complete picture of the locations of the rotated factors could be obtained by plotting all combinations of pairs of the latest rotated positions of the factors. For five factors 10 plots would be required. Examination of these graphs should indicate whether or not further rotations would improve the simple structure or positive manifold.

After it has been determined that no further rotations are indicated, the rotated values can be read directly from the graphs, if the plotting and rotating have been done accurately, by placing a piece of graph paper marked with the scale to which the loadings were plotted under the final rotated plots and reading off the values. If this is to be done, it is well to do the plotting and rotating on onion skin or other transparent paper.

The accuracy of the results can be checked by comparing h^2's and reproduced r's obtained from the rotated loadings with those which have been previously obtained from the centroid loadings. The rotated loadings, as read from the graphs, are shown in Table 7.1 and the communalities and reproduced r's obtained from the

TABLE 7.1. FACTOR LOADINGS AFTER ELEVEN GRAPHICAL ROTATIONS

Test	Factor					h^2	h^2 from Centroid Loadings
	I	II	III	IV	V		
1. Dial and Table Reading...	.22	.55	.34	.01	.39	.62	.62
2. Spatial Orientation I...	.06	.15	.65	.02	.20	.49	.49
3. Reading Comprehension.	.54	.29	.07	.22	.21	.47	.47
4. Instrument Comprehension	.16	.15	.22	.31	.46	.40	.40
5. Mechanical Principles...	.20	-.02	.07	.66	.26	.55	.55
6. Speed of Identification..	.07	.10	.63	.10	.15	.44	.44
7. Numerical Operations I.	.08	.79	.09	-.10	.13	.67	.67
8. Numerical Operations II.	.16	.81	.14	.02	.02	.70	.70
9. Mechanical Information.	.17	-.11	.01	.61	.06	.42	.42
10. Practical Judgment	.54	.11	.07	.27	.15	.40	.40
11. Complex Coordination ..	.04	.10	.29	.22	.47	.36	.36

Tests	Corr. Reproduced from Rotated Loadings	Corr. Reproduced from Centroid Loadings
1,2	.40	.40
2,3	.17	.18
3,4	.31	.31
4,5	.37	.37
5,6	.16	.17
6,7	.15	.15.
7,8	.67	.67
8,9	-.05	-.05
9,10	.25	.25
10,11	.18	.19
11,1	.35	.34

rotated loadings are compared with those obtained from the centroid loadings (originally given in Table 5.18). The communalities all agree to two decimal places, but there are some discrepancies of 0.01 in the two sets of values for the reproduced correlation coefficients. A more complete check would be to reproduce the entire correlation matrix rather than only those correlation coefficients immediately above the principal diagonal.

CALCULATING THE TRANSFORMATION MATRIX

If the rotated loadings obtained graphically are not sufficiently accurate, more accurate loadings can be calculated by means of a transformation matrix. The procedure for setting up a transformation matrix for the eleven-variable problem is illustrated in Tables 7.2 through 7.8. The transformation matrix

TABLE 7.2. ROTATION 1

Matrix Λ_{11}

	I	II	III	IV	V
I	1.00	0	0	0	0
II	0	1.00	0	0	0
III	0	0	1.00	0	0
IV	0	0	0	1.00	0
V	0	0	0	0	1.00

Matrix S_{12}

	I_1	II_1	III_2	IV_1	V
I_c	1.00	.95	0	0	0
II_c	.95	-1.00	0	0	0
III_1	0	0	1.00	.23	0
IV_c	0	0	-.23	1.00	0
V	0	0	0	0	1.00

Matrix $L_{12} = \Lambda_{11} S_{12}$

	I	II	III	IV	V
I	1.00	.95	0	0	0
II	.95	-1.00	0	0	0
III	0	0	1.00	.23	0
IV	0	0	-.23	1.00	0
V	0	0	0	0	1.00
Σl^2	1.9025	1.9025	1.0529	1.0529	1.0000
$\sqrt{\Sigma l^2}$	1.3793	1.3793	1.0261	1.0261	1.0000
d_2	.7250	.7250	.9746	.9746	1.0000

Matrix D_2

	I	II	III	IV	V
I	.7250				
II		.7250			
III			.9746		
IV				.9746	
V					1.0000

Matrix Λ_{12}

	I	II	III	IV	V	$\Sigma\lambda^2$
I	.7250	.6888	0	0	0	1.0001
II	.6888	-.7250	0	0	0	1.0001
III	0	0	.9746	.2242	0	1.0001
IV	0	0	-.2242	.9746	0	1.0001
V	0	0	0	0	1.0000	1.0000

(represented by the Greek letter Λ_{11}) in Table 7.2 is an identity matrix, indicating that at the beginning no rotations have been made.[6] Matrix Λ_{12}, the transformation matrix which represents

---

[6] If the first rotation were a Landahl transformation, as suggested in the note on pages 115-116, Λ_{11} would be the Landahl matrix rather than the identity matrix.

TABLE 7.3. ROTATION 2

Matrix Λ₁₂

	I	II	III	IV	V
I	.7250	.6888	0	0	0
II	.6888	-.7250	0	0	0
III	0	0	.9746	.2242	0
IV	0	0	-.2242	.9746	0
V	0	0	0	0	1.0000

Matrix S₂₃

	I₂	II₂	III₁	IV₂	V
I₁	1.00	0	0	.72	0
II₁	0	1.00	.72	0	0
III_c	0	-.72	1.00	0	0
IV₁	-.72	0	0	1.00	0
V	0	0	0	0	1.00

Matrix L₁₃ = Λ₁₂ S₂₃

	I	II	III	IV	V
I	.7250	.6888	.4959	.5220	0
II	.6888	-.7250	-.5220	.4959	0
III	-.1614	-.7017	.9746	.2242	0
IV	-.7017	.1614	-.2242	.9746	0
V	0	0	0	0	1.0000
Σl^2	1.5185	1.5185	1.5185	1.5185	1.0000
$\sqrt{\Sigma l^2}$	1.2323	1.2323	1.2323	1.2323	1.0000
d_3	.8115	.8115	.8115	.8115	1.0000

Matrix D₃

	I	II	III	IV	V
I	.8115				
II		.8115			
III			.8115		
IV				.8115	
V					1.0000

Matrix Λ₁₃

	I	II	III	IV	V	$\Sigma \lambda^2$
I	.5883	.5590	.4024	.4236	0	.9999
II	.5590	-.5883	-.4236	.4024	0	.9999
III	-.1310	.5694	.7909	.1819	0	1.0000
IV	-.5694	.1310	-.1819	.7909	0	1.0000
V	0	0	0	0	1.0000	1.0000

the rotation of the axes from position 1 to position 2, is obtained by the following steps:

1. Obtain matrix S_{12}. This is done by selecting plots so that none of the factors appears more than once. Plot 1 (Figure 7.5) was selected because it contains axes I_c and II_c. Plot 3 (Figure 7.7) was selected because it contains axes III_1 and IV_c.[7] Plot 2 was passed over temporarily because it contains axis II, which is already represented for this algebraic rotation in plot 1. The projection of each rotated axis on the unrotated axes is determined from the plot and entered in the proper cell in matrix S_{12}. Thus

---

[7] III_{11} may be taken before III_c. The order in which the rotations are taken will not affect the final rotated positions of the axes.

It might be pointed out here that the order in which the axes are listed and numbered in the factor matrix is also arbitrary and any two columns may be interchanged. Thus if the rotation in plot 1 had been considered as clockwise rather than counterclockwise the factor labeled II would have been labeled I, and vice versa.

TABLE 7.4. ROTATION 3

Matrix Λ_{13}

	I	II	III	IV	V
I	.5883	.5590	.4024	.4236	0
II	5590	−.5883	−.4236	.4024	0
III	−.1310	.5694	.7909	.1819	0
IV	−.5694	.1310	−.1819	.7909	0
V	0	0	0	0	1.0000

Matrix S_{34}

	I_3	II_4	III	IV_3	V_1
I_2	1.00	0	0	0	.64
II_3	0	1.00	0	−.34	0
III	0	0	1.00	0	0
IV_2	0	.34	0	1.00	0
V_c	−.64	0	0	0	1.00

Matrix $L_{14} = \Lambda_{13} S_{34}$

	I	II	III	IV	V
I	.5883	.7030	.4024	.2335	.3765
II	.5590	−.4515	−.4236	.6024	.3576
III	−.1310	−.5076	.7909	.3755	−.0838
IV	−.5694	.3999	−.1819	.7464	−.3644
V	−.6400	0	0	0	1.0000
Σl^2	1.4096	1.1156	1.0000	1.1155	1.4094
$\sqrt{\Sigma l^2}$	1.1873	1.0562	1.0000	1.0562	1.1872
d_4	.8422	9468	1.0000	.9468	.8423

Matrix D_4

	I	II	III	IV	V
I	.8422				
II		.9468			
III			1.0000		
IV				.9468	
V					.8423

Matrix Λ_{14}

	I	II	III	IV	V	$\Sigma \lambda^2$
I	.4955	.6656	.4024	.2211	.3171	.9999
II	.4708	−.4275	−.4236	.5704	.3011	.9999
III	−.1103	−.4806	.7909	.3555	−.0706	1.0000
IV	−.4795	.3786	−.1819	.7067	−.3069	1.0000
V	−.5390	0	0	0	.8423	1.0000

the projection of I_1 on I_c in rotation 1 (Figure 7.5) is $+1.00$ and has been so entered. The projection of I_1 on II_c is $+.95$. The unrotated axes are listed down the side and the rotated axes across the top of matrix S_{12}. The projection of II_1 on II_c is -1.00 (the negative sign being due to the fact that axis II was reflected in this rotation). The projection of II_1 on I_c is $+0.95$. The projections from plot 3 are similarly obtained and entered on matrix S_{12}. Matrix S_{12} is always a symmetrical matrix (for orthogonal rotation) with plus or minus one in the diagonal cells.

2. Obtain matrix L_{12} from the product $\Lambda_{11}S_{12}$. Since Λ_{11} is an identity matrix, L_{12} and S_{12} are identical matrices for the first rotation. This is the transformation matrix in terms of "long" vectors (i.e., vectors of greater than unit length). To convert this matrix into one for unit length vectors, it must be normalized (i.e., the sum of squares of each row and column of the matrix should be made equal to 1.00).

TABLE 7.5.   ROTATION 4

Matrix Λ_{14}

	I	II	III	IV	V
I	.4955	.6656	.4024	.2211	.3171
II	.4708	-.4275	-.4236	.5704	.3011
III	-.1103	-.4806	.7909	.3555	-.0706
IV	-.4795	.3786	-.1819	.7067	-.3069
V	-.5390	0	0	0	.8423

Matrix S_{45}

	I_4	II_3	III_4	IV	V_2
I_3	1.00	-.34	0	0	0
II_2	.34	1.00	0	0	0
III_3	0	0	1.00	0	.30
IV	0	0	0	1.00	0
V_1	0	0	-.30	0	1.00

Matrix $L_{15} = \Lambda_{14} S_{45}$

	I	II	III	IV	V
I	.7219	.4971	.3073	.2211	.4378
II	.3255	-.5876	-.5139	.5704	.1740
III	-.2737	-.4431	.8121	.3555	.1667
IV	-.3508	.5416	-.0898	.7067	-.3615
V	-.5390	.1833	-.2527	0	.8423
Σl^2	1.1154	1.1156	1.0900	1.0000	1.0899
$\sqrt{\Sigma l^2}$	1.0561	1.0562	1.0440	1.0000	1.0440
d_5	.9469	.9468	.9579	1.0000	.9579

Matrix D_5

	I	II	III	IV	V
I	.9469				
II		.9468			
III			.9579		
IV				1.0000	
V					.9579

Matrix Λ_{15}

	I	II	III	IV	V	$\Sigma\lambda^2$
I	.6835	.4707	.2944	.2211	.4194	1.0002
II	.3081	-.5563	-.4923	.5704	.1667	.9999
III	-.2592	-.4195	.7779	.3555	1597	1.0000
IV	-.3322	.5128	-.0860	.7067	-.3463	1.0001
V	-.5104	.1735	-.2421	0	.8068	1.0001

3. Normalize matrix L_{12}:

a. Get the sum of squares for each column (Σl^2). As a partial check it can be observed that any two axes that were rotated together (as I and II or III and IV) should have the same column sums.

b. Obtain the square root of $\Sigma l^2 : \sqrt{\Sigma l^2}$.

c. Obtain the reciprocal of $\sqrt{\Sigma l^2} : d_2$.

d. The values in row d_2 are used to write a diagonal matrix D_2.

4. Multiply L_{12} by D_2 (which is the equivalent of multiplying each value in a column of L_{12} by its d_2 value). This will give the normalized matrix Λ_{12}, which is the transformation matrix for the two plots considered thus far. A partial check can be obtained by calculating the sum of squares of each row of matrix Λ_{12} $(\Sigma\lambda^2)$. These values should be 1.0000 within rounding error.

TABLE 7.6. ROTATION 5

Matrix Λ_{15}

	I	II	III	IV	V
I	.6835	.4707	.2944	.2211	.4194
II	.3081	−.5563	−.4923	.5704	.1667
III	−.2592	−.4195	.7779	.3555	.1597
IV	−.3322	.5128	−.0860	.7067	−.3463
V	−.5104	.1735	−.2421	0	.8068

Matrix S_{56}

	I_6	II	III	IV_4	V
I_5	1.00	0	0	.27	0
II	0	1.00	0	0	0
III	0	0	1.00	0	0
IV_3	−.27	0	0	1.00	0
V	0	0	0	0	1.00

Matrix $L_{16} = \Lambda_{15}S_{56}$

	I	II	III	IV	V
I	.6238	.4707	.2944	.4056	.4194
II	.1541	−.5563	−.4923	.6536	.1667
III	−.3552	−.4195	.7779	.2855	.1597
IV	−.5230	.5128	.0860	.6170	−.3463
V	−.5104	.1735	−.2421	−.1378	.8068
Σl^2	1.0731	1.0001	1.0002	1.0729	1.0000
$\sqrt{\Sigma l^2}$	1.0359	1.0000	1.0001	1.0358	1.0000
d_6	.9653	1.0000	.9999	.9654	1.0000

Matrix D_6

	I	II	III	IV	V
I	.9653				
II		1.0000			
III			.9999		
IV				.9654	
					1.0000

Matrix Λ_{16}

	I	II	III	IV	V	$\Sigma\lambda^2$
I	.6022	.4707	.2944	.3916	.4194	1.0001
II	.1488	−.5563	−.4923	.6310	.1667	.9999
III	−.3429	−.4195	.7778	.2756	.1597	1.0000
IV	−.5049	.5128	−.0860	.5957	−.3463	1.0001
V	−.4927	.1735	−.2421	−.1330	.8068	1.0001

For the next rotation matrix we again select two plots which represent four *different* factors (in order to keep the factors orthogonal). Graphical rotation 2 (Figure 7.6) contains axes II_1 and III_c. Graphical rotation 4 (Figure 7.8) contains axes I_1 and IV_1. The work for obtaining the matrix Λ_{13} which will represent these two graphical rotations, and the two already accounted for by Λ_{12} is shown in Table 7.3 and was obtained as follows:

1. Copy matrix Λ_{12} from the preceding table.
2. Fill in the values in matrix S_{23} by obtaining the projections of the rotated "long" axes In graphical plots 2 and 4 on the unrotated axes and entering them in the proper cells.
3. Obtain matrix L_{13} from the product of matrices Λ_{12} and S_{23}.
4. Normalize matrix L_{13}, by multiplying it by matrix D_3.
5. Obtain matrix Λ_{13} from the product of matrices $L_{13}D_3$. Check the sum of squares of the rows to see that they are within rounding error of 1.0000.

TABLE 7.7. ROTATION 6

Matrix Λ_{16}

	I	II	III	IV	V
I	.6022	.4707	.2944	.3916	.4194
II	.1488	-.5563	-.4923	.6310	.1667
III	-.3429	-.4195	.7778	.2756	.1597
IV	-.5049	.5128	-.0860	.5957	-.3463
V	-.4927	.1735	-.2421	-.1330	.8068

Matrix S_{67}

	I_5	II	III_3	IV	V
I_4	1.00	0	.20	0	0
II	0	1.00	0	0	0
III_2	-.20	0	1.00	0	0
IV	0	0	0	1.00	0
V	0	0	0	0	1.00

Matrix $L_{17} = \Lambda_{16} S_{67}$

	I	II	III	IV	V
I	.5433	.4707	.4148	.3916	.4194
II	.2473	-.5563	-.4625	.6310	.1667
III	-.4985	-.4195	.7092	.2756	.1597
IV	-.4877	.5128	-.1870	.5957	-.3463
V	-.4443	.1735	-.3406	-.1330	.8068
Σl^2	1.0401	1.0000	1.0399	1.0000	1.0000
$\sqrt{\Sigma l^2}$	1.0199	1.0000	1.0198	1.0000	1.0000
d_7	.9805	1.0000	.9806	1.0000	1.0000

Matrix D_7

	I	II	III	IV	V
I	.9805				
II		1.0000			
III			.9806		
IV				1.0000	
V					1.0000

Matrix Λ_{17}

	I	II	III	IV	V	$\Sigma \lambda^2$
I	.5327	.4707	.4068	.3916	.4194	1.0001
II	.2425	-.5563	-.4535	.6310	.1667	.9999
III	-.4888	-.4195	.6954	.2756	.1597	.9999
IV	-.4782	.5128	-.1834	.5957	-.3463	1.0001
V	-.4356	.1735	-.3340	-.1330	.8068	1.0000

This routine is continued until all the plots have been used. In rotation 3 (Table 7.4) plots 5 and 7, containing axes I_2, V_c, II_3, and IV_2, are used.

In rotation 4 (Table 7.5) plots 6 and 9, containing axes I_3, II_2, III_3, and V_1 are used.

In rotation 5 (Table 7.6) plot 10, containing I_5 and IV_3 is used. It was necessary to use only one plot in this rotation because all of the other remaining plots contain either axis I or axis IV, which are already represented and could not be put into the same S-matrix without disturbing the orthogonality of the reference axes.

Rotation 6 (Table 7.7) involves I_4 and III_2 from plot 8.

Rotation 7 (Table 7.8) involves III_4 and IV_4 from plot 11.

Matrix Λ_{18} is the transformation matrix by means of which the rotated loadings can be obtained when the centroid matrix is post-multiplied by it. As a partial check on the accuracy of the work the transpose of the transformation matrix (Λ'_{18}) may

TABLE 7.8. ROTATION 7

Matrix Λ_{17}

	I	II	III	IV	V
I	.5327	.4707	.4068	.3916	.4194
II	.2425	-.5563	-.4535	.6310	.1667
III	-.4888	-.4195	.6954	.2756	.1597
IV	-.4782	.5128	-.1834	.5957	-.3463
V	-.4356	.1735	-.3340	-.1330	.8068

Matrix S_{78}

	I	II	III_5	IV_5	V
I	1.00	0	0	0	0
II	0	1.00	0	0	0
III_4	0	0	1.00	-.06	0
IV_4	0	0	.06	1.00	0
V	0	0	0	0	1.00

Matrix $L_{18} = \Lambda_{17} S_{78}$

	I	II	III	IV	V
I	.5327	.4707	.4303	.3672	.4194
II	.2425	-.5563	-.4156	.6582	.1667
III	-.4888	-.4195	.7119	.2339	.1597
IV	-.4782	.5128	-.1477	.6067	-.3463
V	-.4356	.1735	-.3420	-.1130	.8068
Σl^2	.9999	1.0001	1.0035	1.0036	1.0000
$\sqrt{\Sigma l^2}$	1.0000	1.0000	1.0018	1.0018	1.0000
d_8	1.0000	1.0000	.9982	.9982	1.0000

Matrix D_8

	I	II	III	IV	V
I	1.0000				
II		1.0000			
III			.9982		
IV				.9982	
V					1.0000

Matrix Λ_{18}

	I	II	III	IV	V	$\Sigma \lambda^2$
I	.5327	.4707	.4295	.3665	.4194	1.0000
II	.2425	-.5563	-.4149	.6570	.1667	.9999
III	-.4888	-.4195	.7106	.2335	.1597	.9999
IV	-.4782	.5128	-.1474	.6056	-.3463	1.0000
V	-.4356	.1735	-.3414	-.1128	.8068	1.0001

be post-multiplied by the transformation matrix (Λ_{18}). For this or any transformation matrix for orthogonal factors the product should be within rounding error of an identity matrix ($\mathbf{I}$).[8]

It will be observed from the above rotations that the order in which the plots are taken does not matter. Each plot should be used once and once only, and no factor should appear more than once in a single rotation.

CALCULATING THE ROTATED VALUES

As pointed out above, the rotated loadings may be obtained by post-multiplying the matrix of centroid loadings by the transformation matrix.[9] The rotated loadings may be checked by calculating the communalities and "reproducing" the correlation coefficients. They should agree with the corresponding values computed from the centroid loadings.

[8] For orthogonal rotation $\Lambda'\Lambda = \mathbf{I}$.
[9] $\mathbf{F} = \mathbf{F}_c \Lambda$.

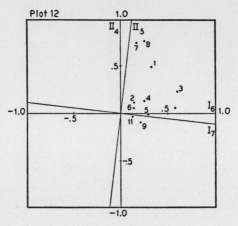

FIGURE 7.9

TABLE 7.9.   ROTATION 8

Matrix Λ_{18}

	I	II	III	IV	V
I	.5327	.4707	.4295	.3665	.4194
II	.2425	-.5563	-.4149	.6570	.1667
III	-.4888	-.4195	.7106	.2335	.1597
IV	-.4782	.5128	-.1474	.6056	-.3463
V	-.4356	.1735	-.3414	-.1128	.8068

Matrix S_{89}

	I_7	II_5	III	IV	V
I_6	1.00	.11	0	0	0
II_4	-.11	1.00	0	0	0
III	0	0	1.00	0	0
IV	0	0	0	1.00	0
V	0	0	0	0	1.00

Matrix $L_{19} = \Lambda_{18} S_{89}$

	I	II	III	IV	V
I	.4809	.5293	.4295	.3665	.4194
II	.3037	-.5296	-.4149	.6570	.1667
III	-.4427	-.4733	-.7106	.2335	.1597
IV	-.5346	.4602	-.1474	.6056	-.3463
V	-.4547	.1256	-.3414	-.1128	.8068
Σl^2	1.0120	1.0122	.9998	1.0000	1.0000
$\sqrt{\Sigma l^2}$	1.0060	1.0061	.9999	1.0000	1.0000
d_9	.9940	.9939	1.0001	1.0000	1.0000

Matrix D_9

	I	II	III	IV	V
I	.9940				
II		.9939			
III			1.0001		
IV				1.0000	
V					1.0000

Matrix Λ_{19}

	I	II	III	IV	V	$\Sigma\lambda^2$
I	.4780	.5261	.4295	.3665	.4194	1.0000
II	.3019	-.5264	-.4149	.6570	.1667	.9998
III	-.4400	-.4704	.7106	.2335	.1597	1.0000
IV	-.5314	.4574	-.1474	.6056	-.3463	1.0000
V	-.4520	.1248	-.3414	-.1128	.8068	1.0001

The more accurate loadings obtained by matrix computation may be sufficiently different from those obtained by graphical rotation to make it advisable that they be examined for further needed rotations. In the illustration rotated factors I and II were plotted (see Figure 7.9) and a small clockwise rotation was made to reduce the loading of test 1 on factor I since its calculated loading was considerably higher than its graphical loading. This

TABLE 7.10. FACTOR LOADINGS AFTER EIGHT ALGEBRAIC ROTATIONS $(F_c\Lambda_{19})$

Test	Factor					h^2	h^2 from Centroid Loadings	r_{1I} [a]
	I	II	III	IV	V			
1 . Dial and Table Reading ..	.27	.53	.33	-.04	.39	.62	.62	.87
2 . Spatial Orientation I ...	.12	.14	.64	.03	.21	.49	.49	.63
3 . Reading Comprehension .	.57	.30	.05	.14	.18	.47	.47	.85
4 . Instrument Comprehension	.23	.15	.20	.29	.44	.40	.40	.84
5 . Mechanical Principles ...	.28	.02	.04	.64	.24	.55	.55	.82
6 . Speed of Identification..	.14	.07	.61	.10	.15	.43	.44	.76
7 . Numerical Operations I .	.08	.78	.12	-.16	.15	.67	.67	.64
8 . Numerical Operations II .	.17	.80	.15	-.05	.05	.70	.70	.70
9 . Mechanical Information .	.22	-.06	-.03	.61	.04	.42	.42	.85
10. Practical Judgment	.57	.13	.03	.22	.11	.40	.40	[b]
11. Complex Coordination ..	.11	.10	.26	.23	.46	.36	.36	.91

Tests	Corr. Reproduced from Rotated Loadings	Corr. Reproduced from Centroid Loadings
1 , 2	.40	.40
2 , 3	.18	.18
3 , 4	.31	.31
4 , 5	.37	.37
5 , 6	.17	.17
6 , 7	.15	.15
7 , 8	.67	.67
8 , 9	-.05	-.05
9 ,10	.25	.25
10,11	.19	.19
11, 1	.34	.34

[a] These reliability coefficients were taken from Guilford (1947b, Appendix B). They were obtained by the separately timed parts method and are corrected for length.

[b] The reliability coefficient for this form is not available. The reliability of a similar form is approximately .50.

rotation is added to the transformation matrix in Table 7.9.   The
rotated loadings and the checks on them are shown in Table 7.10.

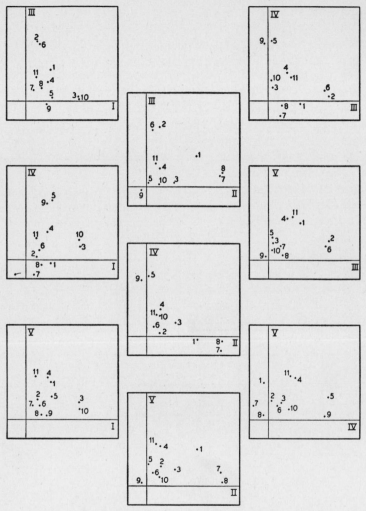

FIGURE 7.10   Positions of axes after eight algebraic rotations.

Plots of the final rotated positions of all combinations of pairs of
axes are shown in Figures 7.9 and 7.10.   Several other minor
adjustments of the axes are indicated in the plots in Figure 7.10
(e.g., III and IV slightly counterclockwise) but will not be made
in this illustration.

PROBLEMS

1. Rotate to simple structure and positive manifold the centroid factors obtained in Problem 5 of Chapter 5 by the graphical method.

2. On the same set of axes plot both the rotated loadings obtained in Problem 1 above and the rotated loadings obtained in Problem 3 of Chapter 5, in order to compare graphically the exact results obtained by the diagonal method with known communalities, and the approximate results obtained from the centroid method with estimated communalities. (*Note:* If the order of numbering the factors in the two solutions does not correspond, put the factors in the same order to facilitate direct comparison.)

3. Rotate the centroid factors obtained in Problem 6 of Chapter 5 to orthogonal simple structure.

4. Rotate the factors obtained in Problem 1 of Chapter 6 to orthogonal simple structure and positive manifold.

5. Rotate the factors obtained in Problem 2 of Chapter 6 to orthogonal simple structure and positive manifold.

CHAPTER 8

Methods of Rotation: Oblique Axes

THERE are several methods by which an oblique solution can be obtained. One fairly obvious way would be to look at the orthogonal solution in the previous chapter and place the hyperplanes oblique to one another, with the axes orthogonal to the hyperplanes wherever the configuration (as between axes I and V, II and III, III and V in Figure 7.10) indicates an oblique structure. The transformation matrix would be obtained by exactly the same procedure as was used for the orthogonal factors, with the addition that it is advisable to obtain a $\Lambda'\Lambda$ matrix after each rotation. This matrix, also referred to as the C-matrix, gives the cosines of the angular separations of the oblique axes. These cosines should be taken into account in plotting oblique axes and also for determining whether the axes are becoming so oblique that they no longer represent independent factors. Of course, it is not necessary to obtain an orthogonal solution as a first step to obtaining an oblique solution. The hyperplanes (and axes) can be rotated to oblique positions as soon as the configuration indicates obliquity. Another useful method, which is used to locate one hyperplane and axis at a time, and usually results in oblique reference factors, is called the single-plane method (Thurstone, 1947c, 216-224).

SINGLE-PLANE METHOD APPLIED TO THE ELEVEN-VARIABLE EXAMPLE

In this method the hyperplanes and corresponding axes are rotated one at a time. The method starts with the selection of one of the variables. If a variable is known or is expected to be a pure, well-saturated measure of a factor, it is best to start with it; if not, any test whose communality is not very low may be selected. In the example, test 7 was selected as representing the start of a possible numerical factor. The steps for obtaining the rotated loadings in the V-matrix and the transformation matrix (Λ-matrix) are as follows:

1. Select a test and write its centroid loadings and communality in a column a_{jm} (as was done for test 7 in the lower part of Table 8.1).

2. Normalize the values in the column by computing $\sqrt{h^2}$ and its reciprocal, and then multiplying each of the five loadings in column a_{jm} by $1/\sqrt{h^2}$. This gives the values in the next column, λ_{mq}, which are the first trial values for the first column of the transformation matrix.

3. Multiply each row of the centroid-loading matrix by the values in the column matrix λ_{mq}, to obtain the first trial rotated loadings. $v_{jp} = \Sigma a_{jm}\lambda_{mq}$. Thus, the first trial rotated loading for test 1 which is entered under trial 1 in the upper right-hand part of Table 8.1 was obtained as follows:

$$.70 \times .61 + -.29 \times -.62 + -.08 \times -.40$$
$$+ -.11 \times .18 + .15 \times .20 = .65$$

The rotated values for the other tests are computed and entered in the column for trial 1.

4. Plot the first trial values against the loadings of each centroid axis, in turn, as shown in Figure 8.1. The plots are then

TABLE 8.1. SINGLE-PLANE METHOD OF ROTATION: CALCULATION OF THE ROTATED OBLIQUE FACTOR LOADINGS FOR THE FIRST COLUMN OF THE V-MATRIX

Test	Centroid Factor Loadings					h^2	Trials		
	I	II	III	IV	V		1	2	3
1. Dial and Table Reading	.70	−.29	−.08	−.11	.15	.62	.65	.44	.47
2. Spatial Orientation I	.50	−.25	.38	−.15	−.09	.49	.26	.02	.08
3 Reading Comprehension . . .	.58	.12	−.29	−.15	−.11	.47	.35	.19	.20
4 Instrument Comprehension .	.57	.17	.11	−.06	.17	.40	.22	.10	.10
5. Mechanical Principles	.50	.52	.08	.16	−.02	.55	−.02	−.07	−.06
6 Speed of Identification	.47	−.16	.39	−.12	−.15	.44	.18	−.09	.00
7. Numerical Operations I	.50	−.51	−.33	.15	.16	.67	.81	.73	.76
8. Numerical Operations II . . .	.57	−.46	−.35	.21	.02	.70	.81	.71	.75
9. Mechanical Information . .	.30	.52	.06	.21	−.13	.42	−.15	−.15	−.14
10. Practical Judgment	.48	.25	−.22	−.15	−.19	.40	.16	.02	.03
11. Complex Coordination	.50	.10	.22	−.07	.22	.36	.19	.06	.07

		Test 7								
		a_{jm}	λ_{mq}	s	$\lambda - s$	$s\lambda$	$1 - s\lambda$	$l = \frac{\lambda - s}{1 - s\lambda}$	$\lambda_{m\rho}$	$\Sigma \lambda_{mq} \lambda_{m\rho} = .8890$
Trial 1	I	.50	.61	.30	.31	.18	.82	.38	.34	
	II	−.51	−.62	−.10	−.52	.06	.94	−.55	−.49	
	III	−.33	−.40	.30	−.70	−.12	1.12	−.62	−.55	
	IV	.15	.18	−.30	.48	−.05	1.05	.46	.41	
	V	.16	.20	−.30	.50	−.06	1.06	.47	.42	

$h^2 = .6671$ $\Sigma l^2 = 1.2638$

$\sqrt{h^2} = .8168$ $\sqrt{l^2} = 1.1243$

$1/\sqrt{h^2} = 1.2243$ $1/\sqrt{l^2} = .8894$

Trial 2	I		.34	.00				.34	.40	$\Sigma \lambda_{mq} \lambda_{m\rho} = .9827$
	II		−.49	.00				−.49	−.57	
	III		−.55	−.20	−.35	.11	.89	−.39	−.46	
	IV		.41	.00				.41	.48	
	V		.42	.20	.22	.08	.92	.24	.28	

$\Sigma l^2 = .7335$

$\sqrt{l^2} = .8564$

$1/\sqrt{l^2} = 1.1677$

examined to try to find clusters of points near the horizontal axis through which the hyperplane, which is perpendicular to the first trial vector, can be passed. (Rotations larger than 30 degrees are usually not advisable, and it is better to underestimate rather than overestimate the amount of rotation.) The rotated position of the plane has been drawn in on each plot of Figure 8.1.

5. At $+1.0$ on each horizontal axis measure the vertical distance between the horizontal axis and the rotated axis. This distance is called s and is entered in the column so labeled in Table 8.1 with proper sign.

6. The method of obtaining the remaining values for trial 1 in Table 8.1 should be fairly obvious:

$$\text{For row I, } \lambda - s = .61 - .30 = .31$$
$$s\lambda = .30 \times .61 = .18$$
$$1.00 - s\lambda = 1.00 - .18 = .82$$
$$l = \frac{\lambda - s}{1 - s\lambda} = \frac{.31}{.82} = .38$$

7. The values in rows II through V are obtained similarly. The values in column l are for long vectors and must be normalized to yield the values in column λ_{mp} which represent the values in the transformation matrix for the latest rotated position of the axis. The normalizing is done by obtaining Σl^2, $\sqrt{\Sigma l^2}$, $1/\sqrt{\Sigma l^2}$. A partial check is that $\Sigma\lambda^2$ should equal unity.

8. The cosine of the angle of the rotation can be determined by the vector product $\Sigma\lambda_{mq}\lambda_{mp}$. For the first trial the value is .8890 which is the cosine of an angle of about $27°$.

9. The second trial values are determined by the same method as the first; each row of the centroid-loading matrix is multiplied, in turn, by the column matrix λ_{mp}. The values are entered in the column for trial 2. The loadings for the second-trial values are plotted, in turn, against each centroid factor, as shown in Figure 8.2. Rotations seem to be called for in the plots of factors III and V.

10. The values in column λ_{mp} for trial 1 are copied as the λ_{mq} values for trial 2 in the lower part of Table 8.1 and the steps for

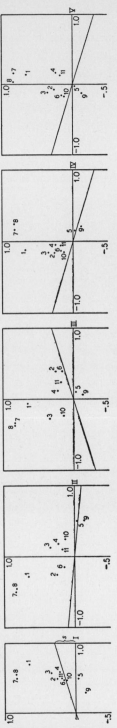

FIGURE 8.1 Plots for first trial values of single-plane method (using test 7).

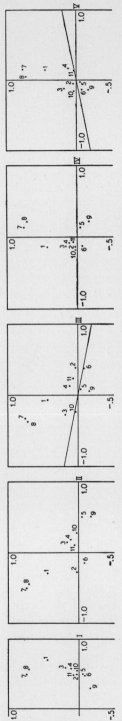

FIGURE 8.2 Plots for second trial values of single-plane method (using test 7).

136

obtaining the values in the various columns of trial 1 are repeated in trial 2. It will be observed that λ_{mq} and l values are equal in rows (such as I, II, and IV) representing axes which have not been rotated. The values in the l-column are then normalized yielding the latest λ_{mp} values. The vector product $\Sigma\lambda_{mq}\lambda_{mp}$ is equal to 0.9337 this time, representing the cosine of an angle of rotation of about 21 degrees.

11. The third trial loadings are obtained by multiplying each row of the centroid-loadings matrix by the latest column matrix

$$\lambda_{mp}, \; v_{jp} = \Sigma a_{jm}\lambda_{mp}.$$

12. The process of obtaining trial loadings and plotting them against centroid-factor loadings is continued until no further rotations are indicated. It is recommended by Thurstone (1947c, p. 222) that the process be continued until the final adjustment represents a rotation of about 5 degrees (cosine of about 0.995 or more). The final column of trial values represents one column in the V-matrix of rotated oblique loadings, and the final λ_{mp} values represent one column of the transformation matrix (Λ).[1]

13. To obtain the next column of the V-matrix and of the Λ-matrix, start by selecting a test that has a low loading on the first rotated factor so as to avoid obtaining the same factor again. (In the example, test 2 with a loading of .08 on factor I was selected.) The procedure that was used to obtain the loadings on rotated factor I is repeated to obtain the second column of the V-matrix of oblique factor loadings and the calculations are illustrated in Table 8.2 and the plots in Figures 8.3 and 8.4.

14. The scalar product of any two columns of the transformation matrix will, of course, give the cosine of the angular separa-

---

[1] If the loadings on the primary axes (see p. 192) rather than on the simple axes are desired, the transformation matrix (T') which will transform the centroid loadings into primary-axis loadings can be obtained from the Λ-matrix by the following steps:

(1) Write matrix Λ', the transpose of matrix Λ.

(2) Find the inverse of matrix Λ' (i.e., Λ'^{-1}) by the method on pages 26 to 31 of Chapter 3, also illustrated in the next section.

(3) Normalize matrix Λ'^{-1} by obtaining the sum of the squared values in each *row* (Σl^2), the square root $(\sqrt{\Sigma l^2})$, and reciprocal $(1/\sqrt{\Sigma l^2})$ and multiplying the values in each *row* of the matrix by the reciprocal value (d_j) for *row* j.

(4) The resulting matrix is **T'**, the transformation to the primary axes and **TT'** gives the cosines of the angular separation of the primary axes.

TABLE 8.2. SINGLE-PLANE METHOD OF ROTATION: CALCULATION OF THE ROTATED OBLIQUE FACTOR LOADINGS FOR THE SECOND COLUMN OF THE V-MATRIX

Test	Trial 1	Trial 2	Trial 3
1	.57	.32	.30
2	.68	.78	.63
3	.26	.18	.17
4	.40	.34	.33
5	.18	.06	.27
6	.65	.62	.63
7	.31	.03	−.01
8	.34	.10	.05
9	.03	.23	.18
10	.19	.19	.19
11	.43	.35	.35

		Test 2								
		a_{jm}	λ_{mq}	s	$\lambda - s$	$s\lambda$	$1 - s\lambda$	$l = \frac{\lambda - s}{1 - s\lambda}$	λ_{mp}	$\Sigma\lambda_{mq}\lambda_{mp} = .8821$
Trial 1	I	.50	.72	.20	52	14	.86	.60	.59	
	II	−.25	−.36	−.30	−.06	11	.89	−.07	−.07	
	III	.38	.54	−.30	.84	−.16	1.16	72	70	
	IV	−.15	−.21	−.20	−.01	.04	.96	−.01	−.01	
	V	−.09	−.13	.30	−.43	−.04	1.04	−.41	−.40	
		h^2 = 4875					Σl^2 = 1.0515			
		$\sqrt{h^2}$ = 6982					$\sqrt{l^2}$ = 1 0254			
		$1/\sqrt{h^2}$ = 1.4323					$1/\sqrt{l^2}$ = 9752			
Trial 2	I		.59	.00				.59	.55	$\Sigma\lambda_{mq}\lambda_{mp} = .9803$
	II		−.07	.00				−.07	−.07	
	III		.70	−.20	.90	−.18	1.18	.76	.71	
	IV		−.01	.20	−.21	−.04	1.04	−.20	−.19	
	V		−.40	.00				−.40	−.38	
							Σl^2 = 1.1306			
							$\sqrt{l^2}$ = 1.0633			
							$1/\sqrt{l^2}$ = .9405			

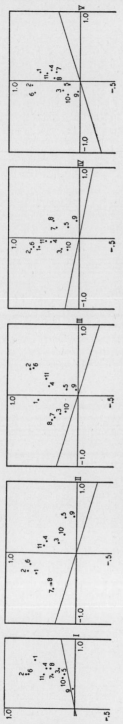

FIGURE 8.3 Plots for first trial values of single-plane method (using test 2).

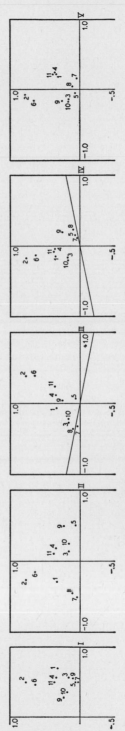

FIGURE 8.4 Plots for second trial values of single-plane method (using test 2).

139

tion of the two factors. (In the example, $\Sigma\lambda_{mp1}\lambda_{mp2} = -.26$ which represents a separation of about 74 degrees between the first two simple axes of the oblique solution.) The remaining columns of the transformation matrix are obtained by the same procedure.

15. The work can be checked by the formula $F_cF'_c = V(\Lambda'\Lambda)^{-1}V'$, where F_c represents the centroid-factor matrix and V represents the matrix of rotated, oblique (structure) loadings and Λ the transformation matrix obtained by the method outlined in this section.

DIRECT ROTATION TO PRIMARY OR SIMPLE STRUCTURE

The method of oblique rotation to be illustrated next was presented by Harris (1948c). At present it is perhaps of more theoretical interest than of practical value since it is a relatively new method and all of the problems of applying it to rotational solutions of large batteries have not been worked out. It has, however, considerable promise for the future not only because it requires only one rotation but also because Harris (1949) has set up some models, based on projective geometry, which may result in new, improved criteria for evaluating rotational solutions. The method as outlined by Harris lends itself most directly to obtaining the loadings on the primary axes (at the intersections of the planes or hyperplanes) which are usually a useful set of loadings. If, however, the loadings on the simple axes (normals to the planes or hyperplanes), that is, the loadings that are appropriate to simple structure and that are more comparable to the loadings obtained by other oblique-solution methods, are the desired ones, they can be obtained by some additional computation as will be explained below.[2]

The first step in applying the method is to obtain the extended values of the centroid loadings (Thurstone, 1947c, Chap. XI). Extending the values of the loadings means extending the vector of each variable so that it has a projection or loading of $+1.00$ on the first centroid (or any other central) axis. Table 8.3 gives the extended values of the centroid loadings in Table 8.1. They are obtained by getting the reciprocal of the first centroid loading of

---

[2] See page 192 for an explanation of primary axes and simple axes.

each test $(1/a_{j1})$ and multiplying all of the centroid loadings in row j by the reciprocal.

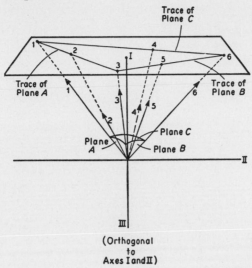

FIGURE 8.5   Representation of extended vectors for a three-dimensional problem.

This method is most appropriate for problems in which there are all high, positive loadings on the first centroid factor. Extending the vectors in a three-dimensional problem so that they have a projection of $+1.00$ on the first centroid axis essentially gives the projection of the configuration on a plane perpendicular to the first axis. The plane intersects axis I at $+1.00$ as is shown in Figure 8.5. This has the effect of showing the three-dimensional configuration in two dimensions. If the vectors lie in three orthogonal planes, the projection should be an equilateral triangle (see Figure 8.6). If they lie in oblique planes, the projection may be a triangle with unequal sides.

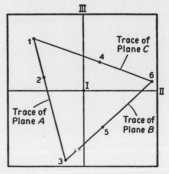

FIGURE 8.6   Plot of extended vectors for the problem in Figure 8.5.

The corners of the triangles represent the intersections of the planes, which is where the primary axes are placed. In other words, if axes are drawn from the origin through the

corners of the triangle, they represent the primary axes and a
transformation matrix for these axes can be written immediately
by observing the projections of the points of intersection. If there
are tests located at these points their extended *or* centroid
loadings can be used to write the (long-vector) transformation
matrix.

Eleven-variable Example. The extended loadings of factors
II through V in Table 8.3 are plotted two factors at a time as

TABLE 8.3. EXTENDED FACTOR LOADINGS OBTAINED
FROM THE CENTROID LOADINGS OF THE ELEVEN-VARI-
ABLE EXAMPLE IN TABLE 5.18

Test	$\frac{1}{a_{ji}}$	Factor				
		I	II	III	IV	V
1	1.4286	1.00	-.41	-.11	-.16	.21
2	2.0000	1.00	-.50	.76	-.30	-.18
3	1.7241	1.00	.21	-.50	-.26	-.19
4	1.7544	1.00	.30	.19	-.11	.30
5	2.0000	1.00	1.04	.16	.32	-.04
6	2.1277	1.00	-.34	.83	-.26	-.32
7	2.0000	1.00	-1.02	-.66	.30	.32
8	1.7544	1.00	-.81	-.61	.37	.04
9	3.3333	1.00	1.73	.20	.70	-.43
10	2.0833	1.00	.52	-.46	-.31	-.40
11	2.0000	1.00	.20	.44	-.14	.44

shown in Figure 8.7. The configurations to be expected from
five-dimensions are not so obvious, although Harris (1949) has
outlined the principles by which they can be determined. We
will restrict ourselves, here, to trying to find the corners at the
intersections of the planes, of the configurations. In Figure 8.7*a*
variables 2 and 6 seem to be at one corner, variables 7 and 8 at
another corner and variable 9 at a third corner, with variables
3 and 10 possibly indicating a fourth corner. Let us inspect the
other plots to see if these corners show up.

In Figure 8.7*b* variables 7 and 8, 3 and 10, 9, and 2 and 6 seem to show up again as corners.

In Figure 8.7*c* the corners seem to be at variables 7, 6, 9, and 11.

In Figure 8.7*d* the corners seem to be at variables 7 and 8, 3 and 10, 2 and 6, and 9.

In Figure 8.7*e* the corners seem to be at variables 7, 10, 6, and 11; and in Figure 8.7*f* at variables 11, 10, and 9.

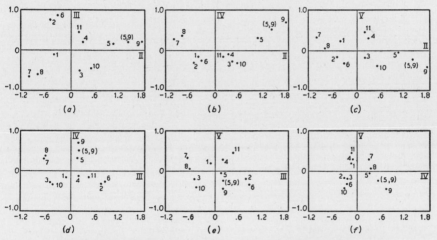

FIGURE 8.7 Plots of the extended factor loadings in Table 8.3.

If we select one variable to represent each corner of the five primary axes, the most consistent corners and also the most meaningful in terms of the nature of the tests represented are variables 6, 7, 9, 10, and 11. Inspection of the graphs indicates that variables 5 and 9 seem to appear in the same vicinity (as would be expected since they are both mechanical tests), but the high projection of 9 on extended factor II tends to distort the figures if it is used as a corner. It was, therefore, decided to establish a point about halfway between the two variables, labeled point (5, 9), to represent the mechanical factor. It should be observed that once a point is placed in Figure 8.7*a*, its projections on axes II and III are established and when, for instance, the point is to be placed in Figure 8.7*b*, its projection on axis II is already set and its projection on axis IV only remains to be determined in that plot.

The extended-factor loadings of the variables or points used to determine the corners of the configuration (i.e., the primary axes at the intersections of the planes) are listed in the columns of a matrix labeled **P′** in Table 8.4. Normalizing this matrix by the

TABLE 8.4. STEPS IN THE CALCULATION OF THE TRANS-FORMATION MATRIX FOR THE OBLIQUE PRIMARY FACTORS

P′

	P_1 (6)	P_2 (7)	P_3 (5,9)	P_4 (10)	P_5 (11)	
I	1.00	1.00	1.00	1.00	1.00	Direction Numbers
II	-.34	-1.02	1.40	.52	.20	for the Primary
III	.83	-.66	.20	-.46	44	Factors
IV	-.26	.30	.52	-.31	-.14	
V	-.32	.32	-.24	-.40	.44	
Σl^2	1.9745	2.6684	3.3280	1.7381	1.4468	
$\sqrt{\Sigma l^2}$	1.4052	1.6335	1.8243	1.3184	1.2028	
d_1	.7116	.6122	.5482	.7585	.8314	

T′=P′D

	P_1	P_2	P_3	P_4	P_5	
I	.7116	.6122	.5482	.7585	.8314	Transformation Matrix
II	-.2419	-.6244	.7675	.3944	.1663	(Direction Cosines)
III	.5906	-.4041	.1096	-.3489	.3658	for the Primary
IV	-.1850	1837	.2851	-.2351	-.1164	Factors
V	-.2277	.1959	-.1316	-.3034	.3658	

T T′

	P_1	P_2	P_3	P_4	P_5	
P_1	.9998	.2694	.2464	.3509	.7057	Cosines of Angular
P_2		1.0001	-.1613	.2565	.3076	Separations between
P_3			1.0002	.6532	5422	Primary Axes
P_4				.9999	.4850	
P_5					1.0000	

steps shown in the table yields a transformation matrix **T′**. If the loadings (structure values) on the *primary* axes, R_{jp}, are desired they can be obtained by multiplying the matrix of the centroid loadings by **T′** (i.e., $F_cT′$). Also the correlations among the primary axes can be obtained from the matrix product **TT′**.

TABLE 8.5. CALCULATION OF MATRIX T^{-1} (THE INVERSE OF MATRIX T)

	a	b	c	d	e	f	g	h	i	j
	T					**T^{-1}**				
	I	II	III	IV	V	I	II	III	IV	V
P₁ 1.	.7116	-.2419	.5906	-.1850	-.2277	1.0000				
2.	1.0000	-.3399	.8300	-.2600	-.3200	1.4053	.0000			
3.		.0000	1.5748	-.5400	-.6399	2.1077	-.8165	.0000		
4.			.0000	.2446	-.0312	.3351	.6649	.6466	.0000	
5.				.0000	-.1630	.4386	.4210	.3012	.3493	.0000
6.					.0000	.2620	.4284	.2307	.2838	2520
P₂ 7.	.6122	-.6244	-.4041	.1837	.1959	.0000				
8.	.0000	-.4163	-.9122	.3429	.3918	-.8603	1.0000			
9.		1.0000	2.1912	-.8237	-.9411	2.0665	-2.4021	.0000		
10.			.0000	.2680	-.0942	-.3999	-.3408	.8997	.0000	
11.				.0000	-.2387	-.2865	-.6080	.5213	.3828	.0000
12.					.0000	-.5451	-.5971	.4180	.2869	.3690
P₃ 13.	.5482	.7675	.1096	.2851	-.1316	.0000				
14.	.0000	.9538	-.3454	.4276	.0438	-.7704	.0000			
15.		.0000	-2.4354	1.2132	.9414	-2.7414	2.2911	1.0000		
16.			1.0000	-.4982	-.3865	1.1256	-.9407	-.4106	.0000	
17.				.0000	-.1180	.9148	-.4439	.2928	-.7115	.0000
18.					.0000	.7869	-.4385	.2416	-.7589	.1824
P₄ 19.	.7585	.3944	-.3489	-.2351	-.3034	.0000				
20.	.0000	.6522	-.9785	-.0379	-.0607	-1.0659	.0000			
21.		.0000	-2.4076	.4993	.5531	-2.4137	1.5666	.0000		
22.			.0000	-.7002	-.3774	.2963	-.6982	-.9886	1.0000	
23.				1.0000	.5390	-.4232	.9971	1.4119	-1.4282	.0000
24.					.0000	.1608	.9725	1.6452	-1.2116	-.8332
P₅ 25.	.8314	.1663	.3658	-.1164	.3658	.0000				
26.	.0000	.4489	-.3243	.0998	.6318	-1.1684	.0000			
27.		.0000	-1.3079	.4696	1.0543	-2.0961	1.0783	.0000		
28.			.0000	-.1820	.5488	-.6239	-.1520	-.5370	.0000	
29.				.0000	.6469	-.7009	.0295	-.2800	-.2599	1.0000
30.					1.0000	-1.0835	.0456	-.4328	-.4018	1.5458

Enter the values from matrix T in rows 1,7,13,19,and 25, columns a through e, and enter the identity matrix in columns f through j, as shown above.

Row 2. Divide 1a through 1f by 1a.
Row 8. 8a=7a-7a•2a =0.0; 8b=7b-7a.2b;8c = 7c-7a•2c;.... 8f = 7f - 7a•2f.
Row 14. 14a=13a-13a• 2a=0.0;14b=13b-13a• 2b;....14f=13f-13a• 2f.
Row 20. 20a=19a-19a• 2a=0.0;20b=19b-19a• 2b;....20f=19f-19a• 2f.
Row 26. 26a=25a-25a• 2a=0.0;26b=25b-25a• 2b;....26f=25f-25a• 2f.

Row 9. Divide 8b through 8g by 8b.
Row 3. 3b= 2b-2b•9b = 0.0; 3c=2c-2b•9c;3d= 2d- 2b•9d;....3g=2g - 2b•9g.
Row 15. 15b=14b-14b• 9b=0.0;15c=14c- 14b• 9c;....15g=14g- 14b• 9g.
Row 21. 21b=20b-20b• 9b=0.0;21c=20c-20b• 9c;21d=20d-20b• 9d;....21g=20g-20b•9g.
Row 27. 27b=26b-26b• 9b=0.0;27c=26c-26b• 9c;....27g=26g-26b• 9g.

Row 16. Divide 15c through 15h by 15c.
Row 4. 4c=3c - 3c•16c =0.0;4d=3d - 3c •16d;4e=3e-3c• 16e; .... 4h=3h-3c•16h.
Row 10. 10c= 9c- 9c•16c=0.0;10d= 9d- 9c•16d;....10h= 9h- 9c•16h.
Row 22. 22c=21c-21c•16c=0.0;22d=21d-21c•16d;....22h=21h-21c•16h.
Row 28. 28c=27c-27c•16c=0.0;28d=27d-27c•16d;....28h=27h-27c•16h.

Row 23. Divide 22d through 22i by 22d.
Row 5. 5d= 4d -4d•23d=0.0; 5e=4e- 4d• 23e;5f = 4f-4d•23f; ....5i=4i -4d•23i.
Row 11. 11d=10d-10d•23d=0.0;11e=10e-10d•23e;....11i = 10i- 10d•23i.
Row 17. 17d=16d- 16d•23d=0.0;17e=16e-16d•23e;....17i = 16i - 16d•23i.
Row 29 29d=28d-28d•23d = 0.0;29e=28e-28d•23e;....29i =28i -28d•23i.

Row 30. Divide 29e through 29j by 29e.
Row 6. 6e= 5e-5e•30e=0.0; 6f= 5f- 5e•30f;6g=5g-5e • 30g;....6j= 5j-5e•30j.
Row 12. 12e=11e-11e•30e=0.0;12f=11f-11e•30f;....12j=11j-11e•30j.
Row 18. 18e=17e-17e•30e=0.0;18f=17f-17e•30f;....18j=17j-17e•30j.
Row 24. 24e=23e-23e•30e=0.0;24f=23f-23e•30f;....24j=23j-23e•30j.

If, however, the loadings (structure values) on the oblique *simple* axes, called a **V**-matrix, are desired, the following steps should be accomplished:

1. Obtain and inspect matrix (**TT′**) to determine that the primary factors are not correlated to a greater extent than you are willing to accept in the rotational solution. (In the example the highest correlation is between P_1 and P_5. The value .7057 represents the cosine of an angle of almost 45° between the axes.)

2. Get matrix **T⁻¹**, which is the inverse of matrix **T** (the latter being the transpose of matrix **T′**). This may be done by the

TABLE 8.6. STEPS IN THE CALCULATION OF THE TRANSFORMATION MATRIX FOR THE OBLIQUE SIMPLE FACTORS

T⁻¹

	I	II	III	IV	V	
P_1	.2620	.4284	.2307	.2838	.2520	(Inverse of the
P_2	-.5451	-.5971	.4180	.2869	.3690	
P_3	.7869	-.4385	.2416	-.7589	.1824	Transpose of
P_4	.1608	.9725	1.6452	-1.2116	-.8332	
P_5	-1.0835	.0456	-.4328	-.4018	1.5458	Matrix **T′**)
Σl^2	2.1848	1.6802	3.1803	2.3682	3.3167	
$\sqrt{\Sigma l^2}$	1.4781	1.2962	1.7833	1.5389	1.8212	
D_2	.6765	.7715	.5608	.6498	.5491	

Λ

	I	II	III	IV	V	
P_1	.1772	.3305	.1294	.1844	.1384	(Transformation Matrix
P_2	-.3688	-.4607	.2344	.1864	.2026	for the Simple
P_3	.5323	-.3383	.1355	-.4931	.1002	
P_4	.1088	.7503	.9226	-.7873	-.4574	Factors)
P_5	-.7330	.0352	-.2427	-.2611	.8488	

C = Λ′Λ

	I	II	III	IV	V	
I	.9999	.1042	2869	-.1928	-.6688	(Cosines of Angular
II		1.0001	.5726	-.4580	-.3948	Separations between
III			1.0001	-.6623	-.5490	
IV				.9999	.1524	Simple Axes)
V					.9999	

procedure for obtaining the inverse matrix described in Chapter 3 (pages 28 to 30). A special work sheet and the procedure for obtaining each value for this 5×5 example are shown in Table 8.5. The accuracy of the work can be checked by multiplication of $TT^{-1} = I$ (within rounding error).

3. Normalize matrix T^{-1} by the steps shown in Table 8.6. This normalized matrix $\Lambda = T^{-1}D$ is the transformation matrix which will rotate the centroid loadings to the projections on the oblique simple axes. In other words, $V = F_c\Lambda$. (See Table 8.7.) These rotated factors will be interpreted in the next chapter.

TABLE 8.7.   ROTATED FACTOR LOADINGS ON THE OBLIQUE SIMPLE AXES (V)

Test	Factor				
	I	II	III	IV	V
1 . Dial and Table Reading....	.07	.32	-.13	.16	.21
2 . Spatial Orientation I......	.43	.04	-.06	.00	.05
3 . Reading Comprehension...	-.03	.12	-.05	.42	.05
4 . Instrument Comprehension .	-.03	.03	.03	.08	.30
5 . Mechanical Principles.....	-.03	.02	.35	.03	.09
6 . Speed of Identification ...	.45	.00	.00	.00	.00
7. Numerical Operations I ...	.00	.63	.00	.00	.00
8 . Numerical Operations II...	.09	.68	.11	.02	-.13
9 . Mechanical Information ..	.01	-.01	.39	-.01	-.05
10. Practical Judgment......	.00	.00	.00	.41	.00
11. Complex Coordination	.00	.00	.00	.00	.33

4. The correlations among the simple axes are obtained from the multiplication $\Lambda'\Lambda = C$ (cosines of the angular separations of the axes). (See Table 8.6.) In general, the signs of the correlations between simple axes will be the opposite of the signs between the corresponding primary axes.

5. The loadings may be checked by reproducing selected, or all of the correlations and communalities by the formula $R = V(\Lambda'\Lambda)^{-1}V'$.

Problems

1. In the illustration for the single-plane method of rotation the first two columns of the **V**-matrix and **Λ**-matrix for the eleven-variable example were obtained. Obtain the remaining three columns of each of these matrices. Also obtain the **Λ'Λ** or **C**-matrix.

2. Apply the direct-rotation-to-primary-structure method of rotation to the centroid factors obtained in Problem 6 of Chapter 5, obtaining the loadings on the primary axes (matrix $\mathbf{R}_{jp}$), the transformation matrix for the primary axes (matrix **T'**) and the cosines of the angular separations of the primary axes (matrix **TT'**).

3. Convert the **T'**-matrix found in Problem 2 above to the corresponding Λ-matrix and compute the loadings on the simple axes (**V**-matrix).

CHAPTER 9

Interpretation of Factors

AFTER the rotated factor loadings have been obtained, an interesting next step is to try to identify the content and nature of the factors. This is done by inferring what the tests with high loadings on a factor have in common that is present to a lesser degree in tests with moderate loadings and absent from tests with zero or near-zero loadings. As with all scientific hypotheses, these inferences need to be verified by prediction and further investigation. (See also pp. 196-197.)

ELEVEN-VARIABLE EXAMPLE

In a new area of investigation it would ordinarily not be feasible to identify five factors derived from only eleven tests. In this case, however, since the correlations are based on a large sample and the factorial content of these tests has been established in other factorial studies (see Guilford, 1947b, Chap. 28) the results can be used to illustrate the procedure for identifying factors. The rotated orthogonal factor loadings in Tables 7.1 and 7.10, and the oblique factor loadings in Table 8.7 will be used for this purpose since they all lead to the same interpretations.

Only two tests (Test 3, Reading Comprehension and Test 10, Practical Judgment) have high loadings on factor I of the orthogonal solutions and factor IV of the oblique solution. The former test reflects individual differences in verbal comprehension. The second test presents verbal descriptions of judgment situations and then several alternative solutions are suggested. It is believed that verbal comprehension is represented in the scores on this test also to a considerable extent. None of the tests with low loadings on this factor seems to require verbal comprehension, so the factor has been identified as a *verbal-comprehension* factor.[1]

The two tests with the highest loadings on factor II are tests of speed and accuracy of arithmetic computation (Test 7, Numerical Operations I and Test 8, Numerical Operations II). Test 1, Dial and Table Reading, which has a sizable loading on this factor, also involves the use and comparison of numbers in reading various dials and tables. Apparently this is a *numerical-facility* some perceptual speed. None of the other tests seems to require numerical facility.

Tests 2 and 6 have high loadings on factor III of the orthogonal solutions and factor I of the oblique solution. Test 2, Spatial Orientation I, requires the matching of a part of an aerial photograph with the whole picture. The perception of small detail is involved. Test 6, Speed of Identification, also involves the matching of small perceptual detail. Since both of these tests are speeded, the factor is identified as a *perceptual-speed* factor. Test 1, Dial and Table Reading, has a moderate loading on this factor. Presumably, working with tables of numbers and dials requires factor. None of the tests with low loadings seems to require appreciable amounts of perceptual speed.

The two mechanical tests, Test 5, Mechanical Principles, and Test 9, Mechanical Information, are highest on factor IV of the orthogonal solutions and factor III of the oblique solution. The Mechanical Information test requires considerable mechanical knowledge and experience. The Mechanical Principles test depends somewhat less on mechanical background although that

---

[1] It might be noted that, with only two tests high on it, the factor would be difficult to identify. Other things these two tests might have in common are judgment, reasoning, etc. The results of this one study would be insufficient to establish this as a verbal factor. Other studies have shown that if a vocabulary test of the appropriate level of difficulty were added to this type of battery it would have a high loading on this factor and on this factor only, thus further establishing it as a verbal factor.

type of background is helpful in obtaining the correct answers. Apparently these two tests have mechanical background as a common source of variance, and the factor is identified as a *mechanical-experience* factor. Tests 4 and 10 also have moderate loadings on this factor in the orthogonal solutions.[2] Some of the items in Test 10 involve judgment in mechanical situations, which probably accounts, in part, for its moderate mechanical-experience loading. It may not be quite so obvious why Test 4, Instrument Comprehension, involves mechanical experience unless, somehow, the reading and interpreting of airplane instruments is related to it.

Also, as was previously noted, mechanical and numerical tests usually have low negative correlations. Hence, the negative loading of Test 7 on the mechanical factor and the negative correlation of the numerical and mechanical primary factors. (See Table 8.4.)

Factor V has three tests (Test 11, Complex Coordination; Test 4, Instrument Comprehension; and Test 1, Dial and Table Reading) moderately loaded on it. The nature of this factor was not obvious when it was first isolated. It is of special interest because it is common to both paper-and-pencil and performance tests. Much research has gone into identifying the common behavior tapped by these and similar tests. It seems to involve comprehending spatial orientation with reference to the position of the observer and has been named a *spatial-relations* or *spatial-orientation* factor. In the Instrument Comprehension test, for instance, the direction and attitude in which a plane would be flying has to be determined from the dials as they would be read in the cockpit of an airplane.

As can be seen from matrix **C** in Table 8.6, some of the factors are correlated and depart considerably from orthogonality in the oblique solution. The highest correlations are between the perceptual and spatial, verbal and mechanical, and mechanical and spatial factors. Inspection of the plots for the orthogonal solution (Figure 7.10) indicates that some of these factors, as represented

---

[2] Loadings of .2 or less are usually regarded as insignificant, loadings of .2 to .3 as low, .3 to .5 as moderate, .5 to .7 as high, and above .7 as very high. This is, of course, an arbitrary classification and varies somewhat depending upon the *N*, the range of talent, the kind of correlation used, etc.

by the tests in the battery, are correlated in this population. Additional examples of the interpretation of factors will be given in Chapter 10.

After the factors have been identified with some certainty, it might be of interest to look at the content of each test individually.

Test 1, *Dial and Table Reading,* seems to be a rather complex test, having appreciable loadings on the numerical-facility, spatial-relations and perceptual-speed factors. Its communality indicates that .62 of its variance is common-factor variance. This is somewhat short of its reliability coefficient of 0.87, the difference indicating specific variance, unaccounted for in this battery of tests.

Test 2, *Spatial Orientation I,* has an appreciable loading on the perceptual-speed factor only. It seems to be a "pure" measure of this factor, although the discrepancy between its communality (.49) and reliability (.63) indicates the possibility of some potential common-factor variance not brought out in this analysis.

Test 3, *Reading Comprehension,* seems to be a relatively pure measure of the verbal-comprehension factor, although its low, possibly significant loadings on the numerical-facility and mechanical-experience factors may reflect mechanical and numerical content in some of the items.

Test 4, *Instrument Comprehension,* has loadings on the spatial-relations and mechanical-experience factors. Its communality (.40) is far short of its reliability (.84), indicating that considerable reliable variance has not been accounted for.

Test 5, *Mechanical Principles,* has its high loading on the mechanical-experience factor. Its communality (.55) is also short of its reliability (.82).

Test 6, *Speed of Identification,* seems to be a rather "pure" measure of the perceptual-speed factor, although the discrepancy between its communality (.44) and reliability (.76) leaves room for significant loadings on factors not isolated in this battery.

Tests 7 and 8, *Numerical Operations I and II,* are pure measures of the numerical-facility factor. Since their communalities approximate their reliabilities, most of their reliable variance is accounted for and these tests should remain pure in other analyses. The communality of Test 7 (.67) slightly exceeds its estimated reliability (.64). This would not be expected from theoretical considerations, and probably indicates that the reliability of the test has been underestimated.

Test 9, *Mechanical Information,* has its only high loading on the mechanical-experience factor. Its communality (.42) is also far short of its reliability (.85), less than half of its reliable variance having been accounted for by its common-factor loadings in this battery.

Test 10, *Practical Judgment,* has its major loading on the verbal-comprehension factor and a secondary loading on the mechanical-experience factor.

Test 11, *Complex Coordination,* has a loading of .46 on the spatial-relations factor and low but possibly significant loadings on the perceptual-speed and mechanical-experience factors. Its communality (.36) is far short of its reliability (.91). If this test were put into batteries with other tests, some of the reliable variance which is specific in this battery might become identifiable common-factor variance.

REPORTING A FACTORIAL STUDY

As is true of all scientific reporting, it is desirable to give a complete account of a factorial study so that the results can be verified and the computations checked. The following are some of the items that should be included in a complete account of a factorial study:

The Measures. The tests or other variables in the battery should be described as completely as possible. If the tests are not generally available, they should be placed on microfilm or made available in some other way. Scoring formulas, reliabilities, time-limits, and special conditions of administration should be stated. Distributions, means, standard deviations, and measures of skewness and kurtosis should be supplied.

The Sample. The population from which the sample is drawn should be described as completely as possible in terms of background variables such as age, sex, education, geographic location, socio-economic level, etc. The method of sampling and size of the sample should be stated.

The Analysis. The method of correlation should be specified. The correlation matrix and matrix of extracted factor loadings should be given. The data for applying the criteria for sufficient factors and the table of residuals following the last factor extracted should be shown. Where the conservation of space is important, as in journals, it has been suggested that only one-half of the symmetrical correlation matrix need be printed and the other half of the table could be devoted to the final residual-correlation coefficients.

The transformation matrix and matrix of rotated factor loadings should be given. For oblique solutions the cosines of the angular separations among the axes (**C**-matrix), or correlations of the primaries (**TT′**) should be shown. For some purposes the loadings of the tests on the primary axes ($\mathbf{R}_{jp} = \mathbf{FT'}$) should be furnished.

For the convenience of the reader, a complete set of diagrams of the rotated axes should be supplied, and a discussion of the interpretation of the factors should be presented.

Not all of the items mentioned will be needed in every report, and several items not mentioned may be needed in others. Where lack of space in a journal or other publication medium makes it impractical to report all of the data, the portion not published can be put on microfilm by the American Documentation Institute, Washington, D. C., and thereby made available to those who desire to examine them.

PROBLEMS

1. Interpret the rotated factor loadings obtained in Problem 3 of Chapter 7.

2. Interpret the rotated factor loadings obtained in Problem 1 of Chapter 8.

3. Interpret the rotated loadings obtained in Problem 2 of Chapter 8 and compare the interpretations with those made in Problem 1 above.

4. Interpret the loadings obtained in Problem 3 of Chapter 8 and compare the interpretations with those made in Problems 1 and 3 above.

CHAPTER 10

Applications in the Literature

A GLANCE at the bibliography at the back of this book will indicate the extensiveness of the literature on factor analysis in recent years. The purpose of this chapter is not to review this voluminous literature, but to summarize a few studies which illustrate the application of some of the methods described in the preceding and succeeding chapters.[1] The studies summarized below have been selected because they illustrate a technique, a point or principle in the theory of factor analysis, an application of the method to the solution of a theoretical problem in science, or a combination of these. Dozens of other studies could have been selected which would have served these purposes equally well. Most of these investigations are much more extensive than the presentation here would indicate. Only the portions which illustrate the above-mentioned points have been abstracted, and the original references should be consulted where there is interest in the subject matter or in the theoretical implications.

[1] Some recent reviews of the literature can be found in Vernon (1951), French (1951 and 1953a), Royce (1950b), Fix (1950), and Carroll and Schweiker (1951).

FACTOR ANALYSIS OF CONDITIONED RESPONSE INDICES

Humphreys (1943) set out to determine whether the concept of excitatory potential established in connection with the continued reinforcement of a conditioned response is unitary or multiple. The potential is not directly measurable but is inferred from such measurable characteristics as frequency, amplitude, and latency of response. These characteristics can be measured in both the acquisition and extinction periods of the conditioning. In addition to the measures listed above, two measures of sensitivity of the reflex on which the conditioning was based, were obtained. The unconditioned response used in this study was the human eyelid reflex to a puff of air directed against the cornea. The conditioned stimulus was an abrupt increase in the amount of illumination. The light measures mentioned above were obtained by several investigators on five groups consisting of 200 subjects in all. The correlations obtained from the separate groups were averaged to obtain more reliable estimates of the various relationships. There were no consistent differences for any one group, and so it was considered to be justifiable to combine the correlations for the several groups.

The intercorrelations for eight measures were factored by the centroid method to three factors, only two of which were determined to be significant and retained for rotation. The centroid loadings, rotated loadings, and communalities are presented in

TABLE 10.1. ORTHOGONAL FACTOR LOADINGS OF STUDY OF EXCITATORY POTENTIAL OF HUMAN EYELID CONDITIONED RESPONSE [1]

(Signs of Latency Variables Reflected)

Variable	Centroid		Rotated		h^2
	I	II	I	II	
1 Reflex to Puff	.44	.32	.07	.54	.30
2 Reflex to Light	.46	.19	.17	.47	.25
3 Acquisition-Frequency	.84	.03	.55	.64	.71
4 Acquisition – Amplitude	.64	.46	.10	.78	62
5 Acquisition - Latency	.56	-.60	.82	.00	.67
6 Extinction-Frequency	.55	-.39	.66	.14	.45
7 Extinction –Amplitude	.45	.48	-.04	.66	.43
8 Extinction - Latency	.40	-.50	.64	-.05	.41

[1] From Humphreys (1943, p. 107).

Table 10.1. A plot of the rotated factor loadings is shown in Figure 10.1.

It was concluded that the concept of excitatory potential as applied to human eyelid conditioning is not unitary as had been previously assumed but is accounted for by two independent factors. Other conclusions were that latency and amplitude are not measures of the same thing and that frequency in acquisition is somewhat different from frequency in extinction.

On the basis of previous nonfactorial work in the area, factor I was identified as attitudinal, i.e., expectancy of stimulating conditions. Factor II was believed to be physiological in origin and is defined by the two measures of sensitivity of the reflexes and the amplitude of the conditioned responses. Variable 3, acquisition-frequency, is loaded on both factors and is influenced by both attitudinal and physiological factors. It contains the most "information" and might be useful if a single measure combining both sources of variance were desired rather than a pure measure of each of the two independent factors.

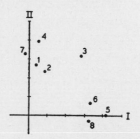

FIGURE 10.1 Plot of rotated factor loadings from Table 10.1. (From Humphreys, 1943, p. 108.)

Is There a General-intellective Factor in Performance Tests?

A group of thirty-four of the most commonly used performance tests was administered by Morris (1939) to determine whether they could be considered to be measures of a general-intelligence factor or, if not, how many and what types of factors were being measured. The battery was administered to fifty-six nine-year-old boys in a New York City grade school who were homogenous with respect to school grade, socio-economic level, and racial background and were above average in intelligence and in mechanical ability.

Seventy-five scores were obtained from the tests, but only the thirty-three listed in Table 10.2 were selected for factor analysis. Those scores which had the largest standard deviations and were the most objectively determined were considered most suitable for analysis. In order to minimize the number of negative correlations, scores based on time, errors, moves, and the like were reflected and are indicated by a negative sign preceding the variable number in Table 10.2. Even after reflection a number of the correlations remained negative, whereas a large number of the correlation coefficients, both positive and negative, did not differ significantly from zero, an indication that a single general factor could not be postulated for the correlation matrix.

TABLE 10.2. ROTATED ORTHOGONAL FACTOR LOADINGS FOR AN ANALYSIS OF PERFORMANCE TESTS [1]

Test	I	II	III	h^2
− 1. Mare and Foal -- Time	-.09	.73	.37	.67
− 2. Seguin Form Board -- Time of Shortest Trial	.10	.42	.53	.47
− 3. Five - Figure Form Board -- Time	-.06	.48	.57	.56
− 4. Two - Figure Form Board -- Time	-.15	.20	.47	.28
− 5. Casuist Form Board -- Time	.08	.54	.33	.41
− 6. Triangle Test -- Time	-.12	.05	.19	.05
− 7. Diagonal Test -- Time	-.16	.05	.25	.09
− 8. Healy Puzzle A -- Time	-.32	.25	.10	.18
− 9. Manikin Test -- Time	.22	.40	.06	.21
−10. Feature Profile -- Time	.05	.40	.20	.20
−11. Ship Test -- Time	.26	.13	.47	.31
12. Picture Completion Score	.44	-.13	.29	.30
−13. Substitution Test -- Time	.52	.23	.27	.40
14. Adaptation Board Score	.10	-.24	.20	.11
15. Cube Test -- Number Correct	.29	-.33	.29	.28
−16. Maxfield Color Cubes Design C -- Time	.14	.09	.56	.34
−17. Witmer Form Board -- Shortest Trial Time	.07	.29	.61	.46
−18. Lincoln Hollow Square -- Total Time	.04	.25	.04	.07
−19. Witmer Cylinder -- Shortest Trial Time	-.01	.46	.00	.21
−20. Dearborn Form Board -- Total Moves	.36	.22	.52	.45
21. Porteus Maze -- Years Credit (M.A.)	.34	-.02	.29	.20
22. Speed of Reaction -- Dominant Hand, Number of Taps	.23	.34	-.07	.18
−23. Aiming -- Dominant Hand, Total Error	.40	.00	.24	.22
−24. Eye-Hand Coordination Maze -- Time	.61	.17	.06	.40
−25. Form Cancellation -- Time	.32	.22	-.16	.18
−26. Dot Counting -- Total Time	.51	.16	-.20	.33
−27. Dot Counting -- Total Errors	.50	-.22	.25	.36
− 28. Circle Block Form Board -- Shortest Trial Time	.38	.23	-.02	.20
−29. Square Block Form Board -- Dominant Hand Time	.43	.34	.19	.40
− 30. Form Card Sorting -- Total Time	.60	.45	.10	.58
31. Manual Dexterity Pegboard A -- Dominant Hand	.20	.40	-.02	.20
−32. Visual Acuity	-.03	-.03	.14	.02
33. Revised Minnesota Paper Form Board -- Total Score	.34	.16	.42	.32

[1] From Morris (1939, p. 96).

The rotated loadings and communalities on three orthogonal factors are shown in Table 10.2. A fourth centroid factor was extracted, but it appeared to be not significant since only one loading contributed more than .10 to the test communalities.

Factor I, although identified with the least confidence of any of the three factors, is believed to represent *induction*. High scores on tests loaded on this factor require the discovery of a pattern or rule of procedure. Thus, for the Dot Counting test (No. 26, time score, and No. 27, error score, incidentally the only two experimentally dependent scores in the analysis), superior performance depends on the subject learning to form clusters to count the dots. Likewise in the Picture Completion and Aiming tests, patterns or rules must be discovered in order to achieve superior performance.

Factor II is identified as a *perceptual-speed* factor. All of the scores loaded on the factor represent time or speed scores of one sort or another, and the factor is interpreted as representing the "ability to make a quick identification of simple perceptual material when mixed with like or similar material."

Factor III has a number of form boards and also the Revised Minnesota Paper Form Board (Test 33) loaded on it and is identified as a *visualizing* factor. "These tests all seem to involve an ability that requires the perception of form and space relations."

The communalities of some of the tests (e.g., Tests 6, 7, 8, and 32) are remarkably low considering that they are correlated with other performance tests, indicating either low reliability or considerable specificity. The three factors were found to be orthogonal to one another, and the hypothesis that the common variance of these tests could be accounted for by a single general factor which could be identified as general intelligence was rejected.

LEARNING DYNAMICS IN BRIGHT AND DULL RATS

Wherry (1941) has made an interesting application of factor analysis to the dynamics of rat maze learning using some data compiled by Tryon for 19 trials on a 17-unit multiple-T maze.[2] The subjects were 530 rats bred for "brightness" and 550 rats bred for "dullness." The 19 trials were divided into ten periods, and the percentage of total entrances into each alley for a given period was considered as the score for that alley. Thus, the correlation matrix consisted of the intercorrelations of the 10 periods over a sample of 17 alleys. Two Pearson product-moment correlation matrices were obtained, one for the bright rats and one for the dull rats, and each one was factored by the centroid method. Three factors were obtained from each matrix and rotated. Table 10.3 gives the rotated loadings and the iden-

TABLE 10.3.   ROTATED ORTHOGONAL FACTOR LOAD-
INGS FOR BRIGHT AND DULL RATS [1]

	Bright			Dull		
	Factor			Factor		
Period	Forward-going	Food-pointing	Goal Gradient	Forward-going	Food-pointing	Goal Gradient
1	.80	.40	.00	.88	.15	.00
2	.73	.62	.23	.93	.36	.00
3	.47	.53	.69	.75	.66	.05
4	.30	.48	.81	.57	.81	.18
5	.24	.45	.86	.46	.85	.28
6	.26	.36	.89	.36	.84	.43
7	.32	.33	.87	.33	.80	.51
8	.40	.25	.86	.31	.73	.61
9	.48	.24	.82	.32	.72	.63
10	.45	.25	.83	.36	.69	.64

[1] From Wherry (1941, p. 239).

tification of the factors. The loadings for the three factors over the ten trials are also graphed in Figure 10.2.

The forward-going factor is interpreted as ". . . when an animal has started to go in a given direction it will, if forced to deviate from that direction, resume it upon the first opportunity."

The food-pointing factor is interpreted as ". . . an animal after learning the general location of the food will tend to enter blinds pointing in that direction and will tend to avoid blinds that point away from the food."

[2] R. C. Tryon, "Studies in Individual Differences in Maze Ability. VII. Specific Components of Maze Ability and a General Theory of Psychological Components," *J. Comp. Psychol.*, 1940, **30**, pp. 283-335.

The goal-gradient factor is defined as ". . . alleys nearer the goal will be learned more quickly than those further away" (Wherry, 1941, p. 245).

Inspection of Figure 10.2 indicates that, although the trends of the loadings of the factors over the entire learning period are similar for the two groups of animals, there are differences in the sizes of the factor loadings at given periods.[3] Thus, for the bright animals there is an earlier, steeper rise for the goal gradient and

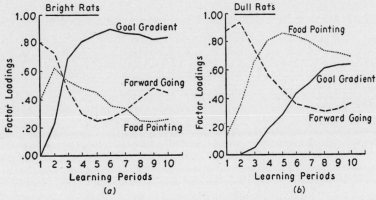

FIGURE 10.2 Profiles of factors obtained by Wherry from Tryon's maze data (see Table 10.3). (From Royce, 1950b, pp. 244-245.)

it remains the dominant factor in the middle and later periods. For the dull group, food-pointing is the dominant factor with goal gradient rising only toward the end. There also seems to be a tendency for the bright rats to make more use of the forward-going factor in the later periods. If forward-goingness can be considered indicative of spatially-oriented behavior and goal gradient of insightful solution of the problem, the results can be interpreted to indicate that the genetically brighter rats are making greater use of "internally-released" hypotheses, whereas the duller rats are more dependent on external stimuli, such as food, for their learning hypotheses. It was also demonstrated in the study that the three factors isolated by Wherry could be used to predict the observed values as accurately as the ten components that Tryon considered necessary for this purpose.

[3] The same factors and similar trends over the learning periods were verified on four other sets of animal data. Cf. Wherry (1939) and Wherry (1940).

AN ANALYSIS OF CRITERION MEASURES

An attempt was made by Fruchter (1952b) to analyze the factor content of Air Force training criteria. If a criterion measure is treated as a variable and its correlations (validities) with the other variables in a prediction battery are obtained, it can be analyzed along with the other variables. This results in a description of the criterion in terms of the common-factor variance. (See Guilford, 1948b.) Such a description may be especially useful for understanding the nature and relative importance of the abilities called for by the criterion and for comparing profiles of abilities required for different courses of training. Thus, it might be found that occupations which are quite different at the level of skilled performance have a similar profile of aptitude requirements at the level of training.

A battery of classification tests is routinely administered to airmen in the USAF Air Training Command, and the results are used to assign them to technical schools for training in various occupational specialties. To evaluate the effectiveness of the tests in selecting successful candidates for the training schools, the scores are validated against the final grades made in the technical courses.

The following two alternative approaches might be used to determine the factor content of these final-grade criteria.

1. Consider each technical specialty a separate population and perform a factor analysis of the intercorrelations of its criterion and the test battery, or,

2. Consider the airmen a single population and perform a factor analysis of the battery on a representative sample. Then estimate the factor content of each training criterion on the basis of the factor loadings obtained from the combined population and the validity of the tests.

The latter approach was adopted because the loadings from specialty to specialty would have a more common basis of comparison and a prohibitive number of factorial analyses would not be required.

A representative sample of 389 airmen who had been assigned to training in technical schools was drawn. Each school was represented in the sample in proportion to the total number of airmen who had been sent into that type of training, and the individuals, all male and mostly 18 and 19 years of age, chosen to represent each school were randomly selected.

The rotated, orthogonal loadings of the nineteen tests used to classify the airmen are shown in Table 10.4. The six factors

TABLE 10.4. ROTATED ORTHOGONAL FACTOR LOADINGS FOR STRATIFIED SAMPLE OF TECHNICAL SCHOOL STUDENTS [1]

Sample: 389 Airmen Assigned to Technical Schools (Decimal points omitted throughout)

Tests[2]	Factor						h^2
	I	II	III	IV	V	VI	
1. Reading Vocabulary	41	62	12	14	23	06	64
2. Arithmetic Computations	72	15	17	04	22	05	62
3. Arithmetic Reasoning	59	31	17	00	22	38	67
4. Pattern Analysis	07	26	-02	33	23	48	47
5. Mechanical Aptitude − 2	14	18	00	27	64	16	56
6. Biographical Inventory #1	01	-09	56	07	-07	-05	33
7. Memory for Landmarks	25	25	16	39	12	32	42
8. Background for Current Affairs	22	74	01	19	16	13	67
9. Biographical Inventory #2	-01	15	53	22	10	16	39
10. Arithmetic Reasoning	57	43	17	-02	26	31	70
11. Aviation Information	13	71	-05	20	36	08	70
12. Dial and Table Reading	49	32	19	38	19	25	62
13. Reading Comprehension	29	69	05	10	28	23	70
14. Electrical Information	06	53	04	18	59	19	70
15. Mechanical Principles	02	10	02	07	38	47	38
16. Numerical Operations #1	70	04	17	36	08	-18	69
17. Numerical Operations #2	78	11	07	28	08	03	71
18. General Mechanics	01	42	08	00	63	14	60
19. Speed of Identification	08	18	08	54	26	16	43
	N	V	SE	P	ME	Vz	

[1] From Fruchter (1952b).
[2] Variables 1 through 4 are part scores of the AGCT. Variable 5 is also an AG test. Variables 6 through 19 are tests from the Airman Classification Battery.

were identified as follows: I, numerical facility (N); II, verbal comprehension (V); III, socio-economic background (SE); IV, perceptual speed (P); V, mechanical experience (ME); VI, visualization (Vz).

The validity coefficients of the nineteen tests for the fourteen technical-school, final-grade criteria were obtained. The factor loadings of the final-grade criteria were computed by a method

for estimating the factor loadings of a variable not included in
the original analysis but whose correlations with the other variables in the battery are known (see Appendix). Since the airmen
had been classified on the basis of the test-battery scores, there was
considerable restriction of the assigned groups on the more valid
tests. This tended to reduce the validity coefficients and the factor
loadings estimated from them. The amount of restriction was
estimated from the standard deviations of the scores of the airmen
assigned to the various specialties and the estimated factor loadings
of the criteria shown in Table 10.5 were adjusted to compensate
for the restriction.

TABLE 10.5. ESTIMATED FACTOR CONTENT OF TECHNI-
CAL SPECIALTY TRAINING CRITERIA CORRECTED FOR
RESTRICTED VARIABILITY [1]

Sample: Graduates of the Technical Specialty Schools (Decimal points
omitted throughout)

Criterion Group	Factor						h^2
	I	II	III	IV	V	VI	
Weather Observer	45	36	22	29	32	13	58
Radio Operator, ACS	22	29	23	24	-02	16	27
Radio Operator, General	38	27	16	26	26	05	38
A & E Mechanic (Conventional)	31	26	04	15	74	44	93
Aircraft Sheet-metal Worker	28	35	07	-01	39	53	64
A & E Mechanic (Jet)	25	42	21	06	58	31	72
Carpenter	17	12	-01	13	18	21	14
Control Tower Operator	31	42	17	06	20	23	40
Draftsman	26	08	20	16	54	32	53
Electrician	57	38	17	-03	36	09	64
Engineman Operator	16	08	12	06	43	16	26
Clerk-typist	71	36	06	21	-01	17	71
Medical Corpsman	30	57	05	15	-07	15	47
Radar Mechanic, General	48	50	01	25	49	30	87
	N	V	SE	P	ME	Vz	

[1] From Fruchter (1952b).

It will be observed that the criteria have a considerable range
of communalities. The very low communalities (e.g., for car-
penter, radio operator ACS, and engineman operator) are probably due to the unreliability of these criteria, although no direct
estimates of their reliabilities are available. It would be desirable
to determine the reliability of the grading systems used in these
schools. If the reliabilities should prove to be satisfactorily high,
then, of course, the indication would be that there is considerable

specific variance in the criteria and that they are not sufficiently covered by the tests in the battery.

It should be kept in mind in evaluating the loadings that the criteria are grades in a course of study rather than performance on the job. The two highest loadings for airplane-and-engine mechanic (conventional) are on the mechanical-experience and visualization factors; for the jet mechanic they are on the mechanical-experience and verbal factors. The curriculum and grading system of the latter school might be examined to determine whether the stress on verbal material is necessary or even desirable. If a similar amount of verbal ability is not needed at the level of skilled performance, a number of airmen who might make skilled jet mechanics are not being sent into training because of the stress on verbal comprehension in the training curriculum. This type of loss of potentially useful workers can become a serious problem in situations where the supply of talent is small relative to the demand (see Dailey, 1952).

The aircraft sheet-metal worker grades have their highest loadings on visualization with a smaller loading on mechanical experience, whereas the draftsman grades have their highest loading on mechanical experience with a somewhat lower loading on visualization. These loadings might also serve as a basis for evaluating these two curricula, as more visualization variance might well be expected in drafting grades and more mechanical experience variance in a sheet-metal course. The high numerical loading for the clerk-typist criterion is also somewhat surprising. A relatively higher verbal loading was anticipated.

The profiles of factor loadings might also be compared to determine the degree of similarity or difference among the criteria, and clusters of training specialties could be set up as a basis for establishing job families.

DIRECT ROTATION TO PRIMARY STRUCTURE IN THE STUDY OF PERSONALITY FACTORS RELATED TO SUCCESS IN STUDENT-TEACHING

Schmid (1950) sought to determine the relationships of such personality measures as the Washburne Social Adjustment Inventory, Mooney Problem Check List, and selected scales of the Minnesota Multiphasic Personality Inventory, to one another and to measures of teaching aptitude, such as total and professional grade-point average, attitude toward teaching, judgment in selecting sound teaching techniques under special conditions, and a rating by critic-teachers of proficiency in practice-teaching. The twenty-four scores listed in Table 10.6 were obtained on fifty-one male and fifty-one female students enrolled in a university school of education. The male and female samples were treated separately for intercorrelational and factorial analysis. Since not all of the scores were available for all individuals, the N's for the correlations, computed from normalized distributions, varied.

The analysis of the correlations derived from the female sample was made by a modified form of the multiple-group method (see Chapter 6) which consisted of the following steps:

1. Estimation of the communalities.
2. Determination of the number of common factors.
3. Construction of an arbitrary, initial oblique structure.
4. Rotation of this initial structure to a primary-axes solution.

The communalities were estimated by the centroid formula [4] and the variables arbitrarily assigned to three groups in order to test the hypothesis that the rank of the correlation matrix is three. In grouping the tests, care was taken to obtain one axis on which all the variables would have positive projections, so that it could be used as a central axis for obtaining the extended-vector loadings of the variables. The loadings on the oblique multiple-group axes were calculated and, also, the correlations among the oblique axes (**C**-matrix).[5] A test of the linear independence of the oblique axes was made by attempting to calculate the inverse of the **C**-matrix (i.e., $\mathbf{C}^{-1}$). If an inverse matrix cannot be computed (because some of the pivotal values become negative) or if some of the entries in the inverse matrix are greater than 1.0, the indication is that the factors are linearly dependent. This usually results where too many groups (factors) have been assumed relative to the rank of the correlation matrix. A satisfactory inverse

---

[4] See p. 88.
[5] See p. 147.

matrix, however, was found for the three groups referred to above, and the projections on the three axes were extended and plotted. The plot revealed no clear-cut configuration for three factors so the process was repeated for four factors. The plots for the extended-vector loadings for four factors seemed to indicate the possibility of five factors. However, the inverse of the C-matrix for five factors contained many entries greater than 1.0, and the plots seemed to indicate the presence of only four factors; so the hypothesis of five common factors was discarded and the hypothesis of four common factors accepted.

The variables were formed, on the basis of the extended-vector plots, into four groups and the factoring process repeated. The inverse matrix (C^{-1}) was computed and did not reject the hypothesis of four linearly independent groups. Examination of the three extended-vector plots, needed to represent the four factors, indicated that the intersections of the hyperplanes, where the primary axes are located were close to variables 9, 10, 13, and 20. The loadings (structure values) of the variables on the primary axes were obtained by direct rotation to primary, oblique structure (cf. Chapter 8 and Harris and Schmid, 1950). Further support for the hypothesis of four factors was obtained by examining the residual correlations. The standard deviation of the distribution of residuals was found to be less than the standard error of a correlation coefficient of zero.

The major loadings of the variables on the four factors are shown in Table 10.6. The factors were identified as:

I. Problem-response Set
II. Professional Maturity
III. Introversion
IV. Social Adjustment

The highest loading of the Practice-Teaching Rating is on the introversion factor, the direction of the measurement being such that a low rating is associated with introversion. The loadings on the professional-maturity factor indicate that grades and the professional-teaching judgment of female students are related to age and interest patterns characteristic of women; female students tend to reflect the same attitudes toward teaching as they

TABLE 10.6. MAJOR LOADINGS ON OBLIQUE PRIMARY AXES IN SCHMID'S STUDY [1]

Variable	Female Sample				Male Sample	
	I	II	III	IV	I	II
1. Washburne Control						.63
2. Washburne Purpose				.65	.62	
3. Washburne Sympathy				.46	.50	
4. Washburne Alienation	.41					.62
5. Washburne Impulse-Judgment				.40		
6. Washburne Subtotal Score				.90	1.00	
7. Washburne Yes-response	.43					.37
8.[2] Professional Grade-Point Average		.54			.36	
9. Total Grade-Point Average		.31			.32	
10.[2] Best's Teacher Attitude Test				.55	43	
11.[2] Age		.43			.33	
12. Mooney Finances, Living Conditions and Employment	.62					.44
13. Mooney Social and Recreational Activities	.78					.48
14. Mooney Social-psychological Relations	.78					.85
15. Mooney Personal-psychological Relations	.52					.96
16. Mooney Adjustment to College Work	.66					.53
17. Mooney The Future: Vocational and Educational	.59					.66
18. Practice Teacher Rating			.49			
19.[2] Minnesota Multiphasic Inventory Hypomania			.37			
20. Minnesota Multiphasic Inventory Masculinity-Femininity Interest		.48				
21. Minnesota Multiphasic Inventory Depression			.97			.30
22. Minnesota Multiphasic Inventory Social Introversion-Extroversion			.68			.42
23. Wright Professional Judgement Examination		.47				
24. Mooney Total Number of Problems	.89					.91

[1] From Schmid (1950).
[2] Reflected.

have toward society in general.   It was also observed that the sub-scores of each personality inventory tend to be separated, factorially, by inventory rather than yielding factors that cut across personality areas.   The correlations among the primary factors (not shown in this summary) indicated no relationship among the problem-response-set, professional-maturity, and social-adjustment factors.   There is a negative relationship between the response-set and introversion factors.   Professional maturity is independent of introversion and negatively related to social adjustment, whereas (poor) social adjustment was highly correlated with the introversion factor.

A procedure similar to the one outlined above was followed in analyzing the correlations derived from the male sample.   Two nearly orthogonal factors fitted the data best, and gave small residual correlations. The two factors, whose major loadings are shown in Table 10.6, were identified as follows:

I. Social and Educational Adjustment
II. Personality-psychological Factor

Factor I was interpreted as indicating that general social adjustment and professional attitude and achievement are related factorially for male students. Apparently a male student who gets good grades in education and general courses is likely to possess a favorable attitude toward teaching and to be rated high in teaching skill. The variables loaded on the second factor are all measures of personality or are psychological in nature.

The differences in the results of the two analyses were attributed largely to sex differences, although instability due to small N's may be partly responsible. In interpreting the results of this study it should also be borne in mind that not all of the variables are experimentally or linearly independent (see Guilford, 1952a). Several of the sub-scores of the personality inventories have items keyed in common, and the correlation of sub-scores with total score leads to spuriously high part-whole correlation which may result in spuriously high loadings and communalities for the variables involved.

RELATIVE ROLES OF CENTRAL AND PERIPHERAL FACTORS IN PITCH DISCRIMINATION

In an attempt to establish the relative roles of peripheral and central factors in pitch variation, Jeffress (1948b) has advanced a theory of pitch perception which hypothesizes a mechanism in the central nervous system that is activated only when both ears are stimulated simultaneously. Tones heard through one ear only are believed to be represented centrally through an entirely different set of pathways, one for each ear. When both ears are stimulated, there is, therefore, a threefold representation of pitch, by way of the pathways for the left and right ears separately, and by way of the central mechanism which responds to the simultaneous stimulation of both ears. If all of these mechanisms exist, the pitch of a tone heard through both ears should be some sort of average of these three heard pitches.

It had been observed previously that there are day-to-day changes in the tuning of each ear when stimulated alone. Thus if one ear were to rise in pitch while the other ear remained the same, the tones heard through both ears simultaneously would be expected to rise also, although not as much, because the tone heard is expected to be an average of the three pitches.

In order to test the expected outcomes of this theory, Jeffress correlated day-to-day changes in pitch discrimination for the following three conditions:

1. Monotic. Stimulation of one ear alone.

2. Diotic. Simultaneous stimulation of both ears by the same stimulus (pure tones of the same frequency, intensity, and phase).

3. Dichotic. Simultaneous stimulation of both ears by different stimuli (pure tones of the same frequency and intensity but of different phase).

Table 10.7 shows the rank-difference correlation coefficients for the following comparisons:

1. Monotic-diotic: The standard tone to the left ear, the variable tone to be matched to it in both ears (*Ls Dv*).

2. Monotic-diotic: The standard tone to the right ear, the variable tone to be matched to it in both ears (*Rs Dv*).

3. Dichotic-diotic: Standard to both ears with the left leading in phase, variable tone to be matched to both ears in phase (*Lls Dv*).

4. Dichotic-diotic: Standard to both ears with the right leading in phase, variable tone to be matched to both ears in phase (*Rls Dv*).

5. Monotic-monotic: Average of the two ears stimulated separately (*LR Av*).

6. Dichotic-dichotic: Average of the left ear leading in phase half of the trials and the right ear leading in phase in the other half (*Ll Rl Av*).

The correlation coefficients were factored by the centroid method and the two factors were rotated in an attempt to separate central and peripheral factors. The rotated loadings are also shown in Table 10.7 and are graphed in Figure 10.3. Since a change in the tuning of one ear would be expected to influence all tones with which it was averaged, a factor with loadings of

TABLE 10.7. CORRELATION AND ROTATED ORTHOGONAL FACTOR MATRIX FOR DAY-TO-DAY VARIATIONS IN PITCH [1]

		Correlations						Rotated Factor Loadings		
Variable		1	2	3	4	5	6	I	II	h^2
Ls Dv	1		-.50	.39	-.57	-.37	-.07	.7	.2	.53
Rs Dv	2			-.36	.28	.61	-.16	-.8	.2	.68
Lls Dv	3				-.55	-.31	-.11	.6	.4	.52
Rls Dv	4					.07	.10	-.6	.7	.85
LR Av	5						-.25	-.6	.4	.52
LlRl Av	6							.1	-.3	.10

[1] From Jeffress (1948b, p. 479).

the same sign for the monotic-monotic (variable 5) and monotic-diotic comparisons (variable 1 and variable 2) would be expected. Factor II shows this expected relationship, since the loading of the monotic average has the same sign as the diotic comparisons. The effect on the dichotic comparisons is not so obvious. Factor I is interpreted as also representing the effect of peripheral change. It shows a tendency for changes in the standard to the left ear and the left-leading dichotic comparisons to go together and in opposition to the standard to the right ear and right-leading dichotic changes. If a change in one of the ears (say the left one) affects

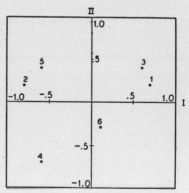

FIGURE 10.3 Plot of rotated loadings for day-to-day variations in pitch (see Table 10.7).

diotic and dichotic comparisons equally, it should have no affect on their relative positions on the factor. If, however, it raises the left-leading dichotic tone more than the diotic, and diotic more than the right-leading dichotic tone, all loadings on the factor would be expected to be positive. The loadings on factor I seem to indicate that a rise in pitch of the left ear has the greatest effect on the right-leading, next to the left-leading, and least on the diotic tone.

Is there any evidence of a central factor? Such a factor should reduce the magnitude of all pitch differences. Such a tendency would result in a factor having loadings with the same sign for the monotic-diotic comparison with the standard applied to the left ear, and loadings of the opposite sign for the changes in the other comparisons. No rotated position of the axes revealed such a factor.

Another possibility, suggested by the large disparity commonly found between the monotic tones and the other tones, however, is that the two types of tones have become separated. If all the fibers were to change their pitch-assignment by the same amount, non-zero opposite-sign loadings for the diotic-comparison changes and zero loadings for the other variables would be expected. If, however, the fiber-assignments for the diotic tones were to shift more than those for the dichotic tones, but the latter were to change in the same direction as the former, the diotic changes would have higher loadings and the left standard and left-leading comparisons would have one sign while the right-standard and right-leading comparisons would have the opposite sign. That is approximately the way in which factor I behaves, except for the loadings of the two averages which are smaller than anticipated. There is then a little supporting evidence for a possible central-mechanism factor.

SECOND-ORDER ANALYSIS OF REASONING TESTS

British factor analysts who follow the lead of Spearman usually seek to establish a general-intellective factor (g) in their analyses of ability tests. The proponents of the multiple-factor approach, on the other hand, tend to minimize the general factor, and it is usually possible to rotate the axes so that no general factor remains. It has been suggested that factoring the intercorrelations of the oblique primary factors obtained by the multiple-factor approach might yield a second-order factor which

TABLE 10.8. FIRST-ORDER AND SECOND-ORDER FACTOR LOADINGS FROM RIMOLDI'S STUDY OF REASONING TESTS [1]

Tests	Rotated Oblique Factor Loadings							h^2	g Loadings	Second-order Factor Loadings		
	I	II	III	IV	V	VI	VII			A	B	C
1 Geometrical Forms No.1	-.05	-.05	.36	-.02	-.02	.46	.07	.53	.54	.48	.01	.06
2 Geometrical Forms No.2	.00	.02	.44	-.08	-.01	-.02	.09	.29	.28	.28	-.12	.18
3 Number Series	.19	.04	.16	.15	.07	.02	.25	.43	.62	.55	.02	.06
4 Verbal Analogies	.34	.11	.00	.19	.20	.21	.03	.64	.78	.62	.05	-.12
5 Pedigrees	-.05	.02	-.01	.00	.87	-.05	.01	.99	.54	.55	-.19	.16
6 Inventive Synonyms	.14	.02	-.02	.68	.05	.33	.01	.84	.60	.44	-.07	-.32
7 Group of Figures	-.04	-.03	.08	.59	-.01	-.08	.34	.47	.38	.33	-.10	-.04
8 Classification of Figures	.01	.10	-.05	.02	-.06	.06	.41	.39	.48	.45	.24	.13
9 Arithmetical Reasoning	.17	-.02	.19	.17	.05	.45	.09	.69	.80	.64	.05	-.07
10 Absurdities	.30	-.09	.02	.01	.16	.33	.02	.45	.60	.49	.08	-.06
11 Group of Letters	.11	.00	.05	.06	.01	.00	.41	.43	.57	.52	.14	.15
12 Code	.32	.10	.01	.15	.10	.06	.11	.42	.61	.51	.06	-.06
13 Secret Writing	.20	.00	.55	-.04	.10	-.06	.03	.56	.49	.45	-.21	.16
14 High Numbers	.00	.52	.08	.08	-.06	-.06	.11	.42	.42	.39	.10	.00
15 Numerical Judgment	.16	.04	-.05	-.04	.05	.03	.38	.45	.58	.53	.21	.14
16 Three Higher	.28	.14	-.05	.18	.09	.16	.07	.45	.64	.51	.09	-.11
17 Letter Series	.18	.09	.18	.27	.03	.09	.26	.56	.74	.62	.02	.00
18 Directions	.14	.01	.09	.09	.36	.05	.09	.42	.58	.51	-.07	.05
19 Areas	-.07	.51	-.11	-.05	.11	.01	-.01	.36	.27	.28	.15	-.02
20 Form or Pattern Analogies	.25	.05	.10	.15	.04	.03	.16	.33	.56	.46	.02	.00
21 Number Pattern	.20	.26	.38	.08	-.06	.10	-.08	.42	.51	.42	-.08	-.04
22 Inventive Opposites	.13	.14	-.06	.32	-.10	.39	.12	.60	.63	.50	.17	-.19
23 Reasoning	.16	-.02	.01	.12	.20	.24	.18	.50	.69	.59	.08	.00
24 Reasoning and Inferences No.1	.63	-.08	-.06	-.05	-.05	-.05	-.03	.44	.28	.22	.08	-.10
25 Reasoning and Inferences No.2	.07	.01	.05	-.09	.19	.34	-.09	.26	.39	.34	.04	-.03

[1] From Rimoldi (1951, pp. 95-99).

is comparable to the general-intellective factor. To test this hypothesis Rimoldi (1951) administered a battery of twenty-five reasoning tests to 384 children between the ages of eleven and fourteen from twelve schools of a large city in Argentina. The intercorrelations of the variables were analyzed by both the multiple-group and two-factor methods. The loadings on both the general factor and seven rotated oblique factors are shown in Table 10.8. The primary factors were identified as follows:

  I. Bringing together of several conflicting *gestalts* (plasticity)
 II. Not interpreted (but possibly Number)
III. Finding relationships
 IV. Finding likenesses
  V. Eduction of correlates
 VI. Verbality
VII. Globalization (bringing parts together for a solution)

The intercorrelations of the seven primary factors are shown in Table 10.9 and were analyzed to three centroid factors. The

TABLE 10.9.   DATA FOR SECOND-ORDER ANALYSIS [1]

Correlations among the Primary Factors

First-order Factor		I	II	III	IV	V	VI	VII
I	Plasticity in Reasoning . .	1.00	.33	.16	.12	.29	.33	.43
II	Unidentified	.33	1.00	.16	.01	.27	.38	.40
III	Finding Relationships . .	.16	.16	1.00	.10	.35	.11	.32
IV	Finding Likenesses . . .	.12	.01	.10	1.00	.07	.08	-.14
V	Eduction of Correlates . .	.29	.27	.35	.07	1.00	.28	.41
VI	Verbal	.33	.38	.11	.08	.28	1.00	.47
VII	Globalization	.43	.40	.32	-.14	.41	.47	1.00

Loadings of the Primary Factors
on the Rotated Oblique Second-order Axes

	A	B	C
I	.25	.08	.47
II	.12	.07	.50
III	.22	.54	-.03
IV	.45	-.07	-.02
V	.25	.45	.20
VI	.17	.01	.59
VII	-.11	.37	.60

Correlations among the Second-order Factors

	A	B	C
A	1.00	.04	.00
B	.04	1.00	.30
C	.00	.30	1.00

[1] From Rimoldi (1951, pp. 97-98).

loadings of the twenty-five tests on the three unrotated second-order factors were calculated and are shown at the right in Table 10.8. The *g*-factor loadings of the tests were plotted against their loadings on the first unrotated, second-order factor, with the results shown in Figure 10.4. The two sets of values are so close as to indicate that the first unrotated second-order factor for these reasoning tests is essentially the general factor that would be obtained by applying Spearman's methods. In addition, two other factors are needed to explain the intercorrelations of the primaries. The second-order centroid factors (not shown in the tables) were then rotated and the loadings of the first-order primary factors on the rotated, oblique, second-order factors, as well as the correlations among the second-order factors, are shown in Table 10.9.

Primary factor IV has the highest loading on second-order factor *A*, which is orthogonal to the other second-order factors. Primary factors I, III, and V show smaller loadings on this factor. Finding likenesses and opposites seem to characterize the element common to the primaries having loadings on this second-order factor.

Primary factors III, V, and VII are loaded on second-order factor *B*. They represent finding relationships, education of correlates, and globalization of parts; and second-order factor *B* was interpreted as referring "to the mechanisms involved in dealing with relations and the eduction of correlates."

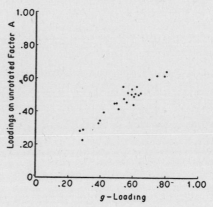

FIGURE 10.4 Plot of *g*-loadings and loadings on the first centroid, second-order factor. (After Rimoldi, 1951, p. 94.)

Primary factors VII, VI, II, and I are loaded on second-order factor *C*. The common element here seems to be the synthesizing of parts into a solution, and the factor was therefore interpreted as representing the "synthetic process, including here all the possible reshaping and redistribution of the elements and the use of the 'instruments' by means of which this process is accomplished."

The results seem to support the hypothesis that the *g*-factor is nonunitary since six of the seven first-order factors have appreciable loadings on it. Also, the general factor can be derived either directly from the variables or through the intermediate step of obtaining the correlations among the first-order oblique factors and then factoring them. It seems to be indicated by this and other studies that the level at which a factor is brought out depends on the complexity of the variables and the method of analysis. Factors which are brought out in the second, or a higher order in one analysis may be brought out in the first-order in another analysis by the appropriate selection of variables.

OBVERSE ANALYSIS OF SUPREME COURT VOTING RECORDS

By far the most frequent type of correlational study has been the correlation of a series of measures over a population of persons (referred to as R-technique). There are, however, a number of other possibilities such as the correlation of a series of measures applied to one person over a population of occasions (P-technique) and the correlation of a series of persons over a population of measures (Q-technique).[6] Analysis of a matrix of Q-correlation coefficients has been variously referred to as inverted, inverse, or obverse factor analysis, since the roles of tests and persons are interchanged as compared with the more conventional R-technique.

An interesting application of obverse factor analysis was made to determine whether the voting records of the nine U. S. Supreme Court justices on a sample of 115 cases decided during 1943-1944 sessions gave evidence of any groupings of the Supreme Court justices. (Thurstone and Degan, 1951.) Only those cases in which there were at least two dissenting opinions were included. Intra-class phi coefficients were computed between each pair of judges on the basis of agreement with, or dissent from, the majority decision. A positive coefficient indicates that two judges tend to agree in their votes. A negative coefficient indicates that they tend to disagree.

Three centroid factors were extracted from the correlations and the communality for each judge was computed (see Table 10.10). There was a large range of communalities, and the voting of those judges with the highest communalities could be predicted best from the three common factors.

The oblique rotations are indicated in the plots in Figure 10.5. In Figure 10.5a, factor II has been rotated so that the trace of the plane orthogonal to it passes through or near the vectors

[6] See pp. 202-204.

TABLE 10.10. FACTOR LOADINGS OF VOTING RECORDS
OF NINE SUPREME COURT JUSTICES DURING 1943–1944 [1]
(N = 115 DECISIONS)

	Justice	Centroid Factor Loadings			h^2	Rotated Oblique Factor Loadings		
		I_c	II_c	III_c		I	II	III
1	Black	.80	.23	.24	.75	.63	-.03	-.05
2	Douglas	.70	.29	.31	.67	.67	.08	.05
3	Rutledge	.64	-.10	-.10	.43	.14	-.33	-.31
4	Murphy	.67	-.24	-.17	.54	.02	-.49	-.39
5	Reed	-.21	.45	-.06	.25	.23	.48	.02
6	Jackson	.28	-.23	.58	.47	-.02	-.01	.64
7	Stone	-.53	.38	-.23	.48	-.04	.49	-.04
8	Frankfurter	-.57	-.19	.08	.37	-.35	.04	.27
9	Roberts	.64	-.23	-.10	.47	-.49	-.01	.12

[1] From Thurstone and Degan (1951, p. 5).

of Justices Douglas, Black, Roberts, and Frankfurter. In Figure
10.5*b* the trace of the plane orthogonal to factor III has been
moved into the position determined by the vectors representing
Justices Douglas, Black, Reed, and Roberts. In Figure 10.5*c*

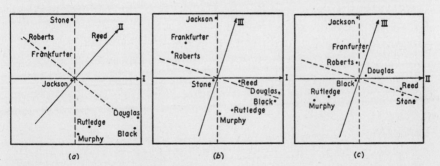

FIGURE 10.5   Plots of rotated oblique factor loadings from Table 10.10. (After
Thurstone and Degan, 1951, pp. 6-7.)

there is a further adjustment of factor III relative to factor II.
In Table 10.10 the oblique factor loadings (**V** matrix) are given,
and the transformation matrix (**Λ**) and cosines of angles between
the oblique axes (**C**-matrix) are shown in Table 10.11. The
authors point out that this is not the only possible solution and
that other locations of the reference frame could be justified.

As is true in all areas of investigation, interpretations cannot
be made automatically. An expert in the subject-matter field is

TABLE 10.11. TRANSFORMATION MATRIX (Λ) AND CO-
SINES OF ANGLES BETWEEN REFERENCE AXES (C) [1]

	Λ				C		
	I	II	III		I	II	III
I_c	.42	-.35	-.34	I	1.00		
II_c	.77	.92	.00	II	.65	1.00	
III_c	.48	.18	.94	III	.31	.29	1.00

[1] From Thurstone and Degan (1951, p. 5).

needed to interpret the results. Factor I represents something
which is shared in common by Justices Black and Douglas and
which is the opposite of something shared by Justices Frankfurter
and Roberts. Factor II represents something common to the
points of view of Justices Reed and Stone but opposite to what is
common to Justices Murphy and Rutledge. Justice Jackson is
not represented on factors I and II.

Justice Jackson is strongly represented on factor III and Justice Frankfurter to a lesser extent, while the points of view of
Justices Rutledge and Murphy have negative projections on this
factor. The entire configuration of test vectors as viewed in three
dimension also seems to suggest that there are actually 5 distinct
but not unrelated points of view represented. These are (1) Reed
and Stone, (2) Murphy and Rutledge, (3) Black and Douglas, (4)
Frankfurter and Roberts, and (5) Jackson and, to a lesser degree,
Frankfurter.

Extracting the factors from a correlation matrix is a relatively
straightforward matter. Rotating to a meaningful position and
interpreting the nature of the factors, however, requires considerable knowledge and insight in the field under investigation, as has
been mentioned above. The authors, therefore, discussed their
results with specialists in political science and law. There was no
general agreement concerning the interpretation of the factors,
although the authors report they were surprised to observe that
the discussions centered around the personalities of the judges
rather than around political, economic, or legalistic concepts such
as civil liberties, economic liberalism, or the rights of the individual.

Another method of interpreting the factors in this type of study might be to list the decisions on which all of the judges on a factor agreed or disagreed and to interpret the factor on the basis of the common principle which the agreements or disagreements seem to embody. Also to be considered in the interpretation are the possible divergent reasons for dissenting to a majority decision and the relative frequency of each type of case considered. The authors felt that this type of interpretation should be done by specialists in the field such as lawyers or political scientists. Pending such further study, no final interpretation of the nature of the factors was attempted.

OBVERSE FACTOR ANALYSIS OF PREPSYCHOTIC PERSONALITY TRAITS

Another application of obverse factor analysis has been made in the study of prepsychotic personality traits in presumably normal female subjects. (Moore, Stafford, and Hsu, 1947.) A personality inventory, consisting of 128 questions concerning prepsychotic and normal mental hygiene traits, was administered to fifty-six juniors and seniors in a Catholic woman's college. The subjects were instructed to check those items to which they would answer "yes." Thirty-eight of the items were checked by more than fifty or fewer than six girls and were, therefore, considered to be nondifferentiating. Tetrachoric correlation coefficients were computed between every pair of girls on the basis of their replies to the remaining ninety items. Thus, since the variables are persons and the sample consists of the tests (i.e., items), a 56×56 matrix of correlation coefficients was obtained, each coefficient based on a sample of ninety traits.[7] Eleven factors were extracted by the centroid method and rotated to simple, oblique structure. The factors were identified by studying the relationship of the answers of a person to her loading on a factor. If all of the persons with high loadings on a factor gave the same answer to a question, that question was used to help interpret

---

[7] Q-technique. Correlations were also computed from the replies to all 128 questions and factor analyzed. This aspect of the study will not be reported here except to say that the authors considered the results from that analysis less satisfactory than from the ninety-item study.

the nature of the factor. The following two questions were answered affirmatively by all thirteen girls who had high loadings on the first factor:

> Have you carried out to some significant degree your first seriously adopted plan of life?
>
> Are you dominantly interested in things going on around you in the world in which you live?

The first factor is identified as "normal, healthy type of adjustment."

Traits held in common by the twelve girls with loadings on the second factor are indicated by affirmative answers to the following questions:

> Do you prefer tasks that are clearly outlined and easy to work at?
>
> Are you dominantly interested in things going on around you in the world in which you live?
>
> Are your plans and wishes mainly concerned with finding someone whom you can love with all your heart?
>
> Are your plans and wishes mainly concerned with finding someone who will love you with deep, abiding devotion?

The second factor is identified as a normal, extraverted, romantic type of adjustment.

Traits held in common by the seven girls with loadings on the third factor are "self-consciousness" and accusing others of doing some of the following things:

> . . . being mean to others and to her; interpreting loosely moral conduct; lacking frankness; cheating on examinations; slandering; being immoral, lying; purposely flattering others; being disloyal or unfaithful; purposely placing her in embarrassing situations; sponging on others; cheating; being insincere; being ungrateful and selfish; being thoughtless; being conceited; separating friends; being arrogant; failing to appreciate qualities in herself or in others; being narrow, stupid, provincial in outlook; trying to bully others; trying to "crush intelligence with organized stupidity"; gossiping and slandering; having ulterior motives; being hypocritical.

The third factor is identified as a social type of maladjustment with ideas of reference, projection, and self-consciousness, and was labeled by the authors as an "inferiority factor."

Traits held in common by the two girls with high loadings on the fourth factor are as follows:

> Has carried out to some significant degree her first seriously adopted plan of life; life and actions are guided at present by a well-defined purpose; prefers tasks that are clearly outlined and easy to work at; prefers tasks in which one is very likely to succeed; music, literature, and art afford her passive enjoyment rather than active accomplishment; if a person is widely admired, she reserves her own judgment until she knows more about him. Is dominantly interested in things going on around her in the world in which she is living; plans and wishes mainly concerned with finding someone who will love her with deep, abiding devotion; plans and wishes concerned mainly with finding someone whom she can love with all her heart; her fear of doing wrong is stronger than her fear of losing love or not being loved; has accused others of lying, stealing, cheating, being sneaky or not being righteous; wants to do something of distinct value for human beings or for the welfare of her own country; wants to do something that will contribute to God's plan for the Universe; has peculiar abnormal fears; is inclined to become excited over what others would consider trifles; is self-conscious

The fourth factor was not considered as clear-cut as the first three but was tentatively identified as "simple-maladjustment." It seems to present a fairly good picture of an introverted, sensitive type of personality maladjustment with perhaps some underlying conflict between principles and desires. It is, of course, only a doublet.[8]

The four girls with high loadings on the fifth factor had the following traits in common as revealed by their answers to the questionnaire:

---

[8] A factor with only two variables with high loadings on it is referred to as a "doublet," a factor with three high loadings on it, as a "triplet."

Plans and wishes mainly concerned with finding someone she can love with all her heart; plans and wishes mainly
concerned with finding someone who will love her with
deep, abiding devotion; has vigorous type of personality
entering the fight rather than seeking shelter; first thought
seriously about what she was going to do in life at 13 or
older; has entertained three or more plans of life seriously
since her 15th year; lacks self-confidence; likes to be with
people constantly rather than apart by herself.

The fifth factor was identified as a romantic-extroverted type
of adjustment.

There were only two traits common to the seven girls who
had high loadings on the sixth factor, namely: "plans and wishes
mainly concerned with finding someone who will love her with
deep, abiding devotion" and "ready to take vigorous steps to
carry out her own plans." The interpretation of this factor is
not very clear, but, when traits which are claimed by six of the
seven girls are also considered, a frustrated-romantic type of adjustment seems to be indicated.

The three girls having high loadings on the seventh factor had
the following traits in common:

Prefers music, literature, and art to less aesthetic pleasures; is self-reliant rather than dependent on aid and comfort received from others; is ready to take vigorous steps
to carry out her own plans; first thought seriously about
what she was going to do in life at 13 or older; began to
plan and work to attain her ambition at 16 or older; has
entertained more than three plans of life seriously since
her 15th year; wants to do something that will contribute
to God's plan for the Universe; is easily influenced; given
to tears with glistening eyes; is self-conscious; likes to study;
likes to be alone.

The seventh factor seems to represent a thinking, introverted
type of adjustment and is identified by the authors as a "schizoid
type" of person.

The eighth factor is another doublet. The traits common to
the two girls with high loadings on it are indicated by the following:

Has a tired, worn-out attitude; suspects others of evil intentions; is unscrupulous; speaks of having vivid dreams; has had nightmares; given to tears with glistening eyes and tears rolling; usually tries to take added responsibilities on herself; likes to be alone; standing is above the average in school; her conscience bothers her more than other people seem to be bothered by theirs; wants to be engaged in tasks that require a great deal of ambition for their accomplishment; music, literature, and art afford her passive enjoyment rather than active accomplishment; plans and wishes are mainly concerned with finding someone whom she can love whole-heartedly; plans and wishes are mainly concerned with finding someone who will love her with a deep, abiding devotion; dominant craving is to love; fear of doing wrong is stronger than her fear of losing love or not being loved; the conflict with conscience in her mind is more acute than in average individuals; is ready to take vigorous steps to overcome opposition; is ready to take vigorous steps to carry out her own plans; helps and supports other people more than she depends on them for help and support; is a vigorous type of personality, entering the fight rather than seeking shelter; has entertained more than three plans of life seriously since her 15th year; wants to do something to contribute to God's plan for the Universe; wants to do something of distinct value for the human race and the welfare of her own country.

The eighth factor is interpreted as a "prepsychotic paranoid" type of maladjustment.

The two girls with high loadings on the ninth factor have the following configuration of traits in common:

Likes to be alone; has been very jealous of other persons; has had an intense dislike bordering on hatred for someone; life and actions guided at present by well-defined purpose; prefers tasks that are clearly outlined and easy to work at; prefers tasks in which she is very likely to succeed; music, literature, and art afford her passive enjoyment rather than active accomplishment; is dominantly interested in things going on around her in the world in which she lives; plans and actions are mainly concerned with finding someone whom she can love with all her heart; plans and wishes are mainly concerned with finding someone who will love her with deep, abiding devotion; dominant craving is to love; is self-reliant rather than dependent on aid and comfort received from others; is ready to take vigorous steps to carry out her own plans; two or more persons have made her feel jealous; first made a serious decision about what she was going to do in life at sixteen or older; wants to do something to contribute to God's plan for the Universe; wants to equip herself for or improve herself in a professional career; is ready to take vigorous steps to overcome opposition.

Jealousy and conscious hatred are the outstanding traits on the ninth factor and it is interpreted as a general schizoid, doublet factor indicating a "jealous" type of maladjustment.

The following traits were common to the three girls with high loadings on the tenth factor:

Has carried out to some significant degree her first seriously adopted plan of life; life and actions are guided at present by a well-defined purpose; wants to be engaged in tasks that require a great deal of ambition for their accomplishment; prefers tasks in which she is very likely to succeed; prefers music, literature, and art to less aesthetic pleasures; if a person is widely admired, she will reserve her own judgment until she knows more about him; is dominantly interested in things going on around her in the world in which she lives; her fear of doing wrong is stronger than her fear of losing love or not being loved; is self-reliant rather than dependent on aid and comfort received from others; is ready to take vigorous steps to carry out her own plans; is ready to take vigorous steps to overcome opposition; helps and supports others more than she depends on them for help and support; wants to do something of distinct value for human beings and for the welfare of her own country; wants to do something to contribute to God's plan for the Universe.

The tenth factor was tentatively identified as an "adjusted, schizoid type of person."

The following traits are held in common by the two girls with high loadings on the eleventh factor:

> Has a tired, worn-out attitude; has peculiar, abnormal fears; would give up and quit if things did not go her way; lacks self-confidence; is self-conscious; daydreams frequently; likes to be alone; has carried out to some significant degree her first seriously adopted plan of life; is more self-conscious than the average person; prefers music, literature, and art to less aesthetic pleasures; plans and wishes are mainly concerned with finding someone whom she can love with all her heart; dominant craving is to love; her fear of doing wrong is stronger than her fear of losing love or not being loved; is self-reliant rather than depending on aid and comfort received from others; has a habitual tendency to keep aloof from almost everybody; wants to do something to contribute to God's plan for the Universe; wants to do something of distinct value for human beings and for the welfare of her own country

The eleventh factor was identified as a withdrawal-from-reality type of maladjustment but without tendency to delusions. It indicates prepsychotic tendency toward simple schizophrenia or catatonia and the need for mental hygiene.

It was noted that several traits appeared on almost all of the factors. Such nondiagnostic traits interfere with the differential interpretation of the factors and might well be eliminated if further refinement of the questionnaire were attempted. It was noted that several of the doublet factors could be readily interpreted, and the small number of variables on these factors was thought to indicate an infrequently occurring type rather than an indeterminate factor.

The results of the study were taken to indicate that "prepsychotic types" do exist in presumably normal groups (just as the same syndromes may exist in both prepsychotic and psychotic individuals) and that personality structure should be considered continuous and multidimensional rather than made up of mutually exclusive qualitative types.

P-TECHNIQUE IN THE STUDY OF PERSONALITY

The conventional approach to intercorrelational studies has been to obtain measures of individual differences at a given point in time and to study their interrelationships. A variation to this approach, introduced by Cattell (1946c), permits the study of the covariation of measures in a single person over a period of time. If a battery of tests is administered to a subject over and over again and his scores are correlated over the sample of occasions, the design is called P-technique (see p. 203). The relationship of factors obtained from this approach to factors obtained by the other techniques is, of course, of interest since, if similar factors should be obtained from intra-individual differences as from inter-individual differences, they would help corroborate the existence and interpretations of the factors obtained from the more conventional designs.

Tests which measure a changed function on re-administration (due to learning, etc.) are not suitable for this method, nor are very unreliable tests, because the variations in score from day to day might reflect chance fluctuation to a greater extent than changes in the function being measured. This approach should be of special interest to clinical psychologists, because it furnishes an objective method of studying the dynamics of an individual over a period of time.

The pioneer study by this approach was done in the area of personality measurement (Cattell, Cattell, and Rhymer, 1947). A battery of "objective" psychological and physiological tests (listed in Table 10.12) was administered to a 29-year-old, normal woman on 55 weekdays. The sessions were held at various times between 8 A.M. and 10 P.M. to get a representative sampling of waking behavior and to determine the effect, if any, of fatigue on the test scores.

The rotated loadings obtained from the intercorrelations of the objective tests are shown in Table 10.12. The factor loadings of two of the memory scores which were not included in the original analysis, because the subject reported she had used different methods of memorizing at various times, were estimated from their correlations after the analysis had been made, when

TABLE 10.12. ROTATED OBLIQUE FACTORS IN OBJECTIVE
PSYCHOLOGICAL AND PHYSIOLOGICAL MEASURES [1]

Tests and Variables	Factor				h^2
	I	II	III	IV	
Time of Day	.02	.02	.71	-.05	.53
Salivary pH (Alkilinity)	-.03	.56	.07	.00	.36
Reversible Perspective, Rapidity	-.17	.43	.56	.09	.56
Myokinesis, Size of Lines Drawn	-.18	.02	.03	.50	.48
Reaction Time, Length of	-.03	.75	-.09	-.04	.59
Reaction Time, Ratio of Reg. to Irreg. Warning	-.02	.28	.34	-.01	.24
Fluency of Association (T.A.T.)	-.03	-.21	-.15	.55	.44
Perseveration (Disposition Rigidity)	.02	-.35	.12	.51	.47
Ataxic Sway Suggestibility	.75	-.02	.02	.35	.58
Size, P.G.R. Deflection	.73	.22	.30	.32	.65
Frequency, P.G.R. Deflection	.27	.03	.48	.01	.29
Upward Drift, P.G.R. After Stress	.39	-.14	.40	.01	.34
Approximate Estimates Only					
Ratio Emotional to Unemotional Recall	.65	.40	.00	.00	
Efficiency Memory Recall	.00	-.45	.00	.40	

C -Matrix	I	II	III	IV
I	1.00			
II	.19	1.00		
III	.00	-.12	1.00	
IV	.39	.06	-.26	1.00

[1] From Cattell, Cattell, and Rhymer (1947, p. 284).

it became apparent that their loadings would be consistent regardless of the memorizing methods used. The four rotated, oblique factors were identified as follows:

Factor I. *Emotional Abundance vs. Emotional Dearth.*

Indicated by high loadings on sway suggestibility and size of psycho-galvanic response. It is described as "emotional responsiveness to environment which might almost be called a dynamic vigor or readiness, were it not that sway suggestibility has been connected in the past with the more neurotic forms of emotionality."

Factor II. *Physiological Ease vs. Emergency Alertness.*

Indicated by slow reaction time, salivary alkalinity, and slow reversible perspective.

Factor III. *Fatigue vs. Energy Reserve.*

Scores with high loadings on this factor are for time of day, quickness of reversible perspective, frequency of psycho-galvanic response deflection, upward drift of psycho-galvanic response during relaxation after stress, and ratio of warned to unwarned reaction time. These scores are known to be related to fatigue and the factor is interpreted as "clearly one of diurnal fatigue."

Factor IV. *Uncontrol vs. Inhibition.*

Loaded on this factor are scores on fluency of association, perseveration-rigidity (measured negatively), and myokinesis (large movements in drawing lines). Since these tests have been used as measures of "lack of integration and will" the factor is interpreted as "some kind of lack of inhibition, with greater spontaneity and carelessness."

At the beginning of each session, the subject also took a questionnaire, consisting of the two items loaded highest on each of the following ten factors isolated in previous personality studies, and was also rated on these factors by two close observers:

1. Factor A. Cyclothyme vs. Schizothyme. (Rated principally on easy-going cooperativeness vs. obstructiveness.)

2. Factor C. Emotional steadiness vs. general emotionality and neuroticism.

3. Factor D. Hypersensitive, sthenic emotionality vs. phlegmatic frustration tolerance. (Rated principally on excitable, attention-getting behavior.)

4. Factor E. Dominance vs. submissiveness.

5. Factor F. Surgency vs. desurgency. (Rated principally on cheerfulness, placidity, talkativeness vs. worried, depressed.)

6. Factor G. Positive character vs. immature dependence. (Rated principally on perseverance, persistence, and will qualities.)

7. Factor H. Adventurous cyclothymia vs. withdrawn schizothymia. (Rated principally on friendly, outgoing behavior vs. shyness, withdrawal.)

8. Factor I. Sensitive, anxious, imaginative emotionality vs. rigid, tough poise. (Rated principally on jumpiness and over-reaction socially vs. poise.)

9. Factor J. Vigorous determined character vs. neurasthenia.

10. Factor K. Intellectual, cultured mind vs. boorishness. (Rate principally on keenness of intellectual interests and analytical vigor of mind.)

In order to determine the relationships between the factors derived from the "objective" tests and the factors represented in the ratings, a second analysis was done. The four "test" factors were represented by combining the scores of the two or three tests loaded highest on each (e.g., factor I was represented by Suggestibility, P.G.R. Deflection, and half of P.G.R. rise). The ratings and self-ratings (which were derived from the questionnaire) for each factor were combined when all three were positively and significantly correlated. This occurred in all but two of the factors: factor A for which the observer-rating and self-rating were treated as separate scores and factor K for which only the observers' ratings were retained. In addition, there were two scores obtained from the self-ratings only, self-sufficiency and day-dreaming-tendencies. All seventeen of these variables were correlated over the sample of occasions and five factors were extracted. Table 10.13 gives the rotated loadings of the variables as well as the cosines among the oblique factors.

The factors were identified as follows:

Factor I. *Cyclothymia vs. Schizothymia.* Variables 6, 12, and 15 have high loadings on the factor and it is interpreted as the "more simple cyclo-schizo pattern. . . ." This factor agrees with factor A found in R-technique studies.

Factor II. *Surgency vs. Desurgency* (or Hysteria-Dysthemia). Variables 2, 10, 6, 15, 9, and 7 are loaded on this factor which agrees with factor F found in R-technique studies.

Factor III. *Positive Character Integration vs. Immature, Dependent Character.* Variables 11, 16, 12, and 7 are loaded on this factor which is interpreted to agree with factor G of previous R-technique studies. Variable 12 (friendly vs. shy) seems out of place, but it is loaded on this factor to the same extent as in R-technique studies where it was referred to as "reserve" and "self-consciousness.'

TABLE 10.13. ROTATED OBLIQUE FACTORS IN PERSONALITY RATINGS AND MEASURES [1]

	Variable	Factor					h^2
		I	II	III	IV	V	
1	Test Factor I. Emotional Abundance	.05	-.18	-.32	.33	.44	.33
2	Test Factor II. Physiological Ease vs. Emergency Alertness	.16	.53	-.03	-.01	.06	.32
3	Test Factor III. Fatigue vs. Energy	.02	.02	-.07	-.06	.17	.19
4	Test Factor IV. Uncontrol vs. Inhibition	.12	.00	-.06	-.63	-.07	.44
5	Factor A. Cyclothyme – Schiz. (Inverse of Self-Rated Shyness, Slowness)	-.13	.02	.06	.24	.19	.48
6	Factor A. Cyclothyme – Schiz. (Cooperative -Obstructive)	.60	.34	.23	-.02	.37	.69
7	Factor C. Stable Emotionally vs. Emotional	-.03	.30	.37	.50	-.01	.70
8	Factor D. Self-Sufficient, Frustration Tolerant	-.04	-.04	.02	-.07	.23	.77
9	Factor E. Self-Confident, Dominant vs. Submissive Mild Retiring	.02	-.32	-.04	-.02	.36	.62
10	Factor F. Surgent vs. Desurgent; Cheerful, Content vs. Worrying, Anxious	.04	-.37	-.23	-.36	-.02	.60
11	Factor G. Persevering, Integrated, Strong-Willed vs. Quiting, Fickle	-.14	-.04	.44	.06	-.07	.87
12	Factor H. Adventurous Cyclo-Schiz. (Friendly, Interested in People vs. Shy, Cautious)	.40	.05	-.40	.04	.74	.78
13	Factor I. Jumpy, Easily-Embarrassed, Over Active Imagination vs. Poised, Tough, Practical	.25	.03	-.07	.02	.24	.11
14	Factor J. Languid, Absent-Minded Asthenic vs. Vigorous, Orderly	-.26	-.07	-.30	-.25	-.14	.73
15	Daydreaming Tendencies	.50	.32	.06	-.47	.02	.46
16	Self-Sufficiency	-.19	-.27	.42	.49	-.06	.68
17	Factor K. Intellectual, Analytical vs. Uninterested in Cultural Matters	-.05	-.06	.06	.06	-.26	.47

C- Matrix

	I	II	III	IV	V
I	1.00				
II	.50	1.00			
III	.09	.18	1.00		
IV	-.31	-.05	-.13	1.00	
V	.33	.00	-.60	.21	1.00

[1] From Cattell, Cattell, and Rhymer (1947, p. 285).

Factor IV. *Emotionally Stable Character vs. Demoralized General Emotionality.* Variables 4, 7, 16, 15, and 10 are loaded on this factor which agrees with the D factor found in the R-technique studies. It is described as "some sort of sobered, mature inhibition, as opposed to immature, frivolous waywardness."

Factor V. *Adventurous Cyclothymia vs. Withdrawn Schizothymia.* Variables 12, 1, 6, and 9 are loaded on the factor which agrees with factor H of the previous studies. In this P-technique study two cyclothyme-schizothyme factors were found as is also the case in the R-technique studies. The first one (factor I) is considered to be "the more general, generic one" whereas in this factor the "schizothyme pole is distinguished by withdrawal. . . . Also there is a lack of energy, adventurousness, and self-confidence."

It is of interest to find that the day-to-day variations in one person brought out a number of the same personality factors as were derived from inter-individual differences and lends further support to their existence and interpretation. The intercorrelations among the oblique factors, with a few exceptions, agree well with those found in R-technique studies. As Cattell points out, "the exact correlation among factors in one subject promises to furnish a new indication of personality uniqueness and one which may be of considerable diagnostic value."

The alignment of some of the test factors with factors based on ratings and questionnaires suggests a possible objective-test battery for some of the primary personality factors and helps to clarify the functional interpretation of these factors.

CHAPTER 11

Some General Considerations

SIMPLE AXES AND PRIMARY AXES

ONE SOURCE of confusion in the use of oblique solutions has been that two types of coordinate systems have been used. They are illustrated below.

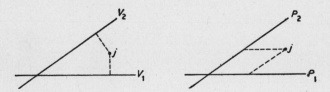

Actually the two types of coordinates are even more different than they appear above, since they are taken with relation to different sets of axes. Those on the left are called *simple* axes, and those on the right are called *primary* axes. Presenting the two sets of axes together as in Figure 11.1 will help to indicate their relationships. Two oblique planes A and B (or rather the traces of the intersections of the planes with the plane of the page) are shown. The normals (unit vectors perpendicular at the origin) to these planes are called the *simple* axes (V_1, V_2), and the loadings called for by simple structure (v_{jk}) are the perpendicular projections of the test vectors on these reference axes. This type of loading has been used by Thurstone because of his interest in simple structure and his intention to pass planes (or hyperplanes) through clusters of test vectors in order to maximize the number of near-zero loadings. The emphasis is on the location of the planes, and the axes are placed orthogonal to the planes. If, however, the emphasis is placed on the axes, and they are passed through the clusters of points, another type of axis is obtained, referred to as the *primary* axes (P_1, P_2). This type of axis has been used by Holzinger and Harman. The first primary axis is in the trace of the *B*-plane and the second primary axis is in the trace of the *A*-plane. From the diagram (Figure 11.1) it can be seen that there is a proportional relationship between the two types of loadings. The values from one can be converted to the values of the other (Harris and Knoell, 1948), and hence the conclusions should be similar, whichever set of axes is used.

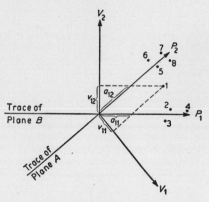

FIGURE 11.1 The relationship of simple and primary reference axes to two oblique planes.

One other distinction should be made. Figure 11.2 indicates the relationships of the axes to three oblique planes. Simple axis V_1 is the normal to plane *A*, etc. Primary axis P_1 is at the intersection of planes *B* and *C*. The projection of test j on V_2 can be obtained by dropping a perpendicular to plane *B*. To obtain the projection of test j on axis P_2, pass a plane through point j parallel to plane *B*. The length of P_2, that lies between plane *B* and the plane parallel to it, is the projection of test j on P_2 (a_{j2}). The less oblique the planes, the closer together are any pair of simple and primary axes (e.g., P_2 and V_2), and in the orthogonal case the two sets of axes coincide. The loadings on the simple axes are perpendicular projections, whereas the loadings on the primary axes are oblique projections. Perpendicular projections represent correlation with an axis and are referred to as *structure* values. Oblique projections represent the coordinates of the points on Cartesian axes and are referred to as *pattern* values. Since pattern values are coordinates rather than correlations, they may be greater than 1.0. Obviously, both types of values can be obtained on either primary or simple axes, and Holzinger and Harman (1941) usually

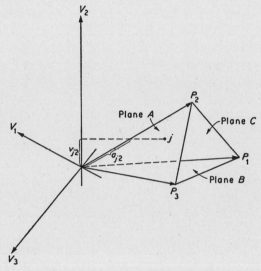

FIGURE 11.2   The relationship of simple and primary axes to three oblique planes.

report both sets of values for the primary axes. It is of interest to note that it is the oblique projections (pattern values) on the primary axes that are the loadings (a_{jk}) needed for the linear equations which describe a person's standard score as a weighted combination of his factor scores.

OBLIQUE VS. ORTHOGONAL SOLUTIONS

The location of the reference axes is in the nature of an interpretation of the data, and differing recommendations for the best type of reference frame have been made. The recommendations have depended to some extent on the purposes of the analysis and to some extent on the theoretical biases of the investigator. One source of disagreement has been the issue of whether the reference axes (and hyperplanes) should be restricted arbitrarily to orthogonality or whether the angles among them should be allowed to vary from analysis to analysis as indicated by the data. Some of the arguments advanced by those partial to *orthogonal* axes include:

Independence. Orthogonal axes are uncorrelated and represent theoretically independent factors. If the practical measures (tests, etc.) are not as independent as are the theoretical factors, this may be an indication that independent measures have not yet been developed rather than that the factors are interdependent. Such an interpretation would represent a challenge to construct new measures, based on the interpretations of the factors, that would vary independently. Not until it has been demonstrated that such independent measures cannot be constructed for a given population should one resort to correlated factors.

Simplicity. Orthogonal factors are much simpler to work with computationally and graphically. Graph paper, of course, usually is ruled orthogonally, and orthogonal axes can be represented on it accurately. If orthogonal graph paper is used to represent oblique axes, as is sometimes done, allowance must be made for distortion in the representation. Computationally, likewise, orthogonal axes are simpler since the identity matrix represents the angular separation of the orthogonal factor vectors and does not have to enter into the reproduction of the correlation matrix from the factor matrix. Also the calculation of an inverse is avoided when dealing with orthogonal factors since the inverse of an identity matrix is itself an identity matrix. Furthermore, there are a number of distinctions such as simple axes and primary axes, pattern and structure, which are needed for oblique axes but are unnecessary for orthogonal axes since the distinctions disappear in the orthogonal case.

Instability of Angular Separations. To some extent at least the obliqueness of the axes in any one study is determined by sampling instability and the angular separations can be expected to fluctuate from sample to sample.

Similarity of Results. Except for instances of highly correlated factors, there is little difference in the interpretation of the factors derived from the two approaches and the added theoretical and computational complications of oblique factors make little practical difference. There is also the problem of how oblique the axes should be permitted to be before they no longer can be considered independent, but blend into one factor.

The following are a few of the advantages claimed by those partial to *oblique* axes:

Important Information. The amount of obliqueness is itself important information. If factors indicated by the data are correlated (dependent), this should be taken into account in interpreting the results. Also second and higher-order analyses can be made of the intercorrelations of the factors.

Better Fit of Axes. If the hyperplanes are passed exactly through the clusters of test vectors representing the sample data, a more compelling simple structure can be obtained. This might be simple structure for one analysis rather than simultaneous simple structure over a series of analyses (see Chap. 8), however, since sampling fluctuations will determine, in part, the location of the oblique axes. It is true that there is some "play" in the location of orthogonal axes when the test vectors themselves are not orthogonal, which might lead to a less unique rotational solution for a specific matrix.

Closer Duplication of Nature. A number of measures, as they commonly appear in nature, tend to be related. A commonly cited example is the height and weight of persons. Even though independent measures of these traits could be developed the correlated measures of height and weight are useful.

Frequently Identified Factors

Factors are hypothetical constructs or intervening variables which can be related both to the stimulus (test items, situations, etc.) and to the response (answers or behavior of examinees). If a factor can be recognized and identified in a wide variety of situations and conditions, it is thought to represent a functional unity. There are probably a large number of "transient" factors which have a temporary or limited existence because they represent a temporary or local influence. Thus in the Air Force studies during World War II a pilot-interest factor was found in several analyses (Guilford, 1947b). During that period this was an important, stable dimension for describing the behavior of the aviation-cadet population. Such limited factors probably can be obtained from any group subjected to uniform influences, training, and background. Most of the factors in which we are interested have a broader scope. They have a more common basis such as schooling, widespread cultural influences, and possibly genetic background. Factors, then, are statistically derived unities, and their interpretation and generalization follow the accepted scientific methods for interpreting and generalizing data. The factor content of a test should be invariant for a given population when analyzed in successive batteries having the same sets of factors. As selection of the population varies with age, training, and other background variables, shifts in the factor loadings may be expected.

A number of aptitude and achievement factors have been identified in an adequate number of studies over sufficiently broad populations to lend some confidence in their stability and wide scope. Such a list of factors based largely on adolescent and adult populations is given by French (1952, p. 12) as:

Established	*Tentative*
Aiming (eye-hand coordination)	Age
Attention?	Ambidexterity
Deduction ("general reasoning")?	Auditory resistance
Finger dexterity	Articulation
Flexibility of closure?	Carefulness
Fluency of expression	Culture
Grades?	Eduction of perceptual relations
Induction?	Eduction of conceptual relations
Ideational fluency?	Eduction of conceptual patterns
Judgment	Eduction of correlates
Length estimation	Figure illusions
Associative (rote) memory	Integration
Manual dexterity	Logical reasoning
Mechanical experience	Loudness
Number	Mathematics background

Established	*Tentative*
Perceptual speed	Musical memory
Psychomotor coordination	Music
Pilot interest	Naming
Schooling	Perceptual alternations
Social studies	Pitch quality
Space	Planning
Spatial orientation	Public speaking
Speed?	Reaction time
Speed of closure	Sex
Verbal comprehension	Speed of judgment
Visualization	Span memory
Visual memory	Symbol substitution
Word fluency	Tapping

After reviewing the literature of factor analysis, French (1951) listed as "established" those factors which had been found with reasonable clarity in at least three different analyses. The question marks placed after some of the established factors indicate that the factors could be expected to appear with some confidence if suitable tests were included in the battery, but their psychological interpretation or scope is not well determined. If a factor was interpreted with reasonable clarity in only one or two analyses it was listed as tentative. Descriptions of the factors and tests which define them are given in French (1951).

Results in the area of personality have been even less conclusive. Several tentative lists of personality factors have been compiled. After reviewing the evidence from three types of personality measures (behavior ratings, self-inventories, and objective tests) Cattell (1946c) considers the following twelve bipolar factors, which are indicated by their extremes, to be the most general:

1. Cyclothymia vs. schizothymia.
2. Intelligence, general mental capacity vs. mental defect.
3. Emotionally mature stable character vs. demoralized general emotionality.
4. Dominance-ascendance vs. submissiveness.
5. Surgency vs. agitated melancholic desurgency.
6. Sensitive, anxious emotionality vs. rigid tough poise.

7. Trained, socialized, cultured mind vs. boorishness.

8. Positive character integration vs. immature dependent character.

9. Charitable, adventurous cyclothymia vs. obstructive, withdrawn schizothymia.

10. Neurasthenia vs. vigorous, "obsessional determined" character.

11. Hypersensitive infantile sthenic emotionality vs. phlegmatic frustration tolerance.

12. Surgent cyclothymia vs. paranoia.

Considerable modification of both of these lists of factors can be expected as a result of further investigations.[1]

A group of factor analysts who met at the Educational Testing Service in Princeton, New Jersey, in November, 1951, is engaged in the task of clarifying some of the more common aptitude factors and recommending several standard reference tests for each factor (French, 1952).[2] The Educational Testing Service intends to serve as a repository for these tests and make copies available to persons who desire to use them for research purposes. Similar batteries of reference tests of personality and achievement factors are to be developed in the future.

INFLUENCES ON FACTOR LOADINGS

A number of conditions that influence the outcome of a factor analysis must be taken into account in the setting up and interpreting the results of a factorial study. Some of these considerations are the selection of the sample, the type of correlation coefficient used, the conditions of administration, and the scoring formulas applied to the tests.

Selection of the Sample. The major considerations in the selection of the sample are the range of the group on the traits

---

[1] Since the above was written, French (1953a) has issued an extensive compilation of factorial studies and results in the area of personality measurements.

[2] Tests of this type which are used to establish the presence of a factor in a given population have been variously referred to as reference tests, marker tests, tie-in variables, anchor tests, etc.

measured by the tests, and the degree of selection on traits correlated with the factors. If the purpose of the study is merely the identification of factors in a new area of investigation, the wider the range the better. If, however, the results are to be generalized to a carefully defined population, the sample must be representative of that population. Since factor loadings (pattern values) are average weights, putting scores from unlike populations (e.g., men and women on strength tests or mechanical tests) together will result in loadings which are averages for the groups which have been combined (Jeffress, 1948a).

Background, Training, Experience, and Set. Selective background population characteristics, such as age, sex, education, and training, may influence factor content. As has been pointed out by Thurstone (1947c), "factors cannot be expected to be invariant from one population to a different population." A vocabulary test of moderate difficulty may be a measure of reasoning for elementary school children but a measure of perceptual speed for college students. Items at different difficulty levels in an apparently homogenous test may emerge as measures of different functions even though methods of correlation that minimize the influence of difficulty level are used.

Even more vexatious to the test constructor and factor analyst is the problem that different examinees may employ different mental processes in solving an item. In solving a spatial problem, for example, some may rely on verbal and reasoning processes, while others may use visual imagery. Such ambiguity can probably be minimized by trying to find tasks that most persons solve in the same manner and by carefully selecting populations so that such differences are held to a minimum.

The processes by which problems are solved can be controlled somewhat by means of a set given either in the directions or in a training period during which a given routine for solving the problems is taught. If the members of a group are at different stages on the learning curve of the traits being tested, they may use different processes to do a task. Thus, in learning telegraphy, typewriting, or reading, quite different factors are measured by the task at different points along the learning curve. Speeded scores, also, have quite different meanings for different ages, difficulty levels, and stages of learning.

Type of Correlation Coefficient. The most satisfactory type of correlation coefficients for continuous variables are product-moment correlations. The most consistent results are obtained when distributions have been normalized, but satisfactory results are also obtained from the correlations of the raw scores if the assumptions (e.g., rectilinearity) for the correlation method used are satisfied. Biserial and rank-difference correlations may be used as estimates of the product-moment correlation coefficient, although it is probably best to use only one type of correlation coefficient in a study. For large samples tetrachoric coefficients may be used if the splits on the variables are not too extreme and the assumption of rectilinearity can be justified.

The phi coefficient (fourfold point correlation) should not be used unless some correction is made to avoid spurious factors due to differences in splits of the dichotomized variables.

Experimental and Linear Dependence. It has been pointed out by Thurstone (1947c), Guilford (1952a), and others, that scores that are experimentally dependent should not be included in a correlation matrix for factor analysis because of the spurious element introduced by the correlation of chance and error variances. Examples of such experimentally dependent scores are speed and accuracy scores taken from a single performance, rights and wrongs scores, scores derived from overlapping keys as in the case of some interest and personality inventories. If several scores are derived from a single performance as is the case with a number of the Rorschach indices, they would not be experimentally independent scores.

Spurious correlations may also be due to linearly dependent scores such as correlating a total score with a part score which entered into the total score or the correlation of the ratio or difference between two scores with one of the scores which entered into the ratio or difference.

Time Limit and Scoring Formula. The extent to which a test is speeded may have some influence on its factor content, because the correlation between speed and level (power) scores may vary anywhere from high positive to negative. General speed factors have been found in several batteries of speeded tests. Also, the more speeded a test is, the more likely the rights and wrongs scores are to be independent (for "power" tests the correlation between rights and wrongs is -1.0). Relatively independent rights and wrongs scores may differ in their factor content, and the factor composition of a total score which is a combination of such independent rights and wrongs scores will vary depending on the scoring formula used (Fruchter, 1953). The reliabilities of the scores also have an effect on the size of the factor loadings and formulas for estimating the changes in loadings, because of changes in reliability have been presented by Guilford and Michael (1950).

EXPERIMENTAL DESIGNS

Cattell (1946c and 1952a and b) has pointed out six possibilities for studying covariation in tests, persons, and occasions and has designated them O- and P-technique, Q- and R-technique, and S- and T-technique. These designations refer to the experimental designs by which the intercorrelations are obtained, and each technique in a pair is the transpose of the other.

Q- and R-techniques. We will begin with this pair because R-technique has been used in the vast majority of studies to the present and is the most familiar. R-technique is the well-known correlation of tests administered to a sample of persons on a single occasion. It indicates the extent to which the tests covary over a series of persons on one occasion or under one condition. Q-technique, the transpose of R-technique, indicates how two or more persons covary over a series of tests administered on one occasion. Actually the term test is somewhat misleading here, because, in correlating persons, the scores of an individual on all tests must be averaged (just as in correlating tests, the scores of all persons on the test must be averaged). Now, if the scores of the tests are expressed in different units (e.g., so many units of reading comprehension, so many units of perceptual speed, and so many units or reaction time, etc.), it will not make sense to average them. Therefore Q-technique has found its greatest use-fulness where some kind of a "person continuum" can be as-sumed, and the various "tests" (really items) are placed on this continuum. Examples are esthetic and other types of preference, and attitude and personality questionnaires where the subject can tell to what extent he likes or dislikes an item or the extent to which an item describes him. The various "scores" are, conse-quently, in terms of the same units (e.g., the person's preference) and can be averaged. This type of measurement has been termed ipsative (relative to the self) as contrasted with the usual type of measurement, which is normative (relative to the group). If two persons answer a series of questions or rank a series of stimuli similarly, they will be highly correlated. The factors derived from Q-technique (obverse factor analysis) have persons loaded on them and each factor represents a hypothetical person of a given "type." (For examples of obverse factor analysis, see Chap-ter 10.)

O- and P-techniques. Of these two, the more common is P-technique. It consists of correlating a group of tests adminis-tered over a series of occasions to one person. By this design it should be possible to determine whether, where a battery of tests is administered repeatedly to one person, any of the tests covary in time. Tests which measure the same factors in an individual should vary as that factor in the individual fluctuates with time. This approach is especially useful with dynamic variables such as personality traits that do fluctuate with time. It could also serve to help identify and confirm the factors obtained from R-technique if the same factors were found in a battery of tests, used to obtain intra-individual differences, as were found in a battery of tests used to obtain inter-individual differences. It should make possible a description of the dynamics of an indi-vidual in terms of relatively objective factors as well as the com-parison of the factors involved in the dynamics of two or more individuals. (See Chapter 10 for an example of the application of P-technique.)

O-technique, involving the correlation of occasions for a series of tests for one individual, is the transpose of P-technique. It indicates the extent to which two or more occasions covary over a series of tests for one person. By this type of analysis it should be possible to group occasions by the ways in which they influence performance. It has been observed that the same person may behave quite differently on different occasions; he may be independent or dependent, shy or not shy, moral or immoral under varying circumstances as his role changes. It should be possible to determine whether different occasions or conditions systematically affect the performance of a person. If the occasions have been varied in some systematic way the interpretations of the factors should be more meaningful. Since this method (as was also true of Q-technique) requires summing over a series of "tests," the scores must be in terms of similar units.

S- and T-techniques.[3] S-technique consists of determining the extent to which two or more individuals vary together over a series of occasions or trials on one task. It should be useful for determining groups homogenous with regard to a given trait over a series of occasions. Traits which vary in the individual on different trials or occasions, as in learning studies or in different social situations, would be most appropriate for this type of analysis also. Varying the occasions in a systematic or controlled manner would probably lead to the most meaningful "person" factors.

T-technique, the transpose of S-technique, indicates how two or more occasions covary over a series of individuals on one test. The most familiar example of this is, of course, test-retest reliability. If the test is of a dynamic trait that fluctuates considerably under differing circumstances, this approach might be useful for determining the basic types of occasion factors affecting performance on the test. O-, S-, and T-techniques have been outlined as theoretical possibilities. Few if any applications have been made of them up to the present time. (However, see the study by Wherry reported in Chapter 10 as a possible application of T-technique.)

THE ESTIMATION OF FACTOR SCORES

A score derived from a complex test, which is a measure of several factors, may be ambiguous in that we do not

---

[3] Mowrer (1953b) refers to these as M- and N-techniques, respectively.

know what combination of the factors may be represented by any individual's score. A score derived from a "pure" test is relatively unambiguous, since it represents a single trait or functional unity. It is said to be "univocal." Factor scores may be computed in several ways, the fundamental principle being to obtain the weighted combination of the tests, by multiple correlation, that best predict a factor. For this purpose the loadings (structure values) of the tests or variables on the factors are used as validity coefficients.

Of course, if a pure, reliable measure with a satisfactorily high saturation on a factor exists, the scores on it can be used as the factor scores. If a pure measure of a factor is not available, but there are several tests with high loadings on the factor and secondary loadings on nonoverlapping factors, either the sum or a weighted combination of their scores may be uesd as an estimate of the factor scores. Guilford and Michael (1948) have presented convenient equations for obtaining univocal factor scores, where the suppression of one or more secondary factors is desired. Their equations also make it possible to maximize the variance on the desired factor, or minimize the variance on the undesired factors, or obtain any given ratio of the two types of variance.

MECHANICAL AIDS TO COMPUTATION

One practical limitation to the widespread application of the factorial methods has been the large amount of laborious computation involved. Approximate methods, such as are provided by the centroid solution, have been used to reduce the labor within reasonable bounds. The present and future development of high-speed computers should do much to cut the amount of time and labor required for a factorial solution and make feasible the use of more powerful statistical techniques, such as the maximum-likelihood method (Lawley, 1943a, 1950 and 1951), which provide mathematically efficient estimates of factor loadings and suitable tests of significance.

The major computational problems in factor analysis are the extraction of factors, the plotting and rotation of axes, the multiplication of the factor matrix by the transformation matrix, and the calculation of inverse matrices.

A method for extracting principal axes by means of IBM

equipment has been devised by Tucker (1946). The machine setup that is desirable for this method includes a key punch and verifier, a sorter, an alphabetical accounting machine, and a summary punch. Tucker (1942) has also devised a punched-card method for centroid factors, and Hall, Welker, and Crawford (1945) have made an adaptation of this method to more commonly available machines and have also introduced some labor saving steps.

The Watson Scientific Computing Laboratory at Columbia University has an IBM sequence-controlled electronic calculator, which can extract principal-axis or maximum-likelihood factors rapidly and furnish a running chi-square test to test the significance of the extracted factors.

For the plotting of factors the General Electric Company has developed, for the Adjutant General's Office, a device that plots points for two axes at a time on an oscilloscope screen, rotates electronically, and does some of the matrix-multiplication operations involved. A method for matrix multiplication by means of a special attachment to an IBM tabulator has been devised by Tucker (1940b). The only copy of this attachment, however, is at the University of Chicago. The steps in matrix multiplication on electronic calculators have been outlined by Brannan (1952) and an application of electronic computers to factor analysis has been made by Wrigley and Neuhaus (1952). Hotelling (1949) has stated some of the problems that need to be solved to develop more efficient methods for computing inverses.

In general the computing devices are cumbersome and expensive, and they are efficient only for large problems and in laboratories where several analyses are being done simultaneously. The time involved in setting up the equipment for several analyses is usually about the same as is required to set up one analysis, and the time needed to run the data through the machines is usually negligible by comparison.

Next Steps in Factor Analysis

Considerable theoretical development and practical application of factor analysis have occurred in the past decade. Much, however, still remains to be done in both of these areas. In the first place, better planned studies are needed. Applying factor analysis to a table of intercorrelations just because it happens to be available cannot be expected to yield meaningful results. The test battery should be carefully constructed or assembled with specific hypotheses in mind, and all aspects of the area under investigation should be adequately covered (in more technical language "overdetermined") to make possible clear interpretations of the factors obtained.

A great deal of work remains to be done on the interpretation of even the better-known factors. It has been suggested, for instance, that the essence of the numerical-facility factor is not number, but the ability to deal with a highly practiced closed system of associations. Where an interpretation of a factor is made, or there are alternative hypotheses, new tests which call for the hypothesized behavior should be constructed and analyzed in order to verify or reject the interpretations. The nature and extent of the factors should be studied by carefully controlled, nonfactorial methods to determine how they vary under different conditions and with different populations. The following are some questions that need to be answered in this connection: Is the function represented by a factor amenable to training or influenced by set or background? Are some factorially complex tests complex only because different individuals in the population do the task differently? If so, can the methods by which individuals solve problems be ascertained, and can the population be subdivided into more homogenous groups or made more homogenous by training or set?

Very few investigations of how factors change with age, sex, speeding, difficulty level, etc., have been done.

In connection with better designed factorial experiments, improved theoretical models, in hyperspace, are needed for the rotational problem, so that criteria for unique solutions can be developed. Tucker (1951) has developed methods for rotating several batteries to "congruent" solutions for those factors that have overlapping variables and has also developed the factor analysis of covariances so that differences in group variability may be taken into account.[4] Burt (1952) has suggested an approximate formula for the standard error of a factor loading under certain restricted conditions.

The factorial methods need to be extended to nonmetric data also. Steps in that direction have been taken by Lazarsfeld (1950) and Burt (1950b).

With regard to application, many more analyses which include independent criterion measures need to be done, both to help clarify the nature of the criteria and to help determine their rela- tionship to factorially-defined predictive measures. Additional studies need to be made using P- and S-techniques, so that the dynamics of individuals and groups over a series of trials or occa- sions can be determined. O- and T-techniques should be applied more extensively so that trials or occasions can be classified accord- ing to the common factors operating in them for one person on a number of traits, and for single traits on a number of persons. With more rapid methods of computation available, it is expected that factor analysis will be applied more frequently as a method of item analysis in the construction of homogenous tests.

With the increasingly insightful and accurate application of factorial methods not only will new understandings and control of social behavior be achieved, but applications will also be made to the many other sciences where the basic variables underly- ing complex multivariate interrelationships must be isolated and identified.

---

[4] The following are some analytical methods for rotation of axes that have been published recently:

J. B. Carroll. An analytical solution for approximating simple structure in factor analysis. *Psychometrika*, 1953, **18**, 23-38.

J. O. Neuhaus and C. Wrigley. The quadrimax method: an analytical approach to orthogonal simple structure. Memorandum Report A-6, University of Illinois, Contract No. AF 33(038)-25726, August 1953, 33 pp. (mimeographed).

D. R. Saunders. An analytical method for rotation to orthogonal simple struc- ture. *Educational Testing Service Research Bulletin* 53-10, August 1953, 28 pp.

L. L. Thurstone. Analytical method for simple structure. *Psychometric Labora- tory, University of North Carolina*, Report No. 6, July 1953, 14 pp.

Appendix

CALCULATION OF THE ESTIMATED FACTOR LOAD-
INGS OF A VARIABLE NOT INCLUDED IN THE
ORIGINAL ANALYSIS [1]

IF IT is desired to estimate the loadings of a variable, relative to the factors in a battery in which it was not included, and the correlations of the variable with the other tests in the battery are known, it may be done by the following steps:

1. Place the rotated factor loadings of the original test battery in a matrix with the tests running vertically and the factors horizontally. Assume an example with four tests and three factors.

Rotated Factor Matrix

Tests	Factors		
	I	II	III
1	.4	.3	.8
2	.1	-.3	.5
3	.7	-.1	.2
4	.9	.2	.3

[1] This method was first presented by Dwyer (1937). An extension of the method to the simultaneous estimation of the loadings of several variables not included in the original analysis was given by Mosier (1938) in matrix notation as follows:

$$V_{tp} = R'_{tj}F'_{jm}G^{-1}_{mM}T_{mp}$$

where V_{tp} = factor loadings of new tests on the rotated factors;

R'_{tj} = transpose of the matrix of intercorrelations of new tests with tests already factor analyzed;

F'_{jm} = transpose of factor loadings of analyzed tests on the unrotated factors;

$G_{mM} = F_{mj}F'_{jm}$;

T_{mp} = transformation matrix from unrotated to rotated loadings.

209

2. From the above matrix, a factor-estimation matrix may be formed by the following steps:

(a) In the factor estimation matrix shown below, the diagonal values, cells (1a, 1), (2a, 2), (3a, 3), etc., are found by summing the squares of the values in each factor column (ΣF^2). Retain all values to twice as many decimal places as they were given in the rotated factor matrix.

Rotated Factor Matrix

	I	II	III
1	.4	.3	.8
2	.1	-.3	.5
3	.7	-.1	.2
4	.9	.2	.3
ΣF^2	1.47	.23	1.02

Factor Estimation Matrix

	1	2	3
1a	1.47		
1b			
2a		.23	
2b			
3a			1.02
3b			

(b) If there are four factors in the rotated factor matrix, the factor estimation matrix is a four-by-four matrix. Similarly, for n factors an $n \times n$ matrix would be obtained.

(c) The value in cell (1a, 2) is the algebraic sum of the products of the factor loadings in factor column I times the corresponding loadings in column II $(\Sigma F_\mathrm{I} F_\mathrm{II})$.

Rotated Factor Matrix

	I	II	III
1	.4	.3	.8
2	.1	-.3	.5
3	.7	-.1	.2
4	.9	.2	.3
$\Sigma F_\mathrm{I} F_\mathrm{II}$ =.20			

Factor Estimation Matrix

	1	2	3
1a	1.47	.20	
1b			
2a		.23	
2b			
3a			1.02
3b			

(d) The value in cell (1a, 3) is the algebraic sum of the products of the factor loadings in column I times the corresponding factor loadings in column III $(\Sigma F_\mathrm{I} F_\mathrm{III})$.

Rotated Factor Matrix

	I	II	III
1	.4	.3	.8
2	.1	-.3	.5
3	.7	-.1	.2
4	.9	.2	.3
$\Sigma F_\mathrm{I} F_\mathrm{III}$ =.78			

Factor Estimation Matrix

	1	2	3
1a	1.47	.20	.78
1b			
2a		.23	
2b			
3a			1.02
3b			

(e) In a four-factor problem, cell (1a, 4) would be the algebraic sum of the products of the factor loadings in column I times the corresponding values in column IV. For larger problems, the additional values in row 1a are obtained by a similar process of cumulative summing of cross-products.

(f) The value in cell (2a, 1) is found by the same procedure as was used for obtaining the value in cell (1a, 2) and may be used as a check on cell (1a, 2). (See step 2c.)

(g) The value in cell (2a, 3) is the algebraic sum of the products of the factor loadings in column II times the corresponding factor loadings in column III ($\Sigma F_{II}\ F_{III}$).

(h) The values in cells (3a, 1) and (3a, 2) are obtained in the same way as those in cells (1a, 3) and (2a, 3) respectively, and may be used as a check on those values.

Rotated Factor Matrix

	I	II	III
1	.4	.3	.8
2	.1	−.3	.5
3	.7	−.1	.2
4	.9	.2	.3

$\Sigma F_{II} F_{III}$ = .13

Factor Estimation Matrix

	1	2	3
1a	1.47	.20	.78
1b			
2a	.20	.23	.13
2b			
3a	.78	.13	1.02
3b			

(i) For larger problems, the values in the remainder of the factor estimation matrix can be found by extending the procedure outlined above.

3. The next column to be added on the right side of the factor estimation matrix is the validities column, which is headed *"Valid."* in the example. This is obtained by the following steps:

(a) List to the right of the rotated factor matrix the intercorrelations of the test (t) whose factor content is to be estimated with the tests of known factor content. (For the example, assume $r_{1t} = .7$, $r_{2t} = .4$, $r_{3t} = .3$, $r_{4t} = .1$.)

Rotated Factor Matrix

	I	II	III	t
1	.4	.3	.8	.7
2	.1	−.3	.5	.4
3	.7	−.1	.2	.3
4	.9	.2	.3	.1

(b) The value in cell (1a, Valid.) of the factor estimation matrix is the algebraic sum of the products of the loadings in column I times the corresponding correlation coefficients in column t ($\Sigma F_I t$).

Rotated Factor Matrix

	I	II	III	t
1	.4			.7
2	.1			.4
3	.7			.3
4	.9			.1
$\Sigma F_I t$	= .62			

Factor Estimation Matrix

	1	2	3	Valid
1 a / b	1.47	.20	.78	.62
2 a / b	.20	.23	.13	
3 a / b	.78	.13	1.02	

(c) The value in cell (2a, Valid.) is found in like manner, using column II and column t ($\Sigma F_{II} t$).

(d) The value in cell (3a, Valid.) is found as above, using column III and column t ($\Sigma F_{III} t$).

(e) For problems with more than three factors, the remainder of the values in the "Validities" column are obtained in a similar manner.

4. The next column in the factor estimation matrix is a "check" column, and the values in it are obtained by summing the values in each row, including the validities column, regarding algebraic signs. The use of the check column will be explained in step 5e.

Factor Estimation Matrix

	1	2	3	Valid.	Check
1 a / b	1.47	.20	.78	.62	3.07 (1.47+.20+.78 +.62=3.07, etc)
2 a / b	.20	.23	.13	.08	.64
3 a / b	.78	.13	1.02	.85	2.78

5. The factor estimation matrix is now completed. Solution for the factor loadings is somewhat analogous to operations on a multiple-correlation matrix in computing beta weights by the Cowles-Crout method.[2]

[2] See J. T. Cowles, "A labor-saving method of computing multiple correlation coefficients, regression weights, and standard errors of regression weights," *Technical Memorandum No. 2* (Lackland AFB: Psychological Research and Examining

(a) Obtain cell (1b, 2) in the factor estimation matrix by dividing cell (1a, 2) by cell (1a, 1). It is suggested that the *b*-row entries be made with colored pencil.

$$(1b, 2) = \frac{.20}{1.47} = .14$$

(b) Obtain cell (1b, 3) by dividing cell (1a, 3) by cell (1a, 1).

$$(1b, 3) = \frac{.78}{1.47} = .53$$

Factor Estimation Matrix

		1	2	3	Valid.	Check
1	a	1.47	.20	.78	.62	3.07
	b		.14	.53	.42	2.09
2	a	.20	.23	.13	.08	.64
	b					
3	a	.78	.13	1.02	.85	2.78
	b					

(c) In a four-factor problem, cell (1b, 4) would be obtained by dividing the value in cell (1a, 4) by the value in cell (1a, 1). For larger problems, the additional cells in the first row are obtained in a similar manner, i.e., the value in cell (1b, n) would be obtained by dividing the value in cell (1a, n) by the value in cell (1a, 1).

(d) The values in cells (1b, Valid.) and (1b, Check) are found in like manner.

(e) For any row the values in the *b* cells of the Check column should equal 1.00 plus the sum of all values in the *b* row to the *right* of the diagonal value, including the entry in the validities column; this sum is entered to the right of the check values of the *b* rows in a column headed "Row Sum + 1.0" (see matrix in step 5s, on page 216). In the example, the first value in this column is:

$$1.00 + .14 + .53 + .42 = 2.09$$

Unit, 17 Feb. 48), and G. H. Dash, "A simplified procedure for computing multiple-correlation coefficients and regression weights by the Cowles-Crout technique," *Technical Memorandum No. 12* (Lackland AFB: 3309th Research and Development Squadron, 25 Feb. 49).

(f) Next, obtain the value in cell (2b, 2) by subtracting from the value in cell (2a, 2) the product of cell (2a, 1) and cell (1b, 2).

$$(2b, 2) = .23 - (.20)(.14) = .20$$

(g) Next, obtain the value in cell (3b, 2) by subtracting from the value in cell (3a, 2) the product of cell (3a, 1) and cell (1b, 2).

$$(3b, 2) = .13 - (.78)(.14) = .02$$

(h) For a four-factor problem, the value in cell (4b, 2) would be obtained by subtracting from the value in cell (4a, 2) the product of (4a, 1) and (1b, 2). For larger problems, values in the additional cells of column 2 would then be determined in a corresponding manner, i.e., subtracting from the value in cell (na, 2) the product of cell (na, 1) and cell (1b, 2).

(i) The value in cell (2b, 3) is obtained by dividing the value in cell (3b, 2) by the value in cell (2b, 2).

$$(2b, 3) = \frac{.02}{.20} = .10$$

(j) For a four-factor problem, the value in cell (2b, 4) is obtained by dividing the value in cell (4b, 2) by the value in cell (2b, 2). For larger problems, the rest of the values in row 2 would be obtained by dividing the entry in cell (nb, 2) by the value in cell (2b, 2) to obtain (2b, n).

(k) The value in cell (2b, Valid.) is obtained by subtracting from cell (2a, Valid.) the product of cell (2a, 1) and cell (1b, Valid.) and dividing by the value in cell (2b, 2).[3]

---

[3] It should be noted here that consistency in rounding off is necessary if the work is to check. For example, in the computation in paragraph 5k, rounding to two decimal places consistently would give:

$$\frac{.08 - (.20)(.42)}{.20} = \frac{.08 - .08}{.20} = .00$$

The use of three decimal places in one of the operations would give:

$$\frac{.08 - (.20)(.42)}{.20} = \frac{.08 - .084}{.20} = -.02$$

When cell (26, Valid.) has the value of .00, the computations will check. When it is given the value −.02, the computations will not check, and the error introduced will affect all further work.

$$(2b, \text{Valid.}) = \frac{.08 - (.20)(.42)}{.20} = .00$$

(l) The value in cell (2b, Check) is obtained by subtracting from cell (2a, Check) the product of cell (2a, 1) and cell (1b, Check) and dividing by the value in cell (2b, 2).

$$(2b, \text{Check}) = \frac{.64 - (.20)(2.09)}{.20} = 1.10$$

(m) The result in (2b, Check) should be equal to 1.00 plus the value obtained by summing algebraically all values in row 2b to the right of the diagonal, including the entry in the validities column.

(n) Next, obtain the value in cell (3b, 3) by summing the products of cell (3a, 1) times cell (1b, 3) and cell (3b, 2) times cell (2b, 3) and subtracting this sum from cell (3a, 3).

$$(3b, 3) = 1.02 - [(.78)(.53) + (.02)(.10)] = .61$$

(o) For a four-factor problem the value in cell (4b, 3) is obtained by:

$$(4b, 3) = (4a, 3) - [(4a, 1)(1b, 3) + (4b, 2)(2b, 3)]$$

For an $n \times n$ matrix,

$$(nb, 3) = (na, 3) - [(na, 1)(1b, 3) + (nb, 2)(2b, 3)]$$

(p) For a four-factor problem,

$$(3b, 4) = \frac{(4b, 3)}{(3b, 3)}$$

For an $n \times n$ matrix,

$$(3b, n) = \frac{(nb, 3)}{(3b, 3)}$$

(q) Next obtain the value in cell (3b, Valid.) by subtracting from cell (3a, Valid.) the sum of the products of cell (3a, 1) times cell (1b, Valid.) and cell (3b, 2) times cell (2b, Valid.) and dividing by the value in cell (3b, 3).

$$(3b, \text{Valid.}) = \frac{.85 - [(.78)(.42) + (.02)(.00)]}{.61} = .85$$

(r) For a four-factor problem, the value in the (4b, validity) cell is obtained as follows:

$$(4b, \text{Valid.}) = \frac{\begin{cases}(4a, \text{Valid.}) - [(4a, 1)(1b, \text{Valid.}) \\ \quad + (4b, 2)(2b, \text{Valid.}) + (4b, 3)(3b, \text{Valid.})]\end{cases}}{(4b, 4)}$$

For an *n*-factor problem,

(nb, Valid.)

$$= \frac{\begin{cases}(na, \text{Valid.}) - [(na, 1)(1b, \text{Valid.}) + (nb, 2)(2b, \text{Valid.}) \\ \quad + \cdots + (nb, n-1)(n-1b, \text{Valid.})]\end{cases}}{(nb, n)}$$

(s) Next, obtain the value in cell (3b, Check) by summing the products of cell (3a, 1) times cell (1b, Check) and cell (3b, 2) times cell (2b, Check) and subtracting this sum from cell (3a, Check) and dividing by the value in cell (3b, 3).

$$(3b, \text{Check}) = \frac{2.78 - [(.78)(2.09) + (.02)(1.10)]}{.61} = 1.85$$

Completed Factor Estimation Matrix

	1	2	3	*Valid.*	*Check*	*Row Sum + 1.0*
1 *a*	1.47	.20	.78	.62	3.07	
b		.14	.53	.42	2.09	2.09
2 *a*	.20	.23	.13	.08	.64	
b		.20	.10	.00	1.10	1.10
3 *a*	.78	.13	1.02	.85	2.78	
b			.02	.61	.85	1.85	1.85

(t) For a four-factor problem:

$$(4b, \text{Check}) = \frac{\begin{cases}(4a, \text{Check}) - [(4a, 1)(1b, \text{Check}) \\ \quad + (4b, 2)(2b, \text{Check}) + (4b, 3)(3b, \text{Check})]\end{cases}}{(4b, 4)}$$

For an *n*-factor problem,

(nb, Check)

$$= \frac{\begin{cases}(na, \text{Check}) - [(na, 1)(1b, \text{Check}) + (nb, 2)(2b, \text{Check}) \\ \quad + \cdots + (nb, n-1)(n-1b, \text{Check})]\end{cases}}{(nb, n)}$$

(u) The general outline of the procedure in step 5 for larger problems is as follows:

(1) Obtain the (nb, n) value. In a four-factor problem,

$$(4b, 4) = (4a, 4) - [(4a, 1)(1b, 4) + (4b, 2)(2b, 4) + (4b, 3)(3b, 4)]$$

And for an *n*-factor problem,

$$(nb, n) = (na, n) - [(na, 1)(1b, n)$$
$$+ (nb, 2)(2b, n) + \cdots + (nb, n - 1)((n - 1)b, n)]$$

(2) Obtain the values in each column (calling the column *m*, where $m < n$) below the diagonal cell. The general formula is:

$$(nb, m) = (na, m) - [(na, 1)(1b, m)$$
$$+ (nb, 2)(2b, m) + \cdots + (nb, m - 1)((m - 1)b, m)]$$

(3) Obtain the values in row nb to the right of the diagonal cell and to the left of the validity column. The general formula for cell (nb, o) where $o > n$ is:

$$(nb, o) = \frac{(ob, n)}{(nb, n)}$$

(4) Obtain the value in the validity column by means of the general formula in step 5r.

(5) Obtain the value in the check column by means of the general formula in step 5t.

(6) Check the work by obtaining the algebraic sum of all values in the row to the right of the diagonal cell plus 1.0. This sum should equal the value in the check column.

6. (a) The loading of the test (t) on the third or last factor is equal to the value in cell (3b, Valid.).

$F_{III} = .85$ (or .8 rounded if the loadings

are being reported to one decimal place)

(b) The loading on the second factor is equal to cell (2b, Valid.) minus the product of cell (2b, 3) times the third factor loading.

$$F_{II} = .00 - (.10)(.85) = -.08 \text{ (or } -.1 \text{ rounded)}$$

(c) The loading on the first factor is equal to cell (1b, Valid.) minus the sum of the products of cell (1b, 3) times the third factor loading, and cell (1b, 2) times the second factor loading.

$$F_{\mathrm{I}} = .42 - [(.53)(.85) + (.14)(-.08)] = -.02 \text{ (or .0 rounded)}$$

(d) For problems with more than three factors, the process is similar to that outlined above. The last factor loading is the value in the last *b* row of the Validities column. Computation of each successive loading involves subtraction of an additional cross-product, as illustrated in steps 6b and 6c above. The general formulas for an *n*-factor problem are:

$$F_{\mathrm{N}} = (\mathrm{nb}, \text{Valid.})$$
$$F_{\mathrm{N}-1} = [(\mathrm{n}-1)\mathrm{b}, \text{Valid.}] - [(\mathrm{n}-1)\mathrm{b}, \mathrm{n}]F_{\mathrm{N}}$$
$$F_{\mathrm{N}-2} = [(\mathrm{n}-2)\mathrm{b}, \text{Valid.}] - [(\mathrm{n}-2)\mathrm{b}, \mathrm{n}]F_{\mathrm{N}}$$
$$+ [(\mathrm{n}-2)\mathrm{b}\,(\mathrm{n}-1)]F_{\mathrm{N}-1}$$
$$F_{\mathrm{II}} = (2\mathrm{b}, \text{Valid.}) - [(2\mathrm{b}, \mathrm{n})F_{\mathrm{N}} + 2\mathrm{b}\,(\mathrm{n}-1)F_{\mathrm{N}-1}]$$
$$+ \cdots + (2\mathrm{b}, 3)F_{\mathrm{III}}$$
$$F_{\mathrm{I}} = (1\mathrm{b}, \text{Valid.}) - [(1\mathrm{b}, \mathrm{n})F_{\mathrm{N}} + 1\mathrm{b}\,(\mathrm{n}-1)F_{\mathrm{N}-1}]$$
$$+ \cdots + (1\mathrm{b}, 3)F_{\mathrm{III}} + (1\mathrm{b}, 2)F_{\mathrm{II}}$$

7. If the factor loadings of a criterion variable rather than a test variable are to be estimated, the validity coefficients of the criterion for the tests of known factorial content are listed in column *t* of the rotated factor matrix.

8. If the factor loadings of more than one variable are to be estimated relative to the same rotated factor matrix, they may be estimated from the same basic factor estimation matrix (i.e., the factor estimation matrix found in step 2g. Also see footnote 1).

9. It is useful as a last step to reproduce from the estimated factor loadings the correlations of the variable not factor-analyzed with the variables that were used in the factor analysis. Reproduced and original correlations for the present example are compared on page 219. Discrepancies are not due to computational errors if work has been checked. Significant discrepancies may be

the result of an inadequate factor description of the enlarged matrix that includes the additional test or criterion. Discrepancies the size of the ones in this example might suggest the presence of one or more additional factors in the enlarged matrix.

Added Variable with	Original Correlation	Reproduced Correlation
1	.7	.6
2	.4	.4
3	.3	.2
4	.1	.2

10. The estimated factor loadings obtained from this method can often be improved by iteration. One such method of iteration is presented by Wherry (1949) and Wherry, Campbell and Perloff (1951).

Bibliography[1]

Abrams, E. N. (1950), Comparative factor analytic study of normal and neurotic veterans. *Microfilm Abstr.,* **10,** 94-95 (Abstract of Ph.D. thesis, N.Y.U.).

Adcock, C. J. (1946), Simplified factor analysis. *Occup. Psychol., Lond.,* **20,** 188-198.

Adcock, C. J. (1948a), A factorial examination of Sheldon's types. *J. Personality,* **16,** 312-319.

Adcock, C. J. (1948b), A re-analysis of Slater's spatial judgment research. *Occup. Psychol., Lond.,* **22,** 213-216.

Adcock, C. J. (1950), A note on the factorial analysis of Sheldon's personality traits. *Aust. J. Psychol.,* **2,** 114-115.

Adcock, C. J. (1951), A factorial approach to Rorschach interpretation. *J. gen. Psychol.,* **44,** 261-272.

Adcock, C. J. (1952), A note on cluster-directed analysis. *Psychometrika,* **17,** 249-254.

Adjutant General's Office, Personnel Research Section (1948), *Studies in visual acuity.* Washington, D. C.: U. S. Government Printing Office (PRS Report No. 742), viii, 161 pp.

Adkins, D. C., and Lyerly, S. B. (1952), *Factor analysis of reasoning tests,* Chapel Hill, N. C.: Univ. of No. Carolina Press, 122 pp.

Albert, A. A. (1944a), The matrices of factor analysis. *Proc. Nat. Acad. Sci., Wash.,* **30,** 90-95.

Albert, A. A. (1944b), The minimum rank of a correlation matrix. *Proc. Nat. Acad. Sci., Wash.,* **30,** 144-148.

---

[1] This bibliography covers the period from 1940 through 1952 mainly. For a comprehensive bibliography prior to 1940, see Wolfle (1940).

Alexander, W. P. (1935), Intelligence, concrete and abstract. *Brit. J. Psychol., Monogr. Suppl.,* **6,** 19, 177 pp.

Anastasi, A. (1938), Faculties versus factors: a reply to Professor Thurstone. *Psychol. Bull.,* **35,** 391-395.

Anastasi, A. (1948), The nature of psychological "traits." *Psychol. Rev.,* **55,** 127-138.

Anderson, G. V. (1946), Factor analysis of attitudes toward community problems. *Amer. Psychologist,* **1,** 462 (Abstract).

Andree, R. V. (1952), A computational short cut in factor analysis. *Psychol. Bull.,* **49,** 144-147.

Andrews, T. G. (1943), A factorial analysis of responses to the comic as a study in personality. *J. gen. Psychol.,* **28,** 209-224.

Ash, P. (1950), A statistical analysis of the Navy's method of position evaluation. *Publ. Personnel Rev.,* **11,** 130-138.

Baehr, M. E. (1952), A factorial study of temperament. *Psychometrika,* **17,** 107-126.

Bair, J. T. (1949), Factor analysis of tests purporting to measure clerical aptitudes. Ph.D., Ohio State Univ. (Thesis).

Bair, J. T. (1951), Factor analysis of clerical aptitude tests. *J. appl. Psychol.,* **35,** 245-249.

Baldwin, A. L. (1946), The study of individual personality by means of the intraindividual correlation. *J. Personality,* **14,** 151-168.

Balinsky, B. (1941), An analysis of the mental factors of various age groups from nine to sixty. *Genetic Psychol. Monogr.,* **23,** 191-234.

Banks, C. (1948a), Flying ability and body-build. *Brit. J. Psychol. Statist. Sect.,* **1,** 107-113.

Banks, C. (1948b), Primary personality factors in women; a re-analysis. *Brit. J. Psychol. Statist. Sect.,* **1,** 204-218.

Banks, C. (1949), Factor analysis of assessments for army recruits. *Brit. J. Psychol. Statist. Sect.,* **2,** 76-89.

Banks, C., and Keir, G. (1952), A factorial analysis of items in the Bernreuter Personality Inventory. *Brit. J. Psychol. Statist. Sect.,* **5,** 19-30.

Barakat, M. K. (1951), A factorial study of mathematical abilities. *Brit. J. Psychol. Statist. Sect.,* **4,** 137-156.

Barnes, C. A. (1952), A statistical study of the Freudian theory of levels of psychosexual development. *Genet. Psychol. Monogr.,* **45,** 105-174.

Baron, M., and Harper, R. (1950), The relation between the mechanical properties of Chesire cheese and graders' judgments. *Dairy Ind.,* **4,** 407-410.

Barratt, E. S. (1952), An analysis of verbal reports of solving spatial problems. Ph.D., Univ. of Texas (Thesis).

Bartlett, M. S. (1947), The general canonical correlation distribution. *Ann. Math. Stat.*, **18**, 1-17.

Bartlett, M. S. (1948a), Internal and external factor analysis. *Brit. J. Psychol. Statist. Sect.*, **1**, 73-81.

Bartlett, M. S. (1948b), The statistical conception of mental factors. *Brit. J. Psychol. Statist. Sect.*, **1**, 204-218.

Bartlett, M. S. (1950a), Tests of significance in factor analysis. *Brit. J. Psychol. Statist. Sect.*, **3**, 77-85.

Bartlett, M. S. (1950b), A further note on tests of significance in factor analysis. *Brit. J. Psychol. Statist. Sect.*, **4**, 1-2.

Baumgarten, F. (1952), Editor, *La psychotechnique dans le monde moderne.* Paris, Presses Universitaires de France, 630 pp.

Bechtoldt, D. C. (1949), An empirical study of the stability of a simple structure multiple factor solution. *Amer. Psychologist*, **4**, 352.

Bechtoldt, H. P. (1949), The use of geometrical concepts of multiple factor analysis in multiple correlation problems. *Amer. Psychologist*, **4**, 246 (Abstract).

Bendig, A. W. (1952), A Q-technique study of the professional interests of psychologists. *J. Psychol.*, **33**, 57-64.

Bennett, E. (1945), Some tests for the discrimination of neurotic from normal subjects. *Brit. J. med. Psychol.*, **20**, 271-277.

Bennett, G. K. (1950), Uses and limitations of factor analysis in psychological research. In *Proc. E.T.S. 1949 inv. conf. on testing probl.* Princeton: Educational Testing Service, 41-44.

Bernyer, G. A. (1945), Un essai d'analyse factorielle des aptitudes. *Année Psychol.*, 41-42, 202-226.

Bernyer, G. (1948), Distribution des facteurs psychologiques dans une population. *Année Psychol.*, **45-46**, 16-29.

Bjorsjo, M. (1951), *Om spatial teknisk och praktisk begåvning. Bidrag till en kvalitativ och kvantitativ analys.* Goteborg: Elanders Boktryckeri Aktiebolag, 268 pp.

Blackwell, A. M. (1940), A comprehensive investigation into the factors involved in mathematical ability of boys and girls. *Brit. J. educ. Psychol.*, **10**, 143-153, 212-222.

Blakey, R. I. (1940), A re-analysis of a test of the theory of two factors. *Psychometrika*, **5**, 121-136.

Blakey, R. I. (1941), A factor analysis of a nonverbal reasoning test. *Educ. psychol. Measmt.*, **1**, 180-198.

Blaisser, M. L. (1948), A factor analysis of personality traits in children from 4 to 7. M.A., Catholic U. America (Thesis).

Bock, R. D., and Husain, S. Z. (1952), Factors of the tele: A preliminary report. *Sociometry*, 15, 206-219.

Bolanovich, D. J. (1946), Statistical analysis of an industrial rating chart. *J. appl. Psychol.*, 30, 23-31.

Bonnardel, R. (1951), Evolution des liasons entre les réussites dans les diverses matières scolaires. *J. Psychol. norm. Path.*, 44, 438-471.

Bonnardel, R., Coumetou, M., Gervaise, R., and Grosjean, M. (1947), Étude comparative de tests géométriques et verbaux appliqués à divers groupes professionals et scolaires. *Travail hum.*, 10, 141-179.

Bordin, E. S. (1941), Factor analysis—art or science? *Psychol. Bull.*, 38, 520-521.

Bordin, E. S. (1943), Factor analysis in experimental designs in clinical and social psychology. *Psychol. Rev.*, 50, 415-429.

Botzum, W. A. (1951), A factorial study of the reasoning and closure factors. *Psychometrika*, 16, 361-386.

Brace, D. K. (1946), Studies in motor learning of gross bodily motor skills. *Res. Quart. Amer. Ass. Hlth.*, 17, 242-253.

Brannon, M. (1952), Essential steps in matrix multiplication by electronic digital calculators. In Cattell, R. B. (1952a). Appendix, 431-439.

Brody, A. B. (1951), A factorial study of intellectual functioning in normal and abnormal adults. *Microfilm Abstr.*, 11, 445-446 (Abstract of Ph.D. thesis, 1950, Columbia Univ.).

Brogden, H. E. (1944), A multiple-factor analysis of the character trait intercorrelations published by Sister Mary McDonough. *J. educ. Psychol.*, 35, 397-410.

Brogden, H. E. (1946), Variation in test validity with variation in the distribution of item difficulties, number of items, and degree of their correlation. *Psychometrika*, 11, 197-214.

Brogden, H. E., and Harman, H. H. (1948), An analysis of factors in physical proficiency. *Amer. Psychologist*, 3, 310 (Abstract).

Brogden, H. E., and Thomas, W. F. (1943), The primary traits in personality items purporting to measure sociability. *J. Psychol.*, 16, 85-97.

Brown, V. M. (1949), A factorial study of the Birkhoff figures. *Amer. Psychologist*, 4, 265-266 (Abstract).

Brown, W., and Stephenson, W. (1933), A test of the theory of two-factors. *Brit. J. Psychol.*, 23, 352-370.

Bryant, N. D., and Zachert, V. (1951), Factor analyses of the Airman Classification Battery with criteria for clerk-typist and radar-mechanic trade schools. *USAF Hum. Resour. Res. Cent. Res. Bull. 51-22*, 12 pp.

Buros, O. K. (1951), Editor, *Statistical methodology reviews, 1941-1950*. New York: John Wiley & Sons, x, 457 pp.

Burt, C. (1917), *The distribution and relations of educational abilities*. London: King, 93 pp.

Burt, C. L. (1937), Correlations between persons. *Brit. J. Psychol.*, **28**, 59-96.

Burt, C. (1938a), The unit hierarchy and its properties. *Psychometrika*, **3**, 151-168.

Burt, C. (1938b), Factor analysis by sub-matrices. *J. Psychol.*, **6**, 339-375.

Burt, C. (1941), *The factors of the mind; an introduction to factor analysis in psychology*. New York: Macmillan. xiv, 509 pp.

Burt, C. (1944a), Mental abilities and mental factors. *Brit. J. educ. Psychol.*, **14**, 85-94.

Burt, C. (1944b), Statistical problems in the evaluation of army tests. *Psychometrika*, **9**, 219-235.

Burt, C. (1946), The assessment of personality. *Egypt. J. Psychol.*, **2**, 1-21.

Burt, C. (1947a), A comparison of factor analysis and analysis of variance. *Brit. J. Psychol. Statist. Sect.*, **1**, 3-26.

Burt, C. (1947b), Factorial analysis and physical types. *Psychometrika*, **12**, 171-188.

Burt, C. (1947c), Critical notice of Thurstone's "multiple factorial analysis." *Brit. J. educ. Psychol.*, **17**, 140-152.

Burt, C. (1947d), Factor-analysis: its aims and chief results. In *Miscellanea Psychologica Albert Michotte*, 49-75.

Burt, C. (1948a), Factor analysis in psychological medicine. *Brit. med. Bull.*, **5**, 375-376.

Burt, C. (1948b), Factor analysis and canonical correlations. *Brit. J. Psychol. Statist. Sect.*, **1**, 95-106.

Burt, C. (1948c), The factorial study of temperamental traits. *Brit. J. Psychol. Statist. Sect.*, **1**, 178-203.

Burt, C. (1949a), Subdivided factors. *Brit. J. Psychol. Statist. Sect.*, **2**, 41-63.

Burt, C. (1949b), Alternative methods of factor analysis and their relations to Pearson's method of "principal axes." *Brit. J. Psychol. Statist. Sect.*, **2**, 98-121.

Burt, C. (1949c), The two-factor theory. *Brit. J. Psychol. Statist. Sect.*, **2**, 151-179.

Burt, C. (1949d), The structure of the mind; a review of the results of factor analysis. *Brit. J. educ. Psychol.*, **19**, 176-199.

Burt, C. (1950a), Group factor analysis. *Brit. J. Psychol. Statist. Sect.*, **3**, 40-75.

Burt, C. (1950b), The factorial analysis of qualitative data. *Brit. J. Psychol. Statist. Sect.*, **3**, 166-185.

Burt, C. (1950c), Symposium on the selection of pupils for different types of secondary schools: IX. conclusion. *Brit. J. educ. Psychol.*, **20**, 1-10.

Burt, C. (1950d), The factorial study of emotions. In Reyinert, M. L., Editor, *Feelings and emotions; the Mooseheart symposium.* New York: McGraw-Hill Book Co., 531-551.

Burt, C. (1951a), The aims and methods of factorial analysis. *Année Psychol.*, **50**, 39-59.

Burt, C. (1951b), The factorial study of the mind. In Ekman *et al.*, *Essays in psychology . . . David Katz*, 18-47.

Burt, C. (1952), Tests of significance in factor studies. *Brit. J. Psychol. Statist. Sect.*, **5**, 109-133.

Burt, C., and Banks, C. (1947), A factorial analysis of body measurements for British adult males. *Ann. Eugen., Camb.*, **13**, 238-256.

Burt, C., and Howard, M. (1952), The nature and causes of maladjustment among children of school age. *Brit. J. Psychol. Statist. Sect.*, **5**, 39-59.

Burt, C., and John, E. (1942), A factorial analysis of Terman-Binet tests. *Brit. J. educ. Psychol.*, **12**, 117-127, 156-161.

Burt, C., and Stephenson, W. (1939), Alternative views on correlations between persons. *Psychometrika*, **4**, 269-281.

Burt, C., and Watson, H. (1951), Factor analysis of assessments for a single person. *Brit. J. Psychol. Statist. Sect.*, **4**, 179-191.

Campbell, D. T., and McCandless, B. R. (1951), Ethnocentrism, xenophobia, and personality. *Hum. Relat.*, **4**, 185-192.

Carlson, H. B. (1937), Factor analysis of memory ability. *J. exp. Psychol.*, **21**, 477-492.

Carlson, H. B. (1945), A simple orthogonal multiple factor approximation procedure. *Psychometrika*, **10**, 283-301.

Carlson, H. B., and Harrell, W. (1942a), An analysis of *Life's* "ablest congressman" poll. *J. soc. Psychol.*, **15**, 153-158.

Carlson, H. B., and Harrell, W. (1942b), Voting groups among leading congressmen obtained by means of the inverted factor technique. *J. soc. Psychol.,* **16,** 51-61.

Carroll, J. B. (1941), A factor analysis of verbal abilities. *Psychometrika,* **6,** 279-308.

Carroll, J. B. (1943), The factorial representation of mental ability and academic achievement. *Educ. psychol. Measmt.,* **3,** 307-332.

Carroll, J. B. (1945), The effect of difficulty and chance success on correlations between items or between tests. *Psychometrika,* **10,** 1-19.

Carroll, J. B. (1950), Problems in the factor analysis of tests of varying difficulty. *Amer. Psychologist,* **5,** 369 (Abstract).

Carroll, J. B. (1952), Ratings on traits measured by a factored personality inventory. *J. Aborm. Soc. Psychol.,* **47,** 626-632.

Carroll, J. B. (1953), An analytical solution for approximating simple structure in factor analysis. *Psychometrika,* **18,** 23-38.

Carroll, J. B., and Schweiker, R. F. (1951), Factor analysis in educational research. *Rev. educ. Res.,* **21,** 368-388.

Carter, G. C. (1951), A factor analysis of student personality traits. *J. educ. Res.,* **44,** 381-385.

Carter, L. F. (1951), Some research on leadership in small groups. (In Guetzkow, H., Editor, *Groups, leadership and men; research in human relations.* Pittsburgh. Carnegie Press), 146-157.

Carter, L. F., and Dudek, F. J. (1947), The use of psychological techniques in measuring and critically analyzing navigators' flight performance. *Psychometrika,* **12,** 31-42.

Cattell, R. B. (1944a), A note on correlation clusters and cluster search methods. *Psychometrika,* **9,** 169-184.

Cattell, R. B. (1944b), Psychological measurement: normative, ipsative, interactive. *Psychol. Rev.,* **51,** 292-303.

Cattell, R. B. (1944c), "Parallel proportional profiles" and other principles for determining the choice of factors by rotation. *Psychometrika,* **9,** 267-283.

Cattell, R. B. (1945a), The principal trait clusters for describing personality. *Psychol. Bull.,* **42,** 129-161.

Cattell, R. B. (1945b), The diagnosis and classification of neurotic states: a re-interpretation of Eysenck's factors. *J. nerv. ment. Dis.,* **102,** 576-589.

Cattell, R. B. (1946a), Personality structure and measurement. I. The operational determination of trait unities. *Brit. J. Psychol.,* **36,** 88-103.

Cattell, R. B. (1946b), Personality structure and measurement. II. The determination and utility of trait modality. *Brit. J. Psychol.,* **36,** 159-174.

Cattell, R. B. (1946c), *Description and measurement of personality.* Yonkers, N. Y.: World Book Co. 602 pp.

Cattell, R. B. (1946d), Simple structure in relation to some alternative factorizations of the personality sphere. *J. gen. Psychol.,* **35,** 225-238.

Cattell, R. B. (1947a), Oblique, second order, and cooperative factors in personality analysis. *J. gen. Psychol.,* **36,** 3-22.

Cattell, R. B. (1947b), Confirmation and classification of primary personality factors. *Psychometrika,* **12,** 197-220.

Cattell, R. B. (1948a), Concepts and methods in the measurement of group syntality. *Psychol. Rev.,* **55,** 48-63.

Cattell, R. B. (1948b), Personality factors in women. *Brit. J. Psychol. Statist. Sect.,* **1,** 102-120.

Cattell, R. B. (1948c), The integration of factor analysis with psychology; a reply to Professor Godfrey Thomson's review of "The description and measurement of personality." *J. educ. Psychol.,* **39,** 227-236.

Cattell, R. B. (1948d), Primary personality factors in the realm of objective tests. *J. Personality,* **16,** 459-487.

Cattell, R. B. (1949a), r_p and other coefficients of pattern similarity. *Psychometrika,* **14,** 279-298.

Cattell, R. B. (1949b), The dimensions of culture patterns by factorization of national characters. *J. abnorm. soc. Psychol.,* **44,** 443-469.

Cattell, R. B. (1949c), A note on factor invariance and the identification of factors. *Brit. J. Psychol. Statist. Sect.,* **2,** 134-139.

Cattell, R. B. (1950a), *Personality: a systematic, theoretical and factual study.* New York: McGraw-Hill Book Co. 689 pp.

Cattell, R. B. (1950b), The discovery of ergic structure in man in terms of common attitudes. *J. abnor. soc. Psychol.,* **45,** 598-618.

Cattell, R. B. (1950c), The principal culture patterns discoverable in the syntal dimensions of existing nations. *J. soc. Psychol.,* **32,** 215-253.

Cattell, R. B. (1950d), The main personality factors in questionnaire, self-estimate material. *J. soc. Psychol.,* **31,** 3-38.

Cattell, R. B. (1951a), On the disuse and misuse of P, Q, Qs, and O techniques in clinical psychology. *J. clin. Psychol.,* **7,** 203-214.

Cattell, R. B. (1951b), P-technique, a new method for analyzing the structure of personal motivation. *Trans. N. Y. Acad. Sci.,* **14,** 29-34.

Cattell, R. B. (1951c), A factorization of tests of personality source traits. *Brit. J. Psychol. Statist. Sect.*, 4, 165-178.

Cattell, R. B. (1952a), *Factor analysis: an introduction and manual for the psychologist and social scientist.* New York: Harper & Bros. xiii, 462 pp.

Cattell, R. B. (1952b), The three basic factor-analytic research designs —their interrelations and derivatives. *Psychol. Bull.*, 49, 499-520.

Cattell, R. B. (1952c), P-technique factorization and the determination of individual dynamic structure. *J. Clin. Psychol.*, 8, 5-10.

Cattell, R. B. (1952d), P-technique factorization. In Brower and Abt, *Progress in clinical psychology*, 536-544.

Cattell, R. B. (in press), The psychological dimensions of social progress in Britain, determined by P-technique, 1835-1935. *Hum. Relat.*

Cattell, R. B., and Adelson, M. (1951), The dimensions of social change in the U. S. A. as determined by P-technique. *Social Forces*, 30, 190-201.

Cattell, R. B., Breul, H., and Hartman, H. P. (1952), An attempt at more refined definition of the cultural dimensions of syntality in modern nations. *Amer. Sociol. Rev.*, 17, 408-421.

Cattell, R. B., Cattell, A. K. S., and Rhymer, R. M. (1947), P-technique demonstrated in determining psycho-physiological source traits in normal individuals. *Psychometrika*, 12, 267-288.

Cattell, R. B., and Luborsky, L. (1950), P-technique demonstrated as a new clinical method for determining personality and symptom structure. *J. gen. Psychol.*, 31, 243-260.

Cattell, R. B., and Miller, A. (1952), A confirmation of the ergic and self-sentiment patterns among dynamic traits (attitude variables by R-technique). *Brit. J. Psychol.*, 43, 280-294.

Cattell, R. B., and Saunders, D. R. (1950), Inter-relation and matching of personality factors from behavior rating, questionnaire, and objective test data. *J. soc. Psychol.*, 31, 243-260.

Cattell, R. B., and Tiner, L. G. (1949), The varieties of structural rigidity. *J. Personality*, 17, 321-341.

Cattell, R. B., and Wenig, P. W. (1952), Dynamic and cognitive factors controlling misperception. *J. abn. soc. Psychol.*, 47, 797-809.

Cattell, R. B., and Winder, A. P. (in press), Structural rigidity in relation to learning theory and clinical psychology. *Psychol. Rev.*

Cattell, R. B., and Wispe, L. G. (1948), The dimensions of syntality in small groups. *J. soc. Psychol.*, 28, 57-78.

Chapman, R. L. (1948), The MacQuarrie test for mechanical ability. *Psychometrika*, 13, 175-179.

Chen, T. L., and Chow, H. (1948), A factor study of a test battery at different educational levels. *J. genet. Psychol.*, **73**, 187-199.

Clark, M. P. (1944), Changes in primary mental abilities with age. *Arch. Psychol.*, No. 291. 30 pp.

Coffman, W. E. (1949), Teacher morale and curriculum development: a statistical analysis of responses to a reaction inventory. Thesis, Teacher Coll., Columbia Univ.

Cohen, J. (1949), Color vision and factor analysis. *Psychol. Rev.*, **56**, 224-233.

Cohen, J. (1950), A comparative analysis of factors underlying intelligence test performance of different neuropsychiatric groups. *Microfilm Abstr.*, **10**, 313-315 (Abstract of Ph.D. thesis, N.Y.U.).

Comrey, A. L. (1949), A factorial study of achievement in West Point courses. *Educ. psychol. Measmt.*, **9**, 193-209.

Cook, E. B. (1948), A factor analysis of acuity and phoria measurements obtained with commercial screening devices and by standard clinical methods. New London, Conn.: Naval Medical Research Laboratory. (*Progr. Rep., No. 4*, Project NM-003-011 (X0493).) 26 pp.

Cook, E. B., and Wherry, R. J. (1949), A study of the interrelationships of psychological and physiological measures on submarine enlisted candidates: I. History, experimental design, and statistical treatment of data. New London, Conn.: Naval Medical Research Laboratory. (*Rep. No. 1*, Project NM-003-017.) 45 pp.

Cook, E. B., and Wherry, R. J. (1950), A factor analysis of MMPI and aptitude test data. *J. appl. Psychol.*, **34**, 260-266

Coombs, C. H. (1941a), A factorial study of number ability. *Psychometrika*, **6**, 161-189.

Coombs, C. H. (1941b), A criterion for significant common factor variance. *Psychometrika*, **6**, 267-272.

Coombs, C. H. (1942), A factor analytical approach to job families. *Psychol. Bull.*, **39**, 452.

Coombs, C. H., and Satter, G. A. (1949), A factorial approach to job families. *Psychometrika*, **14**, 33-42.

Copeland, H. A. (1935), A note on the vectors of mind. *Psychol. Rev.*, **42**, 216-218.

Corter, H. M. (1950), A factor analysis of some individually-administered reasoning tests. *Penn. State Coll. Abstr. Doctoral Dissertations, 1949*, **12**, 325-329.

Cottle, W. C. (1948), A factorial study of selected instruments for measuring personality and interest. *Amer. Psychologist*, **3**, 300 (Abstract).

Cottle, W. C. (1950a), A factorial study of the Multiphasic, Strong, Kuder, and Bell Inventories using a population of adult males. *Psychometrika*, **15**, 25-47.

Cottle, W. C. (1950b), A note on Thurstone's method of computing the inverse of a matrix. *Educ. psychol. Measmt.*, **10**, 134-136.

Counts, S. (1952), Achievement in college mathematics as a function of instructors' and students' patterns of primary mental abilities. Ph.D. thesis, Univ. of Chicago.

Cox, J. A., Jr. (1951), A factor analysis of Airman Classification Battery test scores for Airplane Sheetmetal Worker technical school graduates. *H.R.R.C. Research Note Pers.* 51-23.

Cox, S. M. (1951), A factorial study of the Rorschach responses of normal and maladjusted boys. *J. genet. Psychol.*, **79**, 95-115.

Crissey, W. J. E., and Daniel, W. J. (1939), Vocational interest factors in women. *J. appl. Psychol.*, **23**, 488-494.

Cronbach, L. J. (1953), Correlations between persons as a research tool. In O. H. Mowrer *et al.* (1953), 376-388.

Cross, P. (1951), Comparison of P- and R-technique determinations of ergic structure in common attitudes. Unpublished M.A. thesis, Univ. of Illinois.

Cureton, E. E. (1939), The principal compulsions of factor-analysts. *Harv. educ. Rev.*, **9**, 287-295.

Cureton, E. E. (1947), The verbal relations factor and vocabulary. *Amer. Psychologist*, **2**, 286-287 (Abstract).

Curtin, J. T. (1951), *A factor analysis of verbal and non-verbal tests of intelligence.* Washington: Catholic Univ. of America, 63 pp.

Curtis, H. A. (Aug. 1949), A study of the relative effects of age and of test difficulty upon factor patterns. *Genet. Psychol. Monogr.*, **40**, 99-148.

Dailey, J. T. (1952), The supply and identification of high level talent. In *Proc. E.T.S. 1951 inv. Conf. on testing probl.* Princeton: Educational Testing Service, 17-23.

Dailey, J. G., and McNamara, W. T. (1940), Factor analysis in the establishment of new personality tests. *J. educ. Psychol.*, **31**, 321-334.

Darmois, M. G. (1949), *L'analyse des corrélations.* Paris: Université de Paris, 20 pp.

Davenport, K. S., and Remmers, H. H. (1950), Factors in state characteristics related to average A-12 V-12 test scores. *J. educ. Psychol.*, **41**, 110-115.

Davidson, W. M., and Carroll, J. B. (1945), Speed and level components in time-limit scores: a factor analysis. *Educ. psychol. Measmt.,* 5, 411-427.

Davis, F. B. (1944), Fundamental factors of comprehension in reading. *Psychometrika,* 9, 185-197.

Davis, F. B. (1946a), A brief comment on Thurstone's note on a re-analysis of Davis' Reading Tests. *Psychometrika,* 11, 249-255.

Davis, F. B. (1946b), The factorial composition of two tests of comprehension in reading. *J. educ. Psychol.,* 37, 481-486.

Davis, F. B. (1947a), *The A.A.F. qualifying examination.* Army Air Forces Aviat. Psychol. Prog. Res. Rep., No. 6. Washington, D. C.: U. S. Government Printing Office. 266 pp.

Davis, F. B. (1947b), The interpretation of principal-axis factors. *J. educ. Psychol.,* 38, 471-481.

Davis, F. B. (1948), An analytical study of reasoning among high-school boys. *Amer. Psychologist,* 3, 257 (Abstract).

Dean, D. A. (1951), A factor analysis of the Stanford-Binet and SRA primary abilities battery at the first grade level. In *Penn. State Coll. Abstr. Doctoral Dissertations, 1950,* 13, 394-397 (Abstract).

Deemer, W. L. (1947), Editor, *Records, analysis, and test procedures.* Washington: U. S. Government Printing Office, 1947.

Delaporte, P. (1945), Vérification de l'efficacité d'une methode d'analyse factorielle. *C. R. Acad. Sci. Paris,* 220, 212-214.

Delaporte, P. (1946), Sur l'estimation des corrélations des charactères avec le facteur général et les facteur de groupe et sur l'écarte-type de cette estimation, en l'analyse factorielle. *C. R. Acad. Sci. Paris,* 222, 525-526.

Diaz-Milano, E. (1941), Toward a mathematical theory of aptitudes. (Spanish.) *An. Psicotec., Rosario,* 1, 5-18.

Dickenson, H. F. (1941), Factor analysis of oral group rational learning ability. *Psychol. Bull.,* 38, 692.

Directorate of Personnel Selection (Army) (1944), A factorial analysis of revised Examination M. *Bull. Canad. Psychol. Ass.,* 4, 18-22.

Dixon, A. L. (1952), The estimations of communalities, *Brit. J. Psychol. Statist. Sect.,* 5, 59. (Correspondence and reply by C. Burt.)

Doppelt, J. E. (1950), *The organization of mental abilities in the age range 13 to 17.* Contributions to Education, No. 962. New York: Teachers College, Columbia University. 86 pp.

Drew, L. J. (1947), An investigation into the measurement of technical ability. *Occup. Psychol., Lond.,* 21, 34-38.

Driscoll, Justin A. (1952), *Factors in intelligence and achievement.* Washington, D. C., The Catholic University of America Press, 56 pp.

Dubin, S. S. (1950), A factorial analysis of personality traits in 100 psychopathological subjects. *Microfilm Abstr.,* **10,** 315-316.

Du Bois, P. H., Loevinger, J., and Gleser, G. C. (1952), The construction of homogenous keys for a biographical inventory. *H.R.R.C. Research Report* 52-18.

Dudek, F. J. (1948), The dependence of factorial composition of aptitude tests upon population differences among pilot trainees. I. The isolation of factors. *Educ. psychol. Measmt.,* **8,** 613-633.

Dudek, F. J. (1949), The dependence of factorial composition of aptitude tests upon population differences among pilot trainees. II. The factorial composition of test and criterion variables. *Educ. psychol. Measmt.,* **9,** 95-104.

Dudek, F. J., and Seashore, R. H. (1948), Factorial analysis of arm-hand precision tests. *Amer. Psychologist,* **3,** 252 (Abstract).

Duffy, E. (1940), Evaluative attitudes as related to vocational interests and academic achievement. *J. abn. & soc. Psychol.,* **35,** 226-245.

Duffy, E. (1946), Level of muscular tension as an aspect of personality. *J. gen. Psychol.,* **35,** 161-171.

Dvorak, B. J. (1947), The new United States Employment Service general aptitude test battery. *J. appl. Psychol.,* **31,** 372-376.

Dwyer, P. S. (1937), The determination of the factor loadings of a given test from the known factor loadings of other tests. *Psychometrika,* **2,** 173-178.

Dwyer, P. S. (1939), The contribution of an orthogonal multiple-factor solution to multiple correlation. *Psychometrika,* **4,** 163-171.

Dwyer, P. S. (1940), The evaluation of multiple and partial correlation coefficients from the factorial matrix. *Psychometrika,* **5,** 211-232.

Dwyer, P. S. (1951), *Linear computations.* New York: John Wiley & Sons, Inc.

Eberman, P. (1951), The application of Q-technique to one aspect of teaching competency. Unpublished Ph.D. thesis. Univ. of Chicago.

Emmett, W. G. (1949a), Evidence of a space factor at 11+ and earlier. *Brit. J. Psychol. Statist. Sect.,* **2,** 3-16.

Emmett, W. G. (1949b), Factor analysis by Lawley's method of maximum likelihood. *Brit. J. Psychol. Statist. Sect.,* **2,** 90-97.

English, H. B. (1948), Factor analysis explained (without mathematics). *Egypt. J. Psychol.,* **3,** 475-484.

Ewart, E., Seashore, S. E., and Tiffin, J. (1941), A factor analysis of an industrial merit rating scale. *J. appl. Psychol.*, **25**, 481-486.

Ewers, D. W. F. (1950), Relations between abilities and reading abilities: a problem in psychometrics. *J. exp. Educ.*, **18**, 239-262.

Eysenck, H. J. (1940a), The general factor in aesthetic judgments. *Brit. J. Psychol.*, **31**, 94-102.

Eysenck, H. J. (1940b), Some factors in the appreciation of poetry and their relations to temperamental qualities. *Character and Personality*, **9**, 160-167.

Eysenck, H. J. (1941), A critical and experimental study of colour preferences. *Amer. J. Psychol.*, **54**, 385-394.

Eysenck, H. J. (1942), The appreciation of humor: an experimental and theoretical study. *Brit. J. Psychol.*, **32**, 295-309.

Eysenck, H. J. (1943), An experimental analysis of five tests of "appreciation of humor." *Educ. psychol. Measmt.*, **3**, 191-214.

Eysenck, H. J. (1944), Types of personality: a factorial study of seven hundred neurotics. *J. ment. Sci.*, **90**, 851-861.

Eysenck, H. J. (1947a), Primary social attitudes. 1. The organization and measurement of social attitudes. *Int. J. Opin. Attitude Res.*, **1**, 49-84.

Eysenck, H. J. (1949), *Dimensions of personality*. New York: The Macmillan Co. 308 pp.

Eysenck, H. J. (1950a), Criterion analysis—an application of the hypothetico-deductive method to factor analysis. *Psychol. Rev.*, **57**, 38-53.

Eysenck, H. J. (1950b), Uses and limitations of factor analysis in psychological research. In *Proc. E.T.S. 1949 inv. conf. on testing probl.* Princeton: Educational Testing Service, 45-49.

Eysenck, H. J. (1951), Measurement and prediction; a discussion of Volume IV of studies in social psychology in World War II. *Int. J. Opin. Attitude Res.*, **5**, 95-102.

Eysenck, H. J. (1952a), *The scientific study of personality*. London: Routledge and Kegan Paul, 320 pp.

Eysenck, H. J. (1952b), The uses and abuses of factor analysis. *Appl. Statist.*, **1**, 45-49.

Eysenck, H. J. (1952c), The organization of personality. In Krech and Klein, *Theoretical models and personality theory*, 101-117.

Eysenck, H. J. (1952c), Schizothymia-cyclothymia as a dimension of personality: II. Experimental. *J. Personality*, **20**, 345-384.

Eysenck, H. J. (1953a), The logical basis of factor analysis. *Amer. Psychologist*, **8**, 105-114.

Eysenck, H. J. (1953b), *The structure of human personality.* London: Methuen.

Eysenck, H. J., and Crown, S. (1948), National stereotypes: an experimental and methodological study. *Int. J. Opin. Attitude Res.,* 2 (1), 26-39.

Eysenck, H. J., and Furneaux, W. D. (1945), Primary and secondary suggestibility: an experimental and statistical study. *J. exp. Psychol.,* 35, 485-503.

Eysenck, H. J., and Halstead, H. (1945), The memory function. I. A factorial study of fifteen clinical tests. *Amer. J. Psychiat.,* 102, 174-179.

Eysenck, M. D. (1944), An experimental and statistical study of olfactory preferences. *J. exp. Psychol.,* 39, 246-252.

Eysenck, M. D. (1945), An exploratory study of mental organization in senility. *J. Neurol. Neurosurg. & Psychiat.,* 8, 15-21.

Ferguson, G. A. (1940), A bi-factor analysis of reliability coefficients. *Brit. J. Psychol.,* 31, 172-182.

Ferguson, G. A. (1941), The factorial interpretation of test difficulty. *Psychometrika,* 6, 323-329.

Ferguson, L. W., Humphreys, L. G., and Strong, F. W. (1941), A factorial analysis of interests and values. *J. educ. Psychol.,* 32, 197-204.

Ferguson, L. W., and Lawrence, W. R. (1942), An appraisal of the validity of the factor loadings employed in the construction of the primary social attitude scales. *Psychometrika,* 7, 135-138.

Fiedler, F. E. (1951), Factor analyses of psychoanalytic, nondirective, and Adlerian therapeutic relationships. *J. consult. Psychol.,* 15, 32-38.

Findley, W. G., and Andregg, N. B. (1949), A statistical critique of the USAFI tests of general educational development. *Psychometrika,* 14, 47-60.

Fiske, D. W. (1949), Consistency of the factorial structures in personality ratings from different sources. *J. abnorm. soc. Psychol.,* 44, 329-344.

Fix, E. (1950), Discriminatory analysis: II. Factor analysis and discrimination. *USAF Sch. Aviation Med. Project Report,* Proj. No. 21-49-004, Report No. 2. 82 pp.

Fleishman, E. A. (1953), A factor analysis of intra-task performance on two psychomotor tests. *Psychometrika,* 18, 45-56.

Flemming, E. G. (1942), The "halo" around "personality." *Teach. Coll. Rec.,* 43, 564-569.

Flood, M. M. (1940), A computational procedure for the method of principal components. *Psychometrika,* **5,** 169-172.

Ford, C. F., and Tyler, L. E. (1952), A factor analysis of Terman and Miles' M-F test. *J. appl. Psychol.,* **36,** 251-253.

Ford, R. N., and Henderson, D. E. V. (1942), A multiple factor analysis of Ford's White-Negro experience scales. *Social Forces,* **21,** 28-34.

Franzen, R. (1950), Scaling responses to graded opportunities. *Publ. Opin. Quart.,* **14,** 484-490.

Frawley, P. J. (1948), A study of judgment; a factorial analysis of the anchoring effects. *Stud. Psychol. Psychiat. Cathol. Univ. Amer.,* **7,** viii, 132 pp.

Freeman, G. L., and Katzoff, E. T. (1942), Individual differences in physiological reactions to stimulation and their relation to other measures of emotionality. *J. exp. Psychol.,* **31,** 527-537.

French, J. W. (1950), What is factor analysis? *Coll. Bd. Rev.,* **10,** 129-131.

French, J. W. (1951), The description of aptitude and achievement tests in terms of rotated factors. *Psychometric Monogr.* No. 5, Univ. of Chicago. 278 pp.

French, J. W. (1952), Editor, *Conference on factorial studies of aptitude and personality measures.* Princeton: Educational Testing Service, 33 pp.

French, J. W. (1953a), *The description of personality measurements in terms of rotated factors.* Princeton: Educational Testing Service.

French, J. W. (1953b), A rejoinder to Zimmerman's note. *Psych. Bull.,* **50,** 390.

French, J. W., Tucker, L. R., Newman, S. H., and Bobbitt, J. M. (1952), A factor analysis of aptitude and achievement entrance tests and course grades at the U. S. Coast Guard Academy. *J. educ. Psychol.,* **43,** 65-80.

Friedman, S. T. (1941), A factor analysis of a stenographic proficiency battery. *Psychol. Bull.,* **38,** 567.

Fruchter, B. (1948a), The nature of verbal fluency. *Educ. psychol. Measmt.,* **8,** 35-47.

Fruchter, B. (1948b), Factorial content of right-response and wrong-response scores in a battery of experimental aptitude tests. In *Univ. of So. Calif., Abstracts of Dissertations . . . 1948.* L. A., Calif. 170-173.

Fruchter, B. (1949a), The factorial approach to personality traits. *Texas Personnel Rev.,* **7,** 180-182.

Fruchter, B. (1949b), The factorial content of the Airman Classification Test battery. *Air Training Command Res. Bull. 49-1.* 37 pp.

Fruchter, B. (1949c), Effect of various weighting of wrong responses on the factorial content of speeded tests. *Amer. Psychologist,* 4, 306 (Abstract).

Fruchter, B. (1949d), Note on the computation of the inverse of a triangular matrix. *Psychometrika,* 14, 89-93.

Fruchter, B. (1950b), Error scores as a measure of carefulness. *J. educ. Psychol.,* 41, 279-291.

Fruchter, B. (1952a), Orthogonal and oblique solutions to a battery of aptitude, achievement, and background variables. *Educ. psychol. Measmt.,* 12, 20-38.

Fruchter, B. (1952b), Ability patterns in technical training criteria. *J. appl. Psychol.,* 36, 381-384.

Fruchter, B. (1953), Differences in factor content of rights and wrongs scores. *Psychometrika,* 18, 257-266.

Fruchter, B., and Mahan, W. W. (1952), Some perceptual factors measured by motion picture tests. *J. educ. Psychol.,* 43, 430-435.

Furneaux, W. D. (1948), Some factors affecting the design of 'g' with particular reference to the relation of 'speed' and 'power.' *Proc. Twelfth Intern. Congr. Psychol.,* Edinburgh.

Furst, E. J. (1950), Effect of the organization of learning experiences upon the organization of learning outcomes: II. Study of the problem by means of factor analysis. *J. exp. Educ.,* 18, 343-352.

Gage, N. L. (1948), Scaling and factorial design in opinion poll analysis. *Amer. Psychologist,* 3, 362 (Abstract).

Galvin, J. P. (1950), *A comparative study of personality patterns in boys of different ages.* Washington: Catholic University of America Press. 47 pp.

Garrett, H. E. (1946), A developmental theory of intelligence. *Amer. Psychologist,* 1, 372-378.

Geist, H. (1952), A comparison of personality test scores and medical psychiatric diagnosis by the inverted factor technique. *J. clin. Psychol.,* 8, 184-188.

Gengerelli, J. A. (1948), A binomial method for analyzing psychological functions. *Psychometrika,* 13, 69-77.

Gengerelli, J. A. (1952), A method of factor analysis in which the factors are empirical tests. *J. Psychol.,* 33, 159-174.

Gewirtz, J. L. (1948), Studies in word fluency. *J. genet. Psychol.,* 72, 165-184.

Gibbs, C. A. (1942), Personality traits by factor analysis (I). *Aust. J. Psychol. Phil.,* **20,** 1-15, 203-227.

Gibson, W. A. (1950), A new rotational approach in multiple-factor analysis. *Amer. Psychologist,* **5,** 372-373 (Abstract).

Gibson, W. A. (1952), Orthogonal and oblique simple structure. *Psychometrika,* **17,** 317-324.

Girault, M. (1948), Sur la notion de facteur commun en analyse factorielle générale. *C. R. Acad. Sci. Paris,* **227,** 499-500.

Goldman, F. (1948), Breastfeeding and character-formation. *J. Personality,* **17,** 83-103.

Goldman-Eisler, F. (1951), The problem of "orality" and of its origin in early childhood. *J. Ment. Sci.,* **97,** 765-782.

Goodman, C. H. (1943a), A factorial analysis of Thurstone's seven primary abilities. *Psychometrika,* **8,** 121-129.

Goodman, C. H. (1943b), A factorial analysis of Thurstone's sixteen primary mental abilities tests. *Psychometrika,* **8,** 141-151.

Goodman, C. H. (1944), Prediction of college success by means of Thurstone's primary abilities tests. *Educ. psychol. Measmt.,* **4,** 125-140.

Goodman, C. H. (1947), The MacQuarrie test for mechanical ability. II. Factor analysis. *J. appl. Psychol.,* **31,** 150-154.

Goodman, V. (1940), Factor analysis of twenty personality items. *Penn. St. Coll. Stud. Educ.,* No. 22, 23-24.

Gordon, L. V. (1950), A comparison of the validities of the forced-choice and questionnaire methods in personality measurement. Thesis, Ohio State Univ.

Gordon, M. A. (1952), Orthogonal and oblique rotations of axes, Airman Classification and selected tests from the 1949 Normative Survey. *H.R.R.C. Research Note Pers.* 52-28.

Gordon, O. J. (1952), A factor analysis of human needs and industrial morale. Thesis, Univ. of Utah.

Gourlay, N. (1951), Difficulty factors arising from the use of tetrachoric correlations in factor analysis. *Brit. J. Psychol. Statist. Sect.,* **4,** 65-76.

Grace, H. A. (1951), The geo-ethnic preference inventory: world cultures and autistic thinking. *J. educ. Psychol.,* **42,** 206-214.

Green, B. F. (1952a), The orthogonal approximation of an oblique structure in factor analysis. *Psychometrika,* **17,** 429-440.

Green, B. F. (1952b), Latent structure analysis and its relation to factor analysis. *J. Amer. statist. Ass.,* **47,** 71-76.

Greenal, P. D. (1948), Two criticisms. *Brit. J. Psychol. Statist. Sect.*, **1**, 64.

Greene, E. B. (1943), An analysis of random and systematic changes with practice. *Psychometrika,* **8**, 37-52.

Guertin, W. H. (1951), A factor analysis of some Szondi pictures. *J. clin. Psychol.*, **7**, 232-235.

Guertin, W. H. (1952a), A factor-analytic study of schizophrenic symptoms. *J. consult. Psychol.*, **16**, 308-312.

Guertin, W. H. (1952b), A factor analysis of the Bender-Gestalt tests of mental patients. *J. Clin. Psychol.*, **8**, 362-367.

Guilford, J. P. (1936), *Psychometric Methods.* New York: McGraw-Hill Book Co. xvi, 566 pp.

Guilford, J. P. (1940), Human abilities. *Psychol. Rev.*, **47**, 367-394.

Guilford, J. P. (1941a), The difficulty of a test and its factor composition. *Psychometrika*, **6**, 67-77.

Guilford, J. P. (1941b), A note on the discovery of a G-factor by means of Thurstone's centroid method of analysis. *Psychometrika*, **6**, 205-208.

Guilford, J. P. (1946), New standards for test evaluation. *Educ. psychol. Measmt.*, **6**, 427-438.

Guilford, J. P. (1947a), The discovery of aptitude and achievement variables. *Science,* **106**, 279-282.

Guilford, J. P. (1947b), Editor, *Printed Classification Tests.* Army Air Forces Aviat. Psychol. Prog. Res. Rep., No. 5. Washington, D. C.: U. S. Government Printing Office. xi, 919 pp.

Guilford, J. P. (1948a), Some lessons from aviation psychology. *Amer. Psychologist,* **3**, 3-11.

Guilford, J. P. (1948b), Factor analysis in a test development program. *Psychol. Rev.*, **55**, 79-94.

Guilford, J. P. (1950), Creativity. *Amer. Psychologist,* **5**, 444-454.

Guilford, J. P. (1952a), When not to factor analyze. *Psychol. Bull.*, **49**, 26-37.

Guilford, J. P. (1952b), Progrès récents dans la mesure des aptitudes. *Rev. Psychol Appl.,* **2**, 95 100.

Guilford, J. P. (1952c), Some recent findings on thinking abilities and their implications. *Inform. Bull., Train. Anal. Developm.,* **3**, 48-61.

Guilford, J. P., Fruchter, B., and Zimmerman, W. S. (1952), Factor analysis of the Army Air Forces Sheppard Field Battery of experimental aptitude tests. *Psychometrika*, **17**, 45-68.

Guilford, J. P., Green, R. F., and Christensen, P. R. (1951), A factor-analytic study of reasoning abilities. II. Administration of tests and analysis of results. *Reports from the Psychol. Lab., Univ. of So. Calif.* No. 3. 28 pp.

Guilford, J. P., and Holley, J. W. (1949), A factorial approach to the analysis of variances in esthetic judgments. *J. exp. Psychol.,* **39,** 208-218.

Guilford, J. P., and Michael, W. B. (1948), Approaches to univocal factor scores. *Psychometrika,* 13, 1-22.

Guilford, J. P., and Michael, W. B. (1950), Changes in common-factor loadings as tests are altered homogeneously in length. *Psychometrika,* 15, 237-251.

Guilford, J. P., and Zimmerman, W. S. (1947), Some AAF findings concerning aptitude scores. *Occupations,* 26, 154-159.

Guilford, J. P., and Zimmerman, W. S. (1948), The Guilford-Zimmerman aptitude survey. *J. appl. Psychol.,* 32, 24-34.

Guilford, J. P., *et al.* (1950), A factor-analytic study of reasoning abilities. I. Hypotheses and description of tests. *Reports from the Psychol. Lab., Univ. of So. Calif.* No. 1. 23 pp.

Guilford, J. P., *et al.* (1951), A factor-analytic study of creative thinking. I. Hypotheses and description of tests. *Reports from the Psychol. Lab., Univ. of So. Calif.* No. 4. 27 pp.

Guilford, J. P., *et al.* (1952a), A factor-analytic study of Navy Reasoning Tests with the Air Force Aircrew Classification Battery. *Reports from the Psychol. Lab., Univ. of So. Calif.* No. 6. 23 pp.

Guilford, J. P., *et al.* (1952b), A factor-analytic study of evaluative abilities. I. Hypotheses and description of tests. *Reports from the Psychol. Lab., Univ. of So. Calif.* No. 7. 19 pp.

Guilford, J. P., *et al.* (1952c), A factor-analytic study of creative thinking. II. Administration of tests and analysis of results. *Reports from the Psychol. Lab., Univ. of So. Calif.* No. 8. 24 pp.

Gulliksen, H. (1950), Intrinsic validity. *Amer. Psychologist,* 5, 511-517.

Gulliksen, H., and Tucker, L. R. (1951), A mechanical model illustrating the scatter diagram with oblique test vectors. *Psychometrika* 16, 233-238.

Gunn, D. G. (1951), Factors in the appreciation of poetry. *Brit. J. educ. Psychol.,* 21, 96-104.

Guttman, L. (1940), Multiple rectilinear prediction and the resolution into components. *Psychometrika,* 5, 75-99.

Guttman, L. (1944), General theory and methods for matric factoring. *Psychometrika,* 9, 1-16.

Guttman, L. (1951), Measurement and prediction; a discussion of Volume IV of studies in social psychology in World War II: II. Scale analysis, factor analysis, and Dr. Eysenck. *Int. J. Opin. Attitude Res.,* **5,** 103-120.

Guttman, L. (1952), Multiple group methods for common-factor analysis: their basis, computation, and interpretation. *Psychometrika,* **17,** 209-222.

Guttman, L. (1954), A new approach to factor analysis: radex. (In P. F. Lazarsfeld, Editor, *Mathematical Thinking in the Social Sciences,* Chapter 6. Glencoe, Ill.: Free Press.

Guttman, L., and Cohen, J. (1943), Multiple rectilinear prediction and the resolution into components: II. *Psychometrika,* **8,** 169-183.

Hall, D. M., Welker, E. L., and Crawford, I. (1945), Factor analysis calculations by tabulating machines. *Psychometrika,* **10,** 93-125.

Hall, D. M., and Wittenborn, J. R. (1942), Motor fitness tests for farm boys. *Res. Quart. Amer. Ass. Hlth.,* **13,** 432-443.

Hall, W. E., and Robinson, F. P. (1945), An analytical approach to the study of reading skills. *J. educ. Psychol.,* **20,** 429-442.

Halstead, W. C. (1945), A power factor (P) in general intelligence: the effect of brain injuries. *J. Psychol.,* **20,** 57-64.

Halstead, W. C. (1947), *Brain and intelligence; a quantitative study of the frontal lobes.* Chicago: Univ. of Chicago Press. 206 pp.

Hamilton, M. (1952), An iterative method for computing inverse matrices. *Brit. J. Psychol. Statist. Sect.,* **5,** 181-188.

Hammond, W. H. (1942), An application of Burt's multiple general factor analysis of the delineation of physical types. *Man,* **42,** 4-11.

Hammond, W. H. (1946), Factor analysis as applied to social and economic data. *Brit. J. educ. Psychol.,* **16,** 178 (Abstract of Ph.D. thesis; Univ. of Lond.).

Hampton, N. D. (1951), An analysis of supervisory ratings of elementary teachers graduated from Iowa State Teachers College. *J. exp. Educ.,* **20,** 179-215.

Harman, H. H. (1941), On the rectilinear prediction of oblique factors. *Psychometrika,* **6,** 29-35.

Harper, R., *et al.* (1950), The application of multiple factor analysis to industrial test data. *Brit. J. appl. Phys.,* **1,** 1-6.

Harris, C. W. (1948a), An exploration of language skill patterns. *J. educ. Psychol.,* **39,** 321-336.

Harris, C. W. (1948b), Measurement of comprehension of literature. II. Studies of measures of comprehension. *Sch. Rev.,* **56,** 332-342.

Harris, C. W. (1948c), Direct rotation to primary structure. *J. educ. Psychol.,* **39,** 449-468.

Harris, C. W. (1949), Projections for three types of factor patterns. *J. exp. Educ.* **17**, 335-345. (1951), The symmetric idempotent matrix in factor analysis. *J. exp. Educ.*, **19**, 239-246.

Harris, C. W., and Knoell, D. M. (1948), The oblique solution in factor analysis. *J. educ. Psychol.*, **39**, 385-403.

Harris, C. W., and Schmid, J., Jr. (1950), Further application of the principles of direct rotation in factor analysis. *J. exp. Educ.*, **18**, 175-193.

Harsh, C. M. (1940), Constancy and variation in patterns of factor loadings. *J. educ. Psychol.*, **31**, 335-359.

Hart, H. H., *et al.* (1943), Multiple factor analysis of traits of delinquent boys. *J. soc. Psychol.*, **17**, 191-201.

Hartley, M. (1951), A Q-technique study of changes in the self-concept during psychotherapy. Ph.D. thesis, Univ. of Chicago.

Hartley, R. E., Jr. (1952), On the logical foundations of factor analysis. Ph.D. thesis, Univ. of Chicago.

Hatt, P. (1948), Class and ethnic attitudes. *Amer. sociol. Rev.*, **13**, 36-43.

Havighurst, R. J., and Breeze, F. H. (1947), Relation between ability and social status in a midwestern community. III. Primary mental abilities. *J. educ. Psychol.*, **38**, 241-247.

Heath, H. (1952), A factor analysis of women's measurements taken for garment and pattern construction. *Psychometrika,* **17**, 87-100.

Heese, K. W. (1942), A general factor in improvement with practice. *Psychometrika,* **7**, 213-223.

Hellfritzch, A. G. (1945), Factor analysis of teacher abilities. *J. exp. Educ.,* **14**, 166-199.

Henrysson, S. (1950), The significance of factor loadings. *Brit. J. Psychol. Statist. Sect.,* **3**, 159-165.

Herdan, G. (1943), The logical and analytical relationship between the theory of accidents and factor analysis. *J. Roy. Statist. Soc.,* **106**, 125-142.

Heston, J. C. (1943), A factor analysis of some clinical performance tests. *J. appl. Psychol.,* **27**, 135-149.

Heston, J. C. (1947), The graduate record examination vs. other measures of aptitude and achievement. *Educ. psychol. Measmt.,* **7**, 618-630.

Himmelweit, H. T. (1946), Speed and accuracy of work as related to temperament. *Brit. J. Psychol.,* **35**, 132-144.

Hoel, P. G. (1937), A significance test for component analysis. *Ann. math. Statist.,* **8**, 149-158.

Hoel, P. G. (1939), A significance test for minimum rank in factor analysis. *Psychometrika*, 4, 245-253.

Hofstaetter, P. P. (1951), A factorial study of cultural patterns in the U. S. *J. Psychol.*, 32, 99-113.

Holley, J. W. (1947), A note on the reflection of signs in the extraction of centroid factors. *Psychometrika*, 12, 263-265.

Holley, J. W., and Buxton, C. E. (1950), A factorial study of beliefs. *Educ. psychol. Measmt.*, 10, 400-410.

Holsopple, I. G. (1947), Factorial analysis of the Kuhlmann-Anderson Intelligence tests and the Stanford Achievement tests at fourth and eighth grade levels. In *Penn. St. Coll., Abstracts of Doctoral Dissertations*, 10, 223-229.

Holzinger, K. J. (1940), A synthetic approach to factor analysis. *Psychometrika*, 5, 235-250.

Holzinger, K. J. (1942), Why do people factor? *Psychometrika*, 7, 147-156.

Holzinger, K. J. (1944a), The relationship between the centroid and Spearman's methods. *J. educ. Psychol.*, 35, 347-351.

Holzinger, K. J. (1944b), A simple method of factor analysis. *Psychometrika*, 9, 257-262.

Holzinger, K. J. (1944c), Factoring test scores and implications for the method of averages. *Psychometrika*, 9, 155-167.

Holzinger, K. J. (1945), Interpretation of second-order factors. *Psychometrika*, 10, 21-25.

Holzinger, K. J., and Harman, H. H. (1941), *Factor analysis: a synthesis of factorial methods.* Chicago: Univ. of Chicago Press. xii, 417 pp.

Holzinger, K. J., and Harman, H. H. (1946), A comparison of the principal axis and centroid factor. *J. educ. Psychol.*, 37, 449-472.

Holzinger, K. J., and Harman, H. H. (1947), Factoring factors. *J. educ. Psychol.*, 38, 321-328.

Holzinger, K. J., and Harman, H. H. (1949), Applications of the simple method of factor analysis. *J. educ. Psychol.*, 40, 129-140.

Holzinger, K. J., and Swineford, F. (1946), The relation of two bi-factors to achievement in geometry and other subjects. *J. educ. Psychol.*, 37, 257-265.

Horn, A. M. (1941), Uneven distribution of the effects of specific factors. *Univ. of So. Calif. Educ. Monogr.*, No. 12. x, 107 pp.

Horst, P. (1937), A method of factor analysis by means of which all coordinates of the factor matrix are given simultaneously. *Psychometrika*, 2, 225-236.

Harris, C. W (1948d), A factor analysis of selected Senate roll-calls, 80th Congress. *Educ. psychol. Measmt.*, **8**, 583-591.

Harris, C. W. (1949), Projections of three types of factor pattern. *J. exp. Educ.*, **17**, 335-345.

Horst, P. (1941), A non-graphical method for transforming an arbitrary factor matrix into a simple structure factor matrix. *Psychometrika*, **6**, 77-99.

Horst, P. (1950), Uses and limitations of factor analysis in psychological research. In *Proc. E.T.S. 1949 inv. conf. on testing probl.* Princeton: Educational Testing Service, 50-56.

Hotelling, H. (1933a), Analysis of a complex of statistical variables into principal components. *J. educ. Psychol.*, **24**, 417-441 and 498-520.

Hotelling, H. (1933b), *Analysis of a complex of statistical variables into principal components.* Baltimore: Warwick & York. 48 pp.

Hotelling, H. (1935), Simplified calculation of principal components. *Psychometrika*, **1**, 27-35.

Hotelling, H. (1943a), Some new methods in matrix calculation. *Ann. Math. Stat.*, **14**, 1-34.

Hotelling, H. (1943b), Further points on matrix calculation and simultaneous equations. *Ann. Math. Stat.*, **14**, 440-441.

Hotelling, H. (1949), Practical problems of matrix calculation. *Proc. Berk. Symp. Math. Stat. Probl.*, Univ. Calif. Press, 275-293.

Howard, A. H., and Schutz, H. G. (1952), A factor analysis of a salary job evaluation plan. *J. appl. Psychol.*, **36**, 243-247.

Howard, J. K., and Pickrel, E. W. (1952), Validation of the Airman Classification Battery for Women in the Air Force. *H.R.R.C. Technical Bulletin* 52-5, 31 pp.

Howie, D. (1945), Aspects of personality in the classroom; a study of ratings on personal qualities for a group of schoolboys. *Brit. J. Psychol.*, **36**, 15-28.

Howie, D. (1950), Scholastic aptitude, reasoning, fluency and concentration. *Aust. J. Psychol.*, **2**, 100-113.

Hsü, E. H. (1946a), A factorial analysis of olfaction. *Psychometrika*, **11**, 31-42.

Hsü, E. H. (1946b), On the correlation between a variable and its super-factor. *J. Psychol.*, **22**, 89-92.

Hsü, E. H. (1947), The Rorschach responses and factor analysis. *J. gen. Psychol.*, **37**, 129-138.

Hsü, E. H. (1948a), An experimental demonstration of factor analysis. *J. gen. Psychol.*, **38**, 235-241.

Hsü, E. H. (1948b), Factor analysis, differential bio-process, and mental organization. *J. genet. Psychol.*, **38**, 147-157.

Hsü, E. H. (1949), The intrapersonal factor and its clinical applicability. *J. Personality*, **17**, 273-287.

Hsü, E. H. (1951), A method for isolating presumptive personality profiles from changes in skin conductivity during word association test. *Psychosom Med.*, **13**, 260-261.

Hsü, E. H. (1952a), Comparative study of factor patterns, physiologically and psychologically determined. *J. gen. Psychol.*, **47**, 105-128.

Hsü, E. H. (1952b), Further comments on the Rorschach response and factor analysis. *J. gen. Psychol.*, **47**, 239-241.

Hsü, E. H., and Sherman, M. (1946), The factorial analysis of the electroencephalogram. *J. Psychol.*, **21**, 189-196.

Hughes, R. M. (1950), A factor analysis of Rorschach diagnostic signs. *J. gen. Psychol.*, **43**, 85-103.

Humphreys, L. G. (1939), The stability in pattern of factor loadings: a comment on Dr. Smart's conclusions. *J. educ. Psychol.*, **30**, 231-237.

Humphreys, L. G. (1943), Measures of strength of conditioned eyelid responses. *J. gen. Psychol.*, **29**, 101-111.

Humphreys, L. G. (1946), The place of factor analysis in test experimentation. *Amer. Psychologist*, **1**, 454-455 (Abstract).

Humphreys, L. G. (1952), Individual differences. *Annual Rev. Psychol.*, **3**, 131-150.

Indo, Taro (1950), Factor Analysis of Holzinger and Harman. *Jap. J. Psychol.*, **20**, 38-46.

Jaspen, N. (1949), A factor study of worker characteristics. *J. appl. Psychol.*, **33**, 449-459.

Jastak, J., and Robison, R. K. (1949), The clinical application of factorial measures. *Delaware St. med. J.*, **21**, 169-174.

Jeffress, L. A. (1948a), The nature of primary abilities. *Amer. J. Psychol.*, **61**, 107-111.

Jeffress, L. A. (1948b), Binaural phase difference and pitch variation. *Amer. J. Psychol.*, **61**, 468-486.

Johnson, D. M., and Reynolds, F. (1941), A factor analysis of verbal ability. *Psychol. Rev.*, **4**, 183-195.

Johnson, D. M., Johnson, R. C., and Mark, A. L. (1951), A mathematical analysis of verbal fluency. *J. gen. Psychol.*, **44**, 121-128.

Jones, F. N. (1948), A factor analysis of visibility data. *Amer. J. Psychol.*, **61**, 361-369.

Jones, F. N. (1950), Color vision and factor analysis: some comments on Cohen's comments. *Psychol. Rev.*, **57**, 138-139.

Jones, F. N., and Jones, M. H. (1950), A second factor analysis of visibility data. *Amer. J. Psychol.*, **63**, 206-213.

Jones, L. V. (1949), A factor analysis of the Stanford-Binet at four age levels. *Psychometrika*, **14**, 299-331.

Jones, L. V. (1951), Primary mental abilities in the Stanford-Binet, age 13. *Psychometric Lab. Report* No. 71. Univ. of Chicago. 19 pp.

Kahn, L. A. (1950), The scalability and factorial composition of a universe of content as functions of the level of formal education of the respondents. *Microfilm Abstr.*, **10** (2), 68-71 (Abstract of Ph.D. thesis, 1950, Univ. of Penn.).

Karlin, J. E. (1941), Factor analysis in the field of music. *J. Musicol.*, **3**, 41-52.

Karlin, J. E. (1942a), The factorial isolation of the primary auditory abilities. *Psychol. Bull.*, **39**, 453-454 (Abstract).

Karlin, J. E. (1942b), A factorial study of auditory function. *Psychometrika*, **7**, 251-279.

Keir, G. (1949), The progressive matrices as applied to school children. *Brit. J. Psychol. Statist. Sect.*, **2**, 140-150.

Kell, B. L. (1950), An experimental investigation into the ability to predict the self-concept of an individual receiving psychotherapy. Ph.D. thesis, Univ. of Chicago.

Kelley, H. P. (1951), An investigation to identify and analyze a spatial-relations factor in an airman population. M. A., Univ. of Texas. 92 pp. (Unpublished thesis.)

Kelley, T. L. (1935), Essential traits of mental life. *Harv. Stud. Educ.*, **26**, 145.

Kelley, T. L. (1940), Comment on Wilson and Worcester's "note on factor analysis." *Psychometrika*, **5**, 117-120.

Kelley, T. L. (1944), A variance-ratio test of the uniqueness of principal-axis components as they exist at any stage of the Kelley iterative process for their determination. *Psychometrika*, **9**, 199-200.

Kelley, E. L. (1943), The development of a scale for rating pilot competency. (*CAA Div. Res. Rep.* No. 18; Pub. Bd. No. 50297.) Washington, D. C., U. S. Dept. Commerce.

Kellogg, C. E. (1948), A correction for Thurstone's multiple factor analysis. *Canad. J. Psychol.*, **2**, 137-139.

Kempthorne, O. (1948), The factorial approach to the weighting problem. *Ann. math. Statist.*, **19**, 238-245.

Kendall, M. G. (1950), Factor analysis. *J. Roy. Statist. Soc.*, **12**, 60-73.

Kendall, M. G., and Babington-Smith, B. (1950), Factor analysis. *J. Roy. Statist. Soc.* (B), (London), **12**, No. 1.

Kestelman, H. (1952), The fundamental equation of factor analysis. *Brit. J. Psychol. Statist. Sect.*, **5**, 1-6.

Kleemeier, R. W., and Dudek, F. J. (1950), A factorial investigation of flexibility. *Educ. psychol. Measmt.*, **10**, 107-118.

Knoell, D. M., and Harris, C. W. (1952), A factor analysis of word fluency. *J. educ. Psychol.*, **43**, 131-148.

Koch, H. L. (1942), A factor analysis of some measures of the behavior of preschool children. *J. gen. Psychol.*, **27**, 257-287.

Kremer, A. H. (1942), The nature of persistence. *Stud. Psychol. Psychiat. Cathol. U. Amer.*, **5**, No. 8, 40 pp.

Landahl, H. D. (1938), Centroid orthogonal transformations. *Psychometrika*, **3**, 219-223.

Landahl, H. D. (1940), Time scores and factor analysis. *Psychometrika*, **5**, 67-74.

Langsam, R. S. (1941), A factorial analysis of reading ability. *J. exp. Educ.*, **10**, 57-63.

Laurier, B. (1945), Analyse factorielle des traits de caractère et des aptitudes du maître idéal. *Bull. Canad. Psychol. Ass.*, **5**, 77-78 (Abstract).

Laurier, B. (1948), The tetrad technique and the centroid method in the development of a rating scale for teachers. *Amer. Psychologist*, **3**, 296 (Abstract).

Lawley, D. N. (1940), The estimation of factor loadings by the method of maximum likelihood. *Proc. of the Royal Society of Edinburgh*, **60**, 64-82.

Lawley, D. N. (1941), Further investigations in factor estimation. *Proc. of the Royal Society of Edinburgh*, A, **61**, 176-185.

Lawley, D. N. (1943a), The application of the maximum likelihood method to factor analysis. *Brit. J. Psychol.*, **33**, 172-175.

Lawley, D. N. (1943b), The factorial analysis of multiple item tests. *Proc. of the Royal Society of Edinburgh*, **62**, Section A, Part I, 74-82.

Lawley, D. N. (1950), Factor analysis by maximum likelihood: a correction. *Brit. J. Psychol. Statist. Sect.*, **3**, 76.

Lawley, D. N. (1951), The maximum likelihood method of estimating factor loadings. In G. H. Thomson (1951), 321-327.

Lawshe, C. H., Jr., and Wilson, R. F. (1946), Studies in job evaluation. 5. An analysis of the factor comparison system as it functions in a paper mill. *J. appl. Psychol.*, **30**, 426-434.

Lawshe, C. H., Jr., Dudek, E. E., and Wilson, R. F. (1948), Studies of job evaluation.   7. A factor analysis of two point rating methods of job evaluation. *J. appl. Psychol.*, **32**, 118-129.

Lazarsfeld, P. F. (1947), Factor analysis of qualitative attributes. *Amer. Psychologist*, **2**, 306 (Abstract).

Lazarsfeld, P. F. (1950), The logical and mathematical foundation of latent structure analysis. In *Studies in Social Psychology in World War II*, Vol. 4; *Measurement and Prediction*. (Edited by Samuel A. Stouffer.)   Princeton, N. J.: Princeton Univ. Press.   Chapter 10, 362-412.

Leclere, H. (1952), Bipolar factors as a cause of cyclic overlap. *Brit. J. Psychol. Statist. Sect.*, **5**, 197-200.   (Correspondence and reply by C. Burt.)

Lecznar, W. B., Fruchter, B., and Zachert, V. (1951), A factor analysis of the Airman Biographical Inventory BE601B.   Air Training Command *Human Resources Res. Center Res. Bull. 51-3*, v, 17 pp.

Ledermann, W. (1936), Some mathematical remarks concerning boundary conditions in the factor analysis of ability. *Psychometrika*, **1**, 165-174.

Lehner, G. F. J., Wheeler, W. M., and Little, K. B. (1950), A factor analysis of the MMPI. *Amer. Psychologist*, **5**, 471 (Abstract).

Leiman, J. M., and Hill, F. L., Jr. (1952), The correction of errors of plotting in a rotated factor matrix. *USAF Hum. Resour. Res. Cent., Res. Bull., 52-28,* 13 pp.

Lodge, G. T. (1947), Correlates of criminal behavior. *J. soc. Psychol.*, **25**, 3-51.

Loevinger, J. (1948), The technic of homogeneous tests compared with some aspects of "scale analysis" and factor analysis. *Psychol. Bull.*, **45**, 507-529.

Lorge, I. (1945), Computational technics. *Rev. educ. Res.*, **15**, 441-446.

Lorr, M. (1951), A factorial isolation of two social attitudes. *J. soc. Psychol.*, **34**, 139-142.

Lorr, M., and Murney, R. (1951), Note on factors measured by the Hildreth Feeling and Attitudes Scales. *J. clin. Psychol.*, **7**, 381-382.

Lorr, M., Wittman, P., and Schamberger, W. (1951), An analysis of the Elgin prognostic scale. *J. clin. Psychol.*, **7**, 260-263.

Lovell, C. (1944), The effect of special construction of test items on their factor composition. *Psychol. Monogr.*, **56**, 6, (No. 259), 26 pp.

Lovell, C. (1945), A study of the factor structure of thirteen personality variables. *Educ. psychol. Measmt.*, **5**, 335-350.

Lubin, A. (1950), A note on "criterion analysis." *Psychol. Rev.*, **57**, 54-57.

Luborsky, L. B. (1953), Intraindividual repetitive measurements (P-technique) in understanding psychotherapeutic change. In O. H. Mowrer *et al.* (1953), 389-413.

Luborsky, L. B., and Hornaday, J. A. (1948), A mechanical factor-rotator for demonstration. *Amer. J. Psychol.*, **61**, 104-106.

Luce, R. D., and Perry, A. D. (1949), A method of matrix analysis of group structure. *Psychometrika*, **14**, 95-116.

Lurie, W. A. (1951), A study of Spranger's value types by the method of factor analysis. *J. soc. Psychol.*, **8**, 17-37.

Maccrone, I. D., and Starfield, A. (1949), A comparative study in multiple-factor analysis of "neurotic tendency." *Psychometrika*, **14**, 1-20.

MacDuffee, C. C. (1943), *Vectors and matrices*. New York: Mathematical Association of America, 192 pp.

Martin, G. C. (1948), A factorial analysis of the Bernreuter Personality Inventory. *Educ. psychol. Measmt.*, **8**, 85-92.

Marzolf, S. S., and Larsen, A. H. (1945), Statistical interpretation of symptoms illustrated with a factor analysis of problem check list items. *Educ. psychol. Measmt.*, **5**, 285-294.

Maurer, K. M. (1941), Patterns of behavior of young children as revealed by a factor analysis of trait "clusters." *J. genet. Psychol.*, **59**, 177-188.

McCloy, C. H. (1940), The measurement of speed in motor performance. *Psychometrika*, **5**, 173-182.

McCloy, C. H. (1941), The factor analysis as a research technique. *Res. Quart. Amer. Ass. Hlth.*, **12**, 22-33.

McCloy, C. H., Metheny, E., and Knott, V. (1938), A comparison of the Thurstone method of multiple factors with the Hotelling method of principle components. *Psychometrika*, **3**, 61-67.

McCraw, L. W. (1949), A factor analysis of motor learning. *Res. Quart. Amer. Ass. Hlth.*, **20**, 316-335.

McLeish, J. (1950), The validation of Seashore's measures of musical talent by factorial methods. *Brit. J. Psychol. Statist. Sect.*, **3**, 129-140.

McNemar, Q. (1941), On the sampling errors of factor loadings. *Psychometrika*, **6**, 141-152.

McNemar, Q. (1942a), On the number of factors. *Psychometrika*, **7**, 9-18.

McNemar, Q. (1942b), *The revision of the Stanford-Binet scale*. Boston: Houghton-Mifflin Co. 185 pp.

McNemar, Q. (1945), The mode of operation of suppressant variables. *Amer. J. Psychol.*, **58**, 554-555.

McNemar, Q. (1951), The factors in factoring behavior. *Psychometrika*, **16**, 353-359.

McQuitty, L. L. (1953), A statistical method for studying personality integration. In O. H. Mowrer *et al.* (1953), 414-462.

Medland, F. F. (1947), An empirical comparison of methods of communality estimation. *Psychometrika*, **12**, 101-109.

Meehl, P. E. (1945), A simple algebraic development of Horst's suppressor variables. *Amer. J. Psychol.*, **58**, 550-554.

Meili, R. (1946), L'analyse de l'intelligence. *Arch. Psychol., Geneve*, **31**, 1-64.

Meili, R. (1947), Die faktorentheorie von Charles Edward Spearman (1863-1945). *Schweiz. Z. Psychol. Anwend.*, **6**, 137-140.

Meili, Richard, Factorielle analyse der praktischen Intelligenz (Factorial analysis of practical intelligence). In F. Baumgarten (1952), Editor, 484-485.

Mellone, M. A. (1944), A factorial study of picture tests for young children. *Brit. J. Psychol.*, **35**, 9-16.

Meyer, L. A. (1943), The invariance of factorial composition of a test. Ph.D. dissertation, Univ. of Chicago.

Michael, W. B. (1947), An investigation of the contributions of factors to tests and to their predictive value in two Army Air Force pilot populations. *Amer. Psychologist*, **2**, 417-418.

Michael, W. B. (1949a), Factor analyses of tests and criteria; a comparative study of two AAF pilot population. *Psychol. Monogr.*, **63** (3), (No. 298), v, 55 pp.

Michael, W. B. (1949b), The nature of space and visualization abilities: some recent findings based on factor analysis studies. *Trans. N. Y. Acad. Sci.*, **11**, 275-281.

Michael, W. B., Zimmerman, W. S., and Guilford, J. P. (1951), An investigation of two hypotheses regarding the nature of the spatial-relations and visualization factors. *Educ. psychol. Measmt.*, **10**, 187-213.

Miller, A. W. (1951), Confirmation of ergic structure in man, by R-technique analysis of objectively measured dynamic traits. Unpublished M.A. thesis, Univ. of Illinois.

Mohsin, S. M. (1943), Spearman's tetrad difference criterion and the group factors. *India J. Psychol.*, **18**, 97-105.

Moore, T. V. (1947), Formal causality and the analysis of the general factor. In *Miscellanea Psychologica Albert Michotte*, 544-561.

Moore, T. V., and Hsü, E. H. (1946), Factorial analysis of anthropological measurements in psychotic patients. *Hum. Biol.*, **18**, 133-157.

Moore, T. V., Stafford, J. W., and Hsü, E. H. (1947), Obverse analysis of personality. *J. Personality*, **16**, 11-48.

Morris, C. M. (1939), A critical analysis of certain performance tests. *J. genet. Psychol.*, **54**, 85-105.

Morrow, R. S. (1941), An experimental analysis of the theory of independent abilities. *J. educ. Psychol.*, **32**, 495-512.

Mosier, C. I. (1938), A note on Dwyer: the determination of the factor loadings of a given test. *Psychometrika*, **3**, 297-299.

Mosier, C. I. (1939a), Determining a simple structure when loadings for certain tests are known. *Psychometrika*, **4**, 149-162.

Mosier, C. I. (1939b), Influence of chance error on simple structure: an empirical investigation of the effect of chance error and estimated communalities on simple structure in factor analysis. *Psychometrika*, **4**, 33-44.

Mosier, C. I., Uhlaner, J. E., and Harper, B. P. (1950), Application of factorial logic to spatial abilities. *Amer. Psychologist*, **5**, 277 (Abstract).

Moursy, E. M. (1952), The hierarchical organization of cognitive levels. *Brit. J. Psychol. Statist. Sect.*, **5**, 151-180.

Mowrer, O. H., *et al.* (1953a), *Psychotherapy theory and research.* New York: The Ronald Press Co.

Mowrer, O. H. (1953b), "Q-technique"—description, history and critique. In O. H. Mowrer *et al.* (1953), 316-375.

Muhsam, H. V. (1951), The factor analysis of a simple object. *J. gen. Psychol.*, **45**, 105-111.

Mukherji, N. P. (1942), Why and what in factors. *India J. Psychol.*, **17**, 41-47.

Myers, C. S. (1947), A new analysis of intelligence: a critical notice. *Occup. Psychol., Lond.*, **21**, 17-23.

Myers, C. T. (1950), The factorial composition and validity of a speeded test. *Amer. Psychologist*, **5**, 369-370 (Abstract).

Myers, C. T. (1952), The factorial composition and validity of differently speeded tests. *Psychometrika*, **17**, 347-352.

North, R. D., Jr. (1949), Analysis of the personality dimensions of introversion-extroversion. *J. Personality*, **17**, 352-367.

Obel, H. (1948), Differing factorial abilities of ungraded boys who later became criminals. *Microfilm Abstr.*, **8** (2), 89-90. (Abstract of Ph.D. thesis, Univ. of Michigan, 1948. Microfilm of complete manuscript, 107 pp., $1.34, Univ. Microfilms, Ann Arbor, Mich. Publ. No. 1068.)

Olckers, P. J. (1951), A factorial study of arithmetical ability. *J. Soc. Res., Pretoria,* **2**, 1-21.

Oliver, J. A., and Ferguson, G. A. (1951), A factorial study of tests of rigidity. *Canad. J. Psychol.,* **5**, 49-59.

Olson, H. C. (1950), A factor analysis of depth perception test scores of male subjects having normal acuity. *Amer. Psychologist,* **5**, 263 (Abstract).

Osgood, C. E., and Suci, G. J. (1952), A measure of relationship determined by both mean difference and profile information. *Psychol. Bull.,* **49**, 251-262.

Peatman, J. G. (1947), *Descriptive and sampling statistics.* New York: Harper & Brothers, 1947, 577 pp.

Peckham, R. E. (1953), A comparison of differences in the factorial content of a battery of numerical and reasoning tests when used with high and low ability groups. M.A., University of Texas (Thesis).

Peel, E. A. (1946), A new method for analyzing aesthetic preferences: some theoretical considerations. *Psychometrika,* **11**, 129-137.

Peel, E. A. (1948), Prediction of a complex criterion and battery reliability. *Brit. J. Psychol. Statist. Sect.,* **1**, 84-94.

Peel, E. A. (1949), Symposium on the selection of pupils for different types of secondary schools. VI. Evidence of a practical factor at the age of eleven. *Brit. J. educ. Psychol.,* **19**, 1-15.

Pemberton, C. (1952), The closure factors related to other cognitive processes. *Psychometrika,* **17**, 267-288.

Pemberton, W. A. (1951), Factors involved in clinical judgments made from projective and non-projective behavior samples. Unpublished Ph.D. thesis, Univ. of Chicago.

Perlis, S. (1952), *Theory of Matrices.* Cambridge: Addison-Wesley.

Peters, C. C. (1947), Multiple factor analysis. In Harriman, P. L., *Encyclopedia Psychol.,* New York: Philosophical Library, 393-401.

Peters, C. C., and Van Voorhis, W. R. (1940), *Statistical procedures and their mathematical bases.* New York: McGraw-Hill Book Co.

Peterson, D. A. (1946), Factor analysis of the new United States Navy basic classification test battery. *Office of Scientific Research and Development Report* No. 3004. Washington, D. C.: U. S. Dept. Commerce, 1946. 13 pp.

Phillips, M. (1949), Study of a series of physical education tests by factor analysis. *Res. Quart. Amer. Ass. Hlth.,* **20**, 60-71.

Pickford, R. W. (1946), Factorial analysis of colour vision. *Nature, Lond.,* **157**, 700.

Pickford, R. W. (1948a), "Aesthetic" and "technical" factors in artistic appreciation. *Brit. J. Psychol.*, 38, 135-141.

Pickford, R. W. (1948b), Experiments with pictures. *Advanc. Sci.*, 5, 140.

Pickford, R. W. (1948c), Human colour vision and Granit's theory. *Nature, Lond.*, 162, 414-415.

Pickford, R. W. (1949), Individual differences in colour vision and their measurement. *J. Psychol.*, 27, 153-202.

Pickrel, E. W. (1951), A factor analysis of Airman Classification Battery AC-1A and Aircraft Maintenance Fundamentals final school grade. *H.R.R.C. Research Note Pers.* 51-21.

Piddington, L. S. (1941), A factorial study of types of fear. *Brit. J. Psychol.*, 11, 227 (Abstract).

Price, E. J. J. (1940), The nature of the practical factor (F). *Brit. J. Psychol.*, 30, 341-351.

Primoff, E. S. (1942), Individual correlation and factor analysis. *Psychol. Bull.*, 39, 474.

Primoff, E. S. (1943), Correlations and factor analysis of the abilities of the single individual. *J. gen. Psychol.*, 28, 121-132.

Puranen, E. (1951), Faktorstrukturen av nagra verbila tests. *Nord. Psychol.*, 3, 33-45.

Rafferty, J. A., and Deemer, W. L., Jr. (1950), Factor analysis of psychiatric interviews. *J. educ. Psychol.*, 41, 173-183.

Rees, L. (1947), The physical constitution and mental illness. *Eugen. Rev.*, 39, 50-55.

Rees, L. (1950), A factorial study of physical constitution in women. *J. Ment. Sci.*, 46, 619-632.

Rees, W. L., and Eysenck, H. J. (1945), A factorial study of some morphological and psychological aspects of human constitution. *J. Ment. Sci.*, 41, 8-21.

Reichard, S. (1944), Mental organization and age level. *Arch. Psychol.*, No. 295. 30 pp.

Reiersol, O. (1950), On the identifiability of parameters in Thurstone's multiple factor analysis. *Psychometrika*, 15, 121-149.

Renshaw, T. (1950), A factorial study of two and three dimensional space tests. Ph.D. Thesis, Univ. of Edinburgh.

Renshaw, T. (1952), Factor rotation by the method of extended vectors. A review of Dr. Sutherlands paper. *Brit. J. Psychol. Statist. Sect.*, 5, 7-18.

Rethlingshafer, D. (1941), The learning of a visual discrimination problem under varying motivating conditions. *J. comp. Psychol.,* **32,** 583-591.

Rethlingshafer, D. (1942), Relationship of tests of persistence to other measures of continuance of activities. *J. abnor. soc. Psychol.,* **37,** 71-82.

Reyburn, H. A., and Raath, M. J. (1949), Simple structure: a critical examination. *Brit. J. Psychol.,* **2,** 125-133.

Reyburn, H. A., and Raath, M. J. (1950), Primary factors of personality. *Brit. J. Psychol. Statist. Sect.,* **3,** 150-158.

Reyburn, H. A., and Taylor, J. G. (1941), Factors in introversion and extraversion. *Brit. J. Psychol.,* **31,** 335-340.

Reyburn, H. A., and Taylor, J. G. (1943a), On the interpretation of common factors: a criticism and a statement. *Psychometrika,* **8,** 53-64.

Reyburn, H. A., and Taylor, J. G. (1943b), Some factors of temperament: a re-examination. *Psychometrika,* **8,** 91-104.

Richards, T. W. (1941), Genetic emergence of factor specificity. *Psychometrika,* **6,** 37-42.

Richardson, L. F. (1950), A method for computing principal axes. *Brit. J. Psychol. Statist. Sect.,* **3,** 16-20.

Rimoldi, H. J. A. (1948), Study of some factors related to intelligence. *Psychometrika,* **13,** 27-46.

Rimoldi, H. J. A. (1951), The central intellective factor. *Psychometrika,* **16,** 75-101.

Rippe, D. D. (1951), Statistical rank and sampling variation of the results of factorization of covariance matrices. Unpublished Ph.D. thesis, Univ. of Michigan.

Rippe, D. D. (1953), Application of a large sampling criterion to some sampling problems in factor analysis. *Psychometrika,* **18,** 191-206.

Robinson, W. S. (1940), Preliminary report on factors in radio listening. *J. appl. Psychol.,* **24,** 831-837.

Roff, M. (1937), The relation between results obtainable with raw and corrected correlation coefficients in multiple factor analysis. *Psychometrika,* **2,** 35-39.

Roff, M. (1949), A factorial study of the Fels parent behavior scales. *Child Develpm.,* **20,** 29-45.

Roff, M. F. (1950), Personnel selection and classification procedures: perceptual tests. A factorial analysis. *USAF Sch. Aviation Med. Project Report,* Proj. No. 21-02-009, 23 pp.

Roff, M. F. (1951), Personnel selection and classification procedures:

spatial tests. A factorial analysis. *USAF Sch. Aviation Med. Project Report,* Proj. No. 21-29-002, 46 pp.

Rosner, B. (1948), An algebraic solution for the communalities. *Psychometrika,* **13,** 181-184.

Royce, J. R. (1950a), A factorial study of emotionality in the dog. *Amer. Psychologist,* **5,** 263 (Abstract).

Royce, J. R. (1950b), The factorial analysis of animal behavior. *Psychol. Bull.,* **47,** 235-259.

Royce, J. R. (1950c), A synthesis of experimental designs in program research. *J. gen. Psychol.,* **43,** 295-303.

Rush, C. H., Jr. (1950), Methods for the appraisal of sales personnel: a factorial approach to the analysis of criterion and predictor variates. *Amer. Psychologist,* **5,** 329 (Abstract).

Ryans, D. G. (1952), A study of criterion data (a factor analysis of teacher behaviors in the elementary school). *Educ. psychol. Meas.,* **12,** 333-344.

Ryans, D. G., and Peters, E. F. (1942), Factors affecting the school-satisfaction of students in a woman's college. *Sch. & Soc.,* **55,** 26-28.

Ryans, D. G., and Wandt, E. (1952), A factor analysis of observed teacher behaviors in the secondary school: a study of criterion data. *Educ. psychol. Measmt.,* **12,** 574-586.

Sanai, M. (1950a), A factorial study of social attitudes. *J. soc. Psychol.,* **31,** 167-182.

Sanai, M. (1950b), An experimental study of politico-economic attitudes. *Int. J. Opin. Attitude Res.,* **4,** 563-577.

Sanai, M. (1951), An experimental study of social attitudes. *J. soc. Psychol.,* **34,** 235-264.

Sanai, M. (1952), An empirical study of political, religious, and social attitudes. *Brit. J. Psychol. Statist. Sect.,* **5,** 81-92.

Sandler, J. (1949), The reciprocity principle as an aid to factor analysis. *Brit. J. Psychol. Statist. Sect.,* **2,** 180-182.

Sandler, J. (1952), A technique for facilitating the rotation of factor axes based on an equivalence between persons and tests. *Psychometrika,* **17,** 223-230.

Sastry, N. S. N. (1941), Can there be a factor-analysis of aesthetic judgment? *Sankhya,* **5,** 313-316.

Saunders, D. R. (1948), Factor analysis I: some effects of chance error. *Psychometrika,* **13,** 251-257.

Saunders, D. R. (1949), Factor analysis II: a note concerning rotation of axes to simple structure. *Educ. psychol. Measmt.,* **9,** 753-756.

Saunders, D. R. (1950), Practical methods in the direct factor analysis of psychological score matrices. *Microfilm Abstr.,* **10,** 307-308 (Abstract of Ph.D. thesis, Univ. Illinois).

Saunders, D. R. (unpublished), A further investigation of the relation between questionnaire and behavior rating personality factors. In J. W. French (1953a) (Abstract).

Scheier, I. H., and Ferguson, G. A. (1952), Further factorial studies of tests of rigidity. *Canad. J. Psychol.,* **6,** 18-30.

Schmid, J., Jr. (1950), Factor analyses of prospective teachers' differences. *J. exp. Educ.,* **18,** 287-320.

Searle, L. V. (1947), Application of the "inverted" factor analysis technique to the study of hereditary behavior types in rats. *Amer. Psychologist,* **2,** 320 (Abstract).

Seashore, R. H. (1940), An experimental and theoretical analysis of fine motor skills. *Amer. J. Psychol.,* **53,** 86-98.

Seashore, R. H., and Dudek, F. J. (1950), A factorial analysis of precision, steadiness, and equilibrium in fine motor skills. *Amer. Psychologist,* **5,** 276-277 (Abstract).

Sen, A. (1950), A statistical study of the Rorschach test. *Brit. J. Psychol. Statist. Sect.,* **3,** 21-39.

Shaefer, W. C. (1940), The relation of test difficulty and factorial composition determined from individual and group forms of Primary Mental Abilities tests. *Psychometrika,* **5,** 316-317.

Shaw, D. C. (1949), A study of the relationships between Thurstone Primary Mental Abilities and high school achievement. *J. educ. Psychol.,* **40,** 239-249.

Sheldon, W. H., and Stevens, S. S. (1942), *The varieties of temperament; a psychology of constitutional differences.* New York: Harper & Bros. x, 520 pp.

Skard, Ø. (1949), *Oversikt over test-psykologiens utvikling: intelligensteorier, faktoranalytiske teorier.* Oslo: Universitetets Studentkontor, 58 pp.

Slater, E., and Slater, P. (1944), A heuristic theory of neurosis. *J. Neurol. Neurosurg. & Psychiat.,* **7,** 49-55.

Slater, P. (1947), The factor analysis of a matrix of 2×2 tables. *Suppl.; J. Roy. Statist. Soc.,* **9,** 114-127.

Smalzried, N. T., and Remmers, H. H. (1943), A factor analysis of the Purdue rating scale for instructors. *J. educ. Psychol.,* **34,** 363-367.

Spearman, C. (1904), General intelligence objectively determined and measured. *Amer. J. Psychol.,* **15,** 201-293.

Spearman, C. (1927), *The abilities of man.* London: Macmillan.

Spearman, C. (1934), The factor theory and its troubles: conclusion. Scientific value. *J. educ. Psychol.*, **25**, 383-391.

Spearman, C. (1937), Abilities as sums of factors, or as their products. *J. educ. Psychol.*, **28**, 629-631.

Spearman, C. (1939), Thurstone's work re-worked. *J. educ. Psychol.*, **30**, 1-16.

Spearman, C. (1941a), Professor Thurstone, a correction. *Psychol. Bull.*, **38**, 818.

Spearman, C. (1941b), How 'G' can disappear. *Psychometrika*, **6**, 353-354.

Spearman, C. (1946), Theory of general factor. *Brit. J. Psychol.*, **36**, 117-131.

Spearman, C., and Jones, L. W. (1950), *Human Ability*. London and New York: Macmillan. vii, 198 pp.

Staff, Division of Occupational Analysis, War Manpower Commission (1945), Factor analysis of occupational aptitude tests. *Educ. psychol. Measmt.*, **5**, 147-155.

Staff, Test and Research Section, Training, Standards and Curriculum Division, Bureau of Naval Personnel (1945), Psychological test construction and research in the Bureau of Naval Personnel; development of the basic test battery for enlisted personnel. *Psychol. Bull.*, **42**, 561-571.

Stafford, J. W., and Hsü, E. H. (1947), The super-factor of persons. *J. Psychol.*, **24**, 63-70.

Stagner, R., and Katzoff, E. T. (1942), Fascist attitudes: factor analysis of item correlations. *J. soc. Psychol.*, **16**, 3-9.

Stephenson, W. (1936), The inverted factor technique. *Brit. J. Psychol.*, **26**, 344-361.

Stephenson, W. (1950a), A statistical approach to typology; the study of trait universes. *J. clin. Psychol.*, **6**, 26-38.

Stephenson, W. (1950b), The significance of Q-technique for the study of personality. In Reymert, M. L., Editor, *Feelings and Emotions; the Mooseheart symposium.* New York: McGraw-Hill Book Co., 552-570.

Stephenson, W. (1952a), Some observations on Q-technique. *Psychol. Bull.*, **49**, 483-498.

Stephenson, W. (1952b), A note on Professor R. B. Cattell's methodological adumbrations. *J. Clin. Psychol.*, **8**, 206-207.

Stephenson, W. (1952c), Q-methodology and the projective techniques. *J. Clin. Psychol.*, **8**, 219-229.

Stewart, N., and Bergmann, C. (1951), Cognitive and conative factors in self-ratings by others. In J. W. French (1953a) (Abstract).

Strong, E. K. (1943), *Vocational interests of men and women.* Stanford Univ. Press, 746 pp.

Strong, E. K., and Tucker, A. C. (1952), The use of vocational interest scales in planning a medical career. *Psychol. Monog.,* **66,** 48-51.

Sutherland, J. (1941), An investigation into some aspects of problem solving in arithmetic. *Brit. J. educ. Psychol.,* **11,** 215-222; 1942, **12,** 35-46.

Sutherland, J. (1951), Factor rotation by the method of extended vectors. *Brit. J. Psychol. Statist. Sect.,* **4,** 21-30.

Swineford, F. (1941), Some comparisons of the multiple-factor and the bi-factor methods of analysis. *Psychometrika,* **6,** 375-382.

Swineford, F. (1947), Growth in the general and verbal bi-factors from grade 7 to grade 9. *J. educ. Psychol.,* **38,** 257-272.

Swineford, F. (1948), A study in factor analysis: the nature of the general, verbal, and spatial bi-factors. *Suppl. educ. Monogr.,* No. 67, xi, 70 pp.

Swineford, F. (1949a), A number factor. *J. educ. Psychol.,* **40,** 157-167.

Swineford, F. (1949b), General, verbal, and spatial bi-factors after three years. *J. educ. Psychol.,* **40,** 353-360.

Swineford, F., and Holzinger, K. J. (1940), Selected references on statistics, the theory of test construction and factor analysis. *Sch. Rev.,* **48,** 460-466.

Swineford, F., and Holzinger, K. J. (1942), A study in factor analysis: the reliability of bi-factors and their relation to other measures. *Suppl. educ. Monogr.,* No. 53, 99 pp.

Swineford, F., and Holzinger, K. J. (1950), Selected references on statistics, the theory of test construction and factor analysis. *Sch. Rev.,* **58,** 492-493.

Taylor, C. W. (1947), A factorial study of fluency in writing. *Psychometrika,* **12,** 234-262.

Thomas, L. L. (1952), A cluster analysis of office operations. *J. appl. Psychol.,* **36,** 238-242.

Thomson, D. F. (1948), A treatment of industrial attitude data by means of factor analysis. Ph.D., Ohio State Univ.

Thomson, G. H. (1916), A hierarchy without a general factor. *Brit. J. Psychol.,* **8,** 271-281.

Thomson, G. H. (1935), On complete families of correlation coefficients and their tendency to zero tetrad differences: including a statement of the sampling theory of abilities. *Brit. J. Psychol.,* **26,** 63-92.

Thomson, G. H. (1940), *An analysis of performance test scores of a representative group of Scottish children.* London: Univ. of London Press. 58 pp.

Thomson, G. H. (1941), The speed factor in performance tests. *Brit. J. Psychol.,* **32,** 131-135.

Thomson, G. H. (1946a), Symposium on personality. IV. Both sides of the shield; the reactions of an outsider. *Brit. J. educ. Psychol.,* **16,** 105-115.

Thomson, G. H. (1946b), *Some recent work in factorial analysis, and a retrospect.* Presidential address to British Psychological Society. London: Univ. London Press, 16 pp.

Thomson, G. H. (1949a), Nature of the mind's 'factors.' *Advanc. Sci.,* **6,** 267-274.

Thomson, G. H. (1949b), On estimating oblique factors. *Brit. J. Psychol. Statist. Sect.,* **2,** 1-2.

Thomson, G. H. (1950), *L'analyse factorielle des aptitudes humaines.* Paris: Presses Universitairex de France, ix, 421 pp.

Thomson, G. H. (1951), *The factorial analysis of human ability.* (5th ed.) Boston: Houghton-Mifflin Co. 383 pp.

Thomson, G. H., and Ledermann, W. (1939), The influence of multivariate selection on the factorial analysis of ability. *Brit. J. Psychol.,* **29,** 288-306.

Thorndike, R. L. (1947), Factors determining errors of navigational position errors. In Kelly, G. A., *New Methods in Applied Psychology.* College Park, Md.: Univ. Md., 194-198.

Thorndike, R. L. (1950), Individual differences. *Annual Rev. Psychol.,* **1,** 87-104.

Thurstone, L. L. (1937), Current misuse of the factorial methods. *Psychometrika,* **2,** 73-76.

Thurstone, L. L. (1938), Primary mental abilities. *Psychometric Monogr.,* No. 1, ix, 121.

Thurstone, L. L. (1940a), Current issues in factor analysis. *Psychol. Bull.,* **37,** 189-236.

Thurstone, L. L. (1940b), Experimental study of simple structure. *Psychometrika,* **5,** 153-167.

Thurstone, L. L. (1940c), Factor analysis as a scientific method with special reference to the analysis of human traits. In Wirth, L. (1940), *Eleven twenty six, a decade of social science research.* Chicago: Univ. Chicago Press, 78-112.

Thurstone, L. L. (1944a), Graphical method of factoring the correlational matrix. *Proc. Nat. Acad. Sci., Wash.,* **30,** 129-134.

Thurstone, L. L. (1944b), A factorial study of perception. *Psychometric Monogr.,* No. 4, 148 pp.

Thurstone, L. L. (1944c), Second-order factors. *Psychometrika,* **9,** 71-100.

Thurstone, L. L. (1945a), The effects of selection in factor analysis. *Psychometrika,* **10,** 165-198.

Thurstone, L. L. (1945b), A multiple group method of factoring the correlation matrix. *Psychometrika,* **10,** 73-78.

Thurstone, L. L. (1945c), Factor analysis and body types. *Psychometric Lab. Report* No. 24, Univ. of Chicago.

Thurstone, L. L. (1946a), Theories of intelligence. *Sci. Mon., N. Y.,* **62,** 101-112.

Thurstone, L. L. (1946b), Note on a reanalysis of Davis' reading tests. *Psychometrika,* **11,** 185-188.

Thurstone, L. L. (1946c), A single plane method of rotation. *Psychometrika,* **11,** 71-79.

Thurstone, L. L. (1946d), Analysis of body measurements. *Psychometric Lab. Report* No. 29, Univ. of Chicago.

Thurstone, L. L. (1946e), Factor analysis of body types. *Psychometrika,* **11,** 15-21.

Thurstone, L. L. (1947a), Factorial analysis of body measurements. *Amer. J. Phys. Anthrop.,* **5,** 15-28.

Thurstone, L. L. (1947b), Primary abilities. In Harriman, P. L., *Encyclopedia Psychol.* New York: Philosophical Library, 544-546.

Thurstone, L. L. (1947c), *Multiple-factor analysis; a development and expansion of the vectors of mind.* Chicago: Univ. of Chicago Press. 535 pp.

Thurstone, L. L. (1948), Psychological implications of factor analysis. *Amer. Psychologist,* **3,** 402-408.

Thurstone, L. L. (1949), Note about the multiple group method. *Psychometrika,* **14,** 43-45.

Thurstone, L. L. (1950a), Primary mental abilities. In *A.A.A.S. Centennial.* Washington, D. C.: American Ass. Advanc. Sci., 61-66.

Thurstone, L. L. (1950b), Some primary abilities in visual thinking. *Psychometric Lab. Report* No. 59, Univ. Chicago, 7 pp.

Thurstone, L. L. (1950c), Implicaciones psicologicas del analisis factorial. *Rev. Psicol. gen. apl., Madrid,* **5,** 19-35.

Thurstone, L. L. (1951a), An analysis of mechanical aptitude. *Psychometric Lab. Report* No. 62, Univ. Chicago, 26 pp.

Thurstone, L. L. (1951b), The dimensions of temperament. *Psychometrika*, 16, 11-20.

Thurstone, L. L. (1951c), Factor analysis as a scientific method. *Psychometric Lab. Report* No. 65, Univ. Chicago, 7 pp.

Thurstone, L. L. (1951d), L'analyse factorielle methode scientifique. *Année Psychol.*, 50, 61-75.

Thurstone, L. L., and Degan, J. W. (1951), A factorial study of the Supreme Court. *Psychometric Lab. Report* No. 64, Univ. Chicago, 7 pp.

Thurstone, L. L., and Thurstone, T. G. (1941), Factorial studies of intelligence. *Psychometric Monogr.*, No. 2, 94 pp.

Thurstone, T. G. (1941), Primary mental abilities of children. *Educ. psychol. Measmt.*, 1, 105-116.

Thurstone, T. G. (1948), Factorial studies of mental abilities of children. *Proc. Twelfth Intern. Congr. Psychol.*, Edinburgh.

Torgerson, W. S., and Green, B. F., Jr. (1950), A factor analysis of English readers. *Amer. Psychologist*, 5, 370 (Abstract).

Torr, D. V. (1952), A factor analysis of selected interest inventories. In J. W. French (1953a) (Abstract).

Tryon, R. C. (1939), *Cluster analysis: correlation profile and orthometric (factor) analysis for the isolation of unities in mind and personality.* Ann Arbor: Edwards Bros. 122 pp.

Tschechtelin, S. M. A. (1944), Factor analysis of children's personality rating scale. *J. Psychol.*, 18, 197-200.

Tucker, L. R. (1938), A method for finding the inverse of a matrix. *Psychometrika*, 3, 189-197.

Tucker, L. R. (1940a), The role of correlated factors in factor analysis. *Psychometrika*, 5, 141-152.

Tucker, L. R. (1940b), A matrix multiplier. *Psychometrika*, 5, 289-294.

Tucker, L. R. (1942), *The centroid method of factor analysis by punched cards.* Microfilm Negative No. 1623, Univ. of Chicago Libraries.

Tucker, L. R. (1944a), A semi-analytical method of factorial rotation to simple structure. *Psychometrika*, 9, 43-68.

Tucker, L. R. (1944b), The determination of successive principal components without computation of tables of residual correlation coefficients. *Psychometrika*, 9, 149-153.

Tucker, L. R. (1946), Simplified punched card methods in factor analysis. *Res. Forum.* New York: I. B. M. Corp., 9-19.

Tucker, L. R. (1951), A method of synthesis of factor analysis studies. *Personnel Research Section Research Report* No. 984, 120 pp.

Twedt, D. W. (1952), A multiple factor analysis of advertising readership. *J. appl. Psychol.,* **36,** 207-215.

Tyler, F. T. (1951), A factorial analysis of fifteen MMPI scales. *J. consult. Psychol.,* **15,** 451-456.

Ullman, J. (1944), The probability of convergence of an iterative process of inverting a matrix. *Ann. Math. Stat.,* **15,** 205-213.

Vernon, P. E. (1941), An analysis of the conception of morale. *Character and Personality,* **9,** 283-294.

Vernon, P. E. (1947), Psychological tests in the Royal Navy, Army, and A. T. S. *Occup. Psychol., Lond.,* **21,** 53-74.

Vernon, P. E. (1949a), Classifying high-grade occupational interests. *J. abnorm. soc. Psychol.,* **44,** 85-96.

Vernon, P. E. (1949b), The structure of practical abilities. *Occup. Psychol., Lond.,* **23,** 81-96.

Vernon, P. E. (1949c), Recent developments in the measurement of intelligence and special abilities. *Brit. med. Bull.,* **6,** 21-23.

Vernon, P. E., *et al.* (1949d), How many factors? (Unpublished memorandum.)

Vernon, P. E. (1950), An application of factorial analysis to the study of test items. *Brit. J. Psychol. Statist. Sect.,* **3,** 1-15.

Vernon, P. E. (1951), *The structure of human abilities.* New York: John Wiley & Sons. 160 pp.

Vernon, P. E., and Parry, J. B. (1949), *Personnel selection in the British forces.* London: Univ. of London Press.

Wade, T. L. (1952), *The Algebra of Vectors and Matrices.* Cambridge: Addison-Wesley.

Walker, K. F., Staines, R. J., and Kenna, J. C. (1943), P-tests and the concept of mental inertia. *Character & Personality,* **12,** 32-45.

Waugh, F. V., and Dwyer, P. S. (1945), Compact computation of the inverse of a matrix. *Amer. Math. Statist.,* **16,** 259-271.

Wedeck, J. (1947), The relationship between personality and psychological ability. *Brit. J. Psychol.,* **37,** 133-151.

Weinberg, D. (1945), Une experience de controle des methodes d'analyse factorielle. *C. R. Acad. Sci. Paris,* **220,** 214-216.

Wenger, M. A. (1942), The stability of measurement of autonomic balance. *Psychosom. Med.,* **4,** 94-95.

Wenger, M. A. (1943), An attempt to appraise individual differences in level of muscular tension. *J. exp. Psychol.,* **32,** 213-225.

Wenger, M. A. (1946), A factorial approach to psychophysiological relationships. *Amer. Psychologist,* 1, 454 (Abstract).

Wenger, M. A. (1948), Studies of autonomic balance in Army Air Force personnel. *Comp. Psychol. Monogr.,* 19, No. 4, 1-111.

Wenger, M. A., Holzinger, K. J., and Harman, H. H. (1948), The estimation of pupil ability by three factorial solutions. *Univ. Calif. Publ. Psychol.,* No. 8, 5, viii, 252 pp.

Wenger, M. A., and Voas, R. B. (1950), A new factor solution for Halstead's neuropsychological tests. *Amer. Psychologist,* 5, 468 (Abstract).

Wheeler, W. M., Little, K. B., and Lehner, G. F. J. (1951), The internal structure of the MMPI. *J. consult. Psychol.,* 15, 134-141.

Wherry, R. J. (1939), Factorial analysis of learning dynamics in animals. *J. comp. Psychol.,* 28, 263-272.

Wherry, R. J. (1940), A test by factorial analysis of Honzik's exteroceptive data. *J. comp. Psychol.,* 29, 75-95.

Wherry, R. J. (1941), Determination of the specific components of maze ability for Tryon's bright and dull rats by means of factorial analysis. *J. comp. Psychol.,* 32, 237-252.

Wherry, R. J. (1947), A factorial study of visual acuity, depth, and phoria measurements with three commercial screening devices. *Amer. Psychologist,* 2, 298 (Abstract).

Wherry, R. J. (1949), A new iterative method for correcting erroneous communality estimates in factor analysis. *Psychometrika,* 14, 231-241.

Wherry, R. J., Campbell, J. T., and Perloff, R. (1951), An empirical verification of the Wherry-Gaylord iterative factor analysis procedure. *Psychometrika,* 16, 67-74.

Wherry, R. J., and Fryer, D. H. (1949), Buddy ratings: popularity contest or leadership criteria? *Personnel Psychol.,* 2, 147-159.

Wherry, R. J., and Gaylord, R. H. (1943), The concept of test and item reliability in relation to factor pattern. *Psychometrika,* 8, 247-264.

Wherry, R. J., and Gaylord, R. H. (1944), Factor pattern of test items and tests as a function of the correlation coefficient: content, difficulty, and constant error factors. *Psychometrika,* 9, 237-244.

Whiteman, M., and Whiteman, D. B. (1949), The application of cluster analysis to the Wechsler-Bellevue scale. *Delaware St. med. J.,* 21, 174-176.

Williams, H. V. M. (1949), A P-technique study of personality factors in the psychosomatic areas. Unpublished Ph.D. dissertation, Univ. of Illinois.

Winch, R. F. (1947a), Heuristic and empirical typologies: a job for factor analysis. *Amer. sociol. Rev.,* 12, 68-75.

Winch, R. F. (1947b), Primary factors in a study of courtship. *Amer. sociol. Rev.,* 12, 658-666.

Winch, R. F. (1950), Some data bearing on the Oedipus hypothesis. *J. abnor. soc. Psychol.,* 45, 481-489.

Wing, H. D. (1941), A factorial study of musical tests. *Brit. J. Psychol.,* 31, 341-355.

Winne, J. F. (1950), Common and unique factor patterns in normals and neurotics. *Amer. Psychologist,* 5, 325 (Abstract).

Wittenborn, J. R. (1943), Factorial equations for tests of attention. *Psychometrika,* 8, 19-35.

Wittenborn, J. R. (1945), Mechanical ability, its nature and measurement. I. An analysis of the variables employed in the preliminary Minnesota experiment. II. Manual dexterity. *Educ. psychol. Measmt.,* 5, 241-260, 395-409.

Wittenborn, J. R. (1949), Factor analysis of discrete responses to the Rorschach ink blots. *J. consult. Psychol.,* 13, 335-340.

Wittenborn, J. R. (1950a), A factor analysis of Rorschach scoring categories. *J. consult. Psychol.,* 14, 261-267.

Wittenborn, J. R. (1950b), Level of mental health as a factor in the implications of Rorschach scores. *J. consult. Psychol.,* 14, 469-472.

Wittenborn, J. R. (1951), Symptom patterns in a group of mental hospital patients. *J. consult. Psychol.,* 15, 290-310.

Wittenborn, J. R., Bell, E. G., and Lesser, C. S. (1951), Symptom patterns among organic patients of advanced age. *J. clin. Psychol.,* 7, 328-331.

Wittenborn, J. R., and Holzberg, J. D. (1951), The generality of psychiatric syndromes. *J. consult. Psychol.,* 15, 372-380.

Wittenborn, J. R., and Larsen, R. P. (1944), A factorial study of achievement in college German. *J. educ. Psychol.,* 35, 39-48.

Wittenborn, J. R., Mandler, G., and Waterhouse, I. K. (1951), Symptom patterns in youthful mental hospital patients. *J. clin. Psychol.,* 7, 323-327.

Wolfle, D. (1940), Factor analysis to 1940. *Psychometric Monogr.,* No. 3, 69 pp.

Wolfle, D. (1942), Factor analysis in the study of personality. *J. abnorm. soc. Psychol.,* 37, 393-397.

Woodrow, H. (1938), The relation between abilities and improvement with practice. *J. educ. Psychol., 29,* 215-230.

Woodrow, H. (1939), The common factors in fifty-two mental tests. *Psychometrika, 4,* 99-108.

Woodrow, H. (1940), Interrelationships of measures of learning. *J. Psychol., 10,* 49-73.

Woodrow, H. (1946), The ability to learn. *Psychol. Rev., 53,* 147-158.

Worcester, D. A. (1948), Naming psychological factors. *Amer. Psychologist, 3,* 357 (Abstract).

Wrigley, C. (1952), The predication of a complex aptitude. *Brit. J. Psychol. Statist. Sect., 5,* 93-104.

Wrigley, C., and Neuhaus, J. O. (1952), A re-factorization of the Burt-Pearson matrix with the Ordvac Electronic computer. *Brit. J. Psychol. Statist. Sect., 5,* 105-108.

Yela, M. (1949a), Application of the concept of simple structure to Alexander's data. *Psychometrika, 14,* 121-135.

Yela, M. (1949b), La tecnica del analisis factorial. *Rev. Psicol. gen. apl., Madrid, 4,* 121-140, 317-324, 763-780.

Young, G. (1941), Maximum likelihood estimation and factor analysis. *Psychometrika, 6,* 49-53.

Young, G., and Householder, A. S. (1940), Factorial invariance and significance. *Psychometrika, 5,* 47-56.

Zachert, V. (1951), A factor analysis of vision tests. *Amer. J. Optom., 28,* 405-416.

Zachert, V. (1952), Factor analysis of the Army, Navy, and Air Force classification batteries. *H.R.R.C. Research Bulletin* 52-12.

Zachert, V., and Friedman, G. (1952), Factorial comparisons of two air-crew classification batteries with and without the variable of previous flying experience. *H.R.R.C. Research Bulletin* 52-16.

Zachert, V., and Friedman, G. (1953), The stability of the factorial pattern of aircrew classification tests in four analyses. *Psychometrika, 18,* 219-224.

Zachert, V., and Shibe, E. (1951), Comparison of the USES general Aptitude Test Battery and the Airman Classification Battery. *H.R.R.C. Research Note Pers.* 51-4.

Zagorski, H. J. (1951), A factor study of self-evaluation. Unpublished Ph.D. dissertation. Univ. of Pittsburgh.

Zimmerman, W. S. (1946), A simple graphical method for orthogonal rotation of axes. *Psychometrika, 11,* 51-55.

Zimmerman, W. S. (1949), The isolation, definition, and measurement

of spatial and visualization abilities.   Ph.D., Univ. So. Calif.
(Thesis).

Zimmerman, W. S. (1953a), A revised orthogonal rotational solution
for Thurstone's Primary Mental Abilities test battery.   *Psychometrika,* **18,** 77-94.

Zimmerman, W. S. (1953b), A note on the recognition and interpretation of composite factors.   *Psych. Bull.,* **50,** 387-389.

ANSWERS TO PROBLEMS [1]

CHAPTER 2

1. Two clusters

$$B (7, 8, 3, 6) = 2.274$$
$$B (1, 2, 4, 5) = 2.076$$

2. Graph reveals the same two clusters as were obtained in Problem 1.

CHAPTER 3

1. $$\begin{Vmatrix} .57 & .66 & .60 \\ .33 & .29 & .20 \\ .68 & .89 & .75 \end{Vmatrix}$$

C

2. $$\begin{Vmatrix} .461 & 2.000 & -.769 \\ 1.333 & -2.000 & .000 \\ -1.589 & 2.000 & 1.538 \end{Vmatrix}$$

A^{-1}

6.

Test	Factor		h^2
	I_1	II_1	
1	.6922	-.2024	.52
2	.8454	-.0738	.72
3	2203	-.7291	.58
4	-.1258	-.6279	.41

CHAPTER 4

1. .66
2. Test 2
3. .44

---

[1] Since there are no unique answers to most factor analysis problems, these values are to be regarded as suggested solutions.

4.

Variables	Correlations			
	1	2	3	4
1	(.66)	.52	.46	.41
2	.52	(.56)	.38	.20
3	.46	.38	(.85)	.75
4	.41	.20	.75	(.84)

5. Test 3

6. Increase the loading on factor II and decrease the loading on factor IV.

CHAPTER 5

1. Two factors as follows:

Test	Factor	
	I	II
1	.7616	.0000
2	.8272	.3549
3	.6040	−.3935
4	.6696	−.0392
5	.4596	.1967
6	.2363	−.5516
7	.5909	−.6165
8	.3151	−.7356

3. A clockwise rotation of 66° 50′ gives the following loadings:

Test	Factor		h^2
	I	II	
1	.30	.70	.58
2	.00	.90	.81
3	.60	.40	.52
4	.30	.60	.45
5	.00	.50	.25
6	.60	.00	.36
7	.80	.30	.73
8	.80	.00	.64

4. The algebraically derived values should agree closely with those obtained graphically.

5. The centroid loadings, using the highest correlation or residual correlation in each column as an estimate of the communality, are as follows:

Test	Factor		h^2
	I	II	
1	.713	.317	.609
2	.595	.574	.684
3	.720	−.165	.546
4	.651	.247	.485
5	.393	.385	.303
6	.447	−.448	.401
7	.755	−.365	.703
8	.562	−.555	.624

Tucker's phi for factor II is .158 and for factor III it is .778. The factoring should be repeated once or twice for this small matrix to stabilize the communalities.

6.

Test	Centroid Factor			h^2
	I	II	III	
1	.458	.285	.255	.342
2	.465	.507	.266	.544
3	.483	.329	.580	.677
4	.550	.400	−.406	.627
5	.691	.176	−.462	.722
6	.714	.444	−.225	.707
7	.649	−.425	.150	.758
8	.490	−.673	−.089	.701
9	.675	−.402	.066	.622
10	.483	−.656	−.172	.692

CHAPTER 6

1.

V-Matrix		
Variable	Factor	
	I	II
1	.762	.462
2	.817	.218
3	.520	.698
4	.669	.438
5	.510	.122
6	.130	.590
7	.465	.828
8	.172	.760

F-Matrix $\left[= V\left(F'_{mp} \right)^{-1} \right]$

Variable	Factor	
	I	II
1	.762	.136
2	.817	−.164
3	.520	.520
4	.669	.155
5	.510	−.119
6	.130	.598
7	.465	.692
8	.172	.764

T-Matrix			
	I	II	w
I	7.64	3.57	.361
II	3.57	8.28	.347

U-Matrix		
	I	II
I	2.76	1.29
II	1.24	2.88

R_{pq}		
	I	II
I	1.000	.448
II	.448	1.000

F_{pm}		
	I	II
I	1.000	.000
II	.448	.894

F_{pm}^{-1}		
	I	II
I	1.000	.000
II	−.500	1.120

$(F'_{mp})^{-1}$		
	I	II
I	1.00	−.50
II	.00	1.12

2.

Variable	Factor		h^2
	I	II	
3	.7344	−.0888	.547
4	.5435	−.3706	.433
7	.8260	.1275	.699
8	.7081	.3867	.651

CHAPTER 7

1.

Test	Rotated Factors		h^2
	I	II	
1	.29	.73	.62
2	.02	.85	.72
3	.62	.39	.54
4	.29	.63	.48
5	−.02	.53	.28
6	.61	−.01	.37
7	.81	.28	.73
8	.80	.00	.64

2. The two sets of loadings agree closely.

3.

Test	Rotated Factor		
	I	II	III
1	.12	.22	.53
2	−.03	.31	.67
3	.11	−.04	.84
4	.11	.77	.17
5	.36	.80	.07
6	.19	.72	.44
7	.76	.01	.22
8	.82	−.14	−.04
9	.76	.20	.08
10	.80	.01	−.18

CHAPTER 8

2.

Test	Rotated Factor		
	I	II	III
1	.53	.35	.00
2	.65	.35	-.17
3	.85	.17	-.08
4	.16	.80	.08
5	.08	.84	.30
6	.43	.82	.10
7	31	16	69
8	.07	-.04	.81
9	.29	.31	.73
10	-.08	.08	.82

T'	I	II	III
I	.564	.690	.586
II	.389	.504	-.792
III	.728	-.525	-.170

T T'	I	II	III
I	1.00		
II	.20	1.00	
III	-.10	.10	1.00

CHAPTER 9

1. The rotated factors are identified as a numerical-facility factor (with tests 1, 2, and 3 loaded on it), a verbal-comprehension factor (with tests 4, 5, and 6), and an academic-achievement factor in educational psychology (with tests 7, 8, 9, and 10).

Index

Abilities, 2, 11, 111
Achievement factors, 197
Adjutant General's Office, 206
Analysis of variance, 3
Andree, R. V., 28
Aptitude factors, 197
Assumptions of factor analysis, 44f.
  additive, 46
  correlations due to common factors, 47
Attention, 11
Axes
  Cartesian, 194
  coordinate, 38, 41
  long, 123
  oblique, 107
  primary, 137, 140, 192, 193
  reference, 38
  simple, 146, 192

B-coefficient, 13-16
Basic equation of factor analysis, 44 (footnote), 48
Bi-factor method, 10, 11, 109
Bipolar
  factors, 111
  simple structure, 112
Brannan, M., 206
Burt, C., 104, 207, 208

C-matrix, 177
Campbell, J. T., 219
Carroll, J. B., 155, 208
Cartesian axes, 194

Categories
  classificatory, 1
  diagnostic, 2
Cattell, A. K. S., 186
Cattell, R. B., 13, 113, 186, 191, 198
Centroid formula for estimating communality, 166
Centroid method of factoring, 59f.
  computation of first loadings, 61
  eleven-variable example, 71f.
  general rules for signs of loadings, 66
  reflection of variables, 74
  residual correlation matrix, 73
Checks
  on centroid loadings, 68, 84
  for diagonal loadings, 58
  importance of, 62
  on oblique simple structure loadings, 147
  for reflection, 65
  on rotated factor loadings, 127
  on rotation, 117
  for transformation matrix, 126
Chi-square test for sufficient factors, 206
Clinical psychology, 2, 186
Cluster analysis, 12-17
  comparison with factor analysis, 12
  methods of, 13
  purposes of, 12, 13
  steps in computation, 14, 15
Clusters of test vectors, 193

Columbia University, 206
Common
  factors, 68
  traits, 2
  variance, 2, 45, 47
Communality, 9, 35, 40, 41 (footnote)
  defined, 47, 51
  estimated by centroid method, 166
  estimated by highest r, 61
  re-estimated, 63
  sign of, 61
Computation, mechanical aids to, 205
Conditioned response, 156
Conditions of administration, 199
Configuration
  bipolar simple structure, 112
  complete triangular, 112
  incomplete triangular, 113
  isolated constellations, 111
  of test vectors, 38, 41, 107, 178
Coombs' criterion, 80
Correlation coefficients
  geometrical representation of, 31, 32, 42
  interpretation of, 4
  part-whole, 169
  reproduced from factor loadings, 35, 37, 48, 49
  spurious, 169, 201
  tetrachoric, 179, 201
  types of, 201
Correlation of persons, 176
Correlations between tests calculated from factor loadings, 11
Cosines of angles, 177
Cowles, J. T., 212 (footnote)
Cowles-Crout method, 213 (footnote)
Crawford, I., 206
Criteria for rotation
  Cattell's, 113
  parallel proportional profiles, 114
  positive manifold, 110
  simple structure, 109

Criteria for rotation (Cont.)
  simultaneous simple structure, 114
Criteria for sufficient factors, 69, 77
  Chi-square test, 206
  Coombs' criterion, 80
  Humphrey's rule, 79
  Tucker's phi, 77
Criterion
  measures, 162, 208
  variables, 48
Cross-products of factor loadings, 11, 35, 37, 48, 49
Cureton, E. E., 106

D-matrix, 124
Dailey, J. T., 165
Dash, G. H., 213 (footnote)
Deemer, W. L., 28
Degan, J. W., 176
Determinants
  defined, 21
  evaluation of, 21
  of a matrix, 21
  minors of, 21
Diagonal matrix, 24, 124
Diagonal method of factoring, 52f.
  numerical example, 52f.
  steps in, 57, 58
Difficulty level, 200, 207
Dimensions, number of, 2
Direct rotation, 140, 142, 147, 165-169
Dwyer, P. S., 28, 209
Dynamics of an individual, 186

Educational Testing Service, 199
Elements of a matrix, 18, 26
Electronic
  matrix multiplication, 206
  plotting, 206
Eleven-variable example
  analysis by centroid method, 69
  description of tests for, 69
  direct rotation, 142
  first centroid factor loadings, 69
  interpretation of factors, 149
  reflection of variables, 74

Eleven-variable example (Cont.)
   residual correlation matrix, 73
   rotation by graphical method, 114
   second centroid factor loadings, 73, 75
   transformation matrix, 121
Errors in rotation, 117
Error variance, 3, 45
Example, eleven-variable, *see* Eleven-variable example
Experimental
   conditions, 3
   dependence, 201
   design, 202
Extended factor loadings, 140
Extended vectors, 167

F-matrix, 94
Factor
   general-intellective, 157
   general speed, 202
   induction, 159
   mechanical experience, 151, 163
   numerical, 207
   perceptual speed, 150, 159, 163, 200
   reasoning, 200
   socio-economic background, 163
   spatial orientation, 151
   spatial relations, 151
   verbal, 150, 163
   visualization, 159, 163
Factors
   achievement, 197
   aptitude, 197
   bipolar, 111
   as classificatory categories, 1
   common, 44, 68
   established, 197
   frequently identified, 196
   as functional unities, 196
   general, 7, 8, 9, 109
   as hypothetical constructs, 196
   independent, 44
   interpretation of, 149, 197, 207
   as intervening variables, 196
   invariant, 106, 197
   maximum number, 69

Factors (Cont.)
   occasion, 204
   overdetermination of, 69
   person, 204
   personality, 11, 165, 198, 199
   as statistically derived unities, 197
   tentative, 197
   transient, 196
Factor analysis
   additive, 46
   assumptions in, 44f.
   basic equation of, 48 (footnote)
   experimental designs in, 202
   limitations of, 4
   major application of, 4
   as mathematical model, 2
   of nonmetric data, 207
   obverse, 176, 179, 203
   planning of, 207
      purposes of, 1, 2, 4, 6, 35
   skill needed for, 4
Factor-estimation matrix, 209
Factor loadings
   efficient estimates of, 205
   estimated by iteration, 219
   estimated for tests not in original analysis, 164, 209
   influences on, 199
   shifts in, 197
Factor matrix, 34
Factor scores
   estimation of, 204
   univocal, 205
Factorial
   axis, 42
   structure, 42
Factoring methods
   centroid, 57f.
   diagonal, 52f.
   group-centroid, 104
   grouping, 13
   maximum-likelihood, 104, 205
   multiple group, 13, 52, 87f., 166
   nonlinear, 3
   principal-axes, 59, 99f.
   simple summation, 104
Fix, E., 155

French, J. W., 155, 197, 198, 199, 199 (footnote)
Fruchter, B., 28, 162, 202
Functional unities, 197

G-factor, 7-9, 109, 172
formula for, 9
nonunitariness of, 175
General Electric Co., 206
General factor, 10, 11
General-intellective factor, 7, 157, 173
Geometrical
interpretation of correlation coefficients, 31, 32, 42
interpretation of rank of a matrix, 32
representation of centroid axes, 59, 60
Graphical representation of
one plane at a time, 38-41
table of intercorrelations, 32
three-dimensional example, 35
two-dimensional example, 33
Graphical rotation of axes
advantageous configuration for, 117
Zimmerman's method, 115
Group factors, 10, 11
Guilford, J. P., 50, 149, 169, 197, 201, 202, 205

h², *see* Communality
Hall, D. M., 206
Harman, H. H., 13, 14 (footnote), 193, 194
Harris, C. W., 93, 140, 142, 193
Hierarchy, 8
Holley, J. W., 66
Holzinger, K. J., 10, 11, 13, 14 (footnote), 109, 193, 194
Homogeneous
populations, 207
tests, 200
Hotelling, H., 206
Hsu, E. H., 179
Humphreys, L. G., 156
Humphreys' rule, 79
Hyperplane, 110, 193, 194

IBM method
for matrix multiplication, 206
for principal-axes method, 205
Identity matrix, 24, 27, 195
Imagination, 1, 11
Individual differences, 1, 3, 203
Intelligence, 1, 3
Intercorrelation
pattern of, 2
of test scores, 2
Interpretation of factors, 149, 197, 207
by common element of tests, 11
difficulties in, 177
by inferring underlying traits, 2
tentative nature of, 4
in terms of traits, 2
Intra-class phi coefficients, 176
Intra-individual differences, 186, 203
Invariant factors, 106
Inventories
interest, 201
personality, 201
Inverse matrix, 26, 166
computation of, 28
conditions for, 27 (footnote)
of a triangular matrix, 94
Inverse factor analysis, *see* Obverse factor analysis
Inverted factor analysis, *see* Obverse factor analysis
Ipsative measurement, 203
Isolated constellations, 111
Item analysis, 208
Iterative method of factoring, 219

Jeffress, L. A., 169, 200
Judgment, 1

Kestelman, H., 44 (footnote)
Knoell, D. M., 193

L-matrix, 123
Lambda (Λ) matrix, 39, 133, 137 (footnote), 177
Lawley, D. N., 104, 205
Lazarsfeld, P. F., 208

Learning, studies of, 204
Least-squares solution, 59
Linear dependence, 33, 201
Long vectors, 123, 142

Matrix
  algebra, 18, 27, 27 (footnote)
  defined, 18
  determinant of, 21
  diagonal, 24, 124
  element of, 18, 24
  factor, 34, 41, 42
  factor estimation, 209
  geometrical interpretation of, 32
  geometry, 31
  I-, 24
  identity, 24, 195
  inverse, 26, 166
  multiplication, 24-26, 206
  non-singular, 27 (footnote)
  normalized, 124
  order of, 19
  of rank 1, 107
  rank of, 22, 32, 42
  square, 23
  symmetric, 23
  theory, 18
  transpose of, 19
  triangular, 94
  unidimensional, 107
Maximum-likelihood method, 205
McNemar, Q., 85
Measures
  a priori, 1
  continuous, 4
  interrelationships of, 1
  nature of, 1
Memory factor, 1
Mental organization, 3
Mental testing, 1
Michael, W. B., 202, 205
Minnesota Multiphasic Personality Inventory, 166
Mooney Problem Check List, 165
Moore, T. V., 179
Morris, C. M., 157
Mosier, C. I., 84, 209

Multiple correlation, 205
  by the Cowles-Crout method, 213
Multiple-factor theory, 109, 172
Multiple-group method of factoring, 13, 52, 166
  estimation of communalities, 88
  numerical example, 88
  orthogonal loadings, 98
  S-matrix, 92
  T-matrix, 92
  V-matrix, 92
Multiplication of matrices, 24-26
  column-by-column rule, 26 (footnote)
  row-by-column rule, 26, 26 (footnote)
  row-by-row rule, 26 (footnote)

Near-zero loadings, 118
  maximization of, 193
Neuhaus, J. O., 206, 208
Nonmetric data, 207
Normal to plane or hyperplane, 192, 193
Normalized matrix, 124

O-technique, 202, 203, 204
Oblique
  axes, 107
  factor loadings, 92
  solution, 34 (footnote), 132, 196
Obverse factor analysis, 176, 179, 203
Orthogonal
  axes, 106
  solution, 109, 132, 194, 195
  vectors, 31, 34
Overdetermination of factors, 69

P-matrix, 144
P-technique, 176, 186, 202, 203
Parallel proportional profiles, 114
Pattern values, 194
Peatman, J. G., 13
Perloff, R., 219
Personality
  P-technique in the study of, 186

Personality (Cont.)
  prepsychotic traits, 179
Personality factors, 11, 198, 199
  in student teaching, 165
Phi-coefficients, intra-class, 176
Physiological tests, 186
Pitch discrimination, 169
Planes
  normals to, 192, 193
  traces of, 192
Populations
  adolescent, 197
  adult, 197
Positive manifold, 110, 118
  defined, 42
Prepsychotic personality traits,
  179
Primary axes, 142, 143, 144
  cosines of angular separations,
  137
  transformation matrix for, 137
Primary structure, 140, 165
Principal diagonal, 23, 24
  values in, 51
Principal-axes method of factoring, 59
  first factor loadings, 102
  IBM extraction for, 205
  numerical example, 99
Projections of test vectors, 39, 59
  oblique, 193
  perpendicular, 193
Projective geometry, 130
Proportionality, criterion of, 7, 11
Psycho-galvanic reflex, 189

Q-technique, 176, 202
Questionnaires, 191

R$_{pq}$-matrix, 93
R-technique, 176, 202
Rank of a matrix, 22, 32, 42
  minimized, 52
Ratings, 191
Reasoning ability, 2
Reasoning tests, second-order anal-
  ysis of, 172
Reference
  axes, rotation of, 38

Reference (Cont.)
  factor, 42, 44
  frame, 38, 41, 42, 194
  tests, 199
  variable, 1, 109
  vector, 42, 107
Reflection
  of axes, checks for, 65
  goal of, 60
  signs of correlations in, 66
  steps in, 64
  of test vectors, 42, 60, 62, 64
  of variables, 74
Reliability
  coefficient, 47, 51
  as diagonal entry, 51
  effect on factor loadings, 202
Reporting a factorial study, 153
Reproduction of correlations
  from cross products, 35, 37, 48
  (footnote)
  from factor loadings, 35, 37, 48
Research programs, proper order
  for, 2
Residual correlations, 59, 73
  centroid-factor, 59, 62, 67
  computation of, 62-63
  geometrical interpretation of,
  59
  second and subsequent, 67
Reversals, sign (*see also* Reflection), 42, 59
Rhymer, R. M., 186
Rimoldi, H. J. A., 173
Rorschach test, 201
Rotated factor loadings
  calculation of, 127
  checks on, 127
Rotation of axes, 38, 106
  analytical, 41, 207
  checks for, 117, 120
  clockwise, 39
  counterclockwise, 39
  errors in, 117
  graphical, 41, 114
  maximizing zero loadings, 118
  purposes of, 106
  transformation matrix for, 121
  Zimmerman's method, 115

Rotation methods
  analytical, 41, 207
  direct-rotation, 140, 167
  graphical, 41, 114
  single-plane, 133
Royce, J. R., 2, 155

S-factors, 7, 8
S-matrix
  in multiple-group method, 92
  in rotation, 122
S-technique, 202, 204, 208
Samples
  adolescent, 197
  adult, 197
  selection of, 199
Saunders, D. R., 208
Scalar product, 31, 42
Schmid, J., 93, 165
Schweiker, R. F., 155
Scores
  rights, 202
  standard, 44, 194
  test, intercorrelation of, 1, 2
  wrongs, 202
Scoring formulas, 201, 202
Second-order analysis, 196
  of Reasoning Tests, 172
Significance
  of group differences, 3
  tests of, 205
Signs
  of first centroid loadings, 62
  in computation of second cen-
    troid loadings, 63
  of correlations in reflection, 66
  general rules in centroid
    method, 66
Simple axes, 146, 192
Simple structure, 109, 110, 119,
    140, 193, 196
  bipolar, 111
  criteria for, 110
  simultaneous, 114
  without positive manifold, 112
Single-plane method of rotation,
    133
Sources of variance, 2

Spearman, C., 6, 7, 8, 9, 10, 107,
    109, 172
Specific
  factors, 9
  variance, 45, 47
Speed of working, 5
Speeded scores, 200, 207
Spherical right triangle, 111
Stafford, J. W., 179
Standard scores, 44, 194
Structure
  factorial, 42
  primary, *see* Primary structure
  simple, *see* Simple structure
  values, 144
Suppression of secondary factors,
    205
Supreme Court voting records
    analysis, 176

T-matrix
  in multiple-group method, 92
  in rotation, 137, 144
T-technique, 202, 204, 208
Test
  scores, intercorrelation of, 1, 2
  space, 2
Tests
  addition, 5
  anchor, 199
  arithmetic reasoning, 4, 5
  clerical aptitude, 1
  cognitive, 3
  description of in eleven-variable
    example, 69-72
  general intelligence, 1
  homogeneous, 200
  marker, 199
  mechanical aptitude, 1
  medical aptitude, 1
  physiological, 186
  reading comprehension, 4, 5
  reference, 199
  speeded, 202
  tie-in, 199
Test vectors
  angular separations of, 31, 32,
    42
  clusters of, 193

Test vectors (Cont.)
  configuration of, 38, 41, 107
  length of, 42
Tetrachoric correlations, 179
Tetrads
  equations for, 7
  number of, 7
Thomson, G. H. (Preface)
Thurstone, L. L. (Preface), 28, 31
  (footnote), 59, 85, 88, 104,
  109, 133, 137, 176, 193, 200,
  201, 208
Time limits, 201
Trace of plane, 192
Traits
  common, 2
  hypothetical, 3
  measured by tests, 4
  temperament, 111
  trait-concepts, 1
  underlying, 2
Transformation matrix, 39
  calculation of, 121
  checks on, 126
  for primary axes, 137
Transpose matrix, 19
  defined, 19
Triangular configuration, 112
Triangular matrix inverse, 94
Tryon, R. C., 13, 160
Tucker, L. R., 28, 206, 207
Tucker's phi, 77
Two-factor theory, 6-8
  schematic representation of, 8

U-matrix, 92
Unidimensional matrix, 107
Unique set of factor loadings, 44
Uniqueness defined, 47
Univocal factor scores, 205

V-matrix, 92, 133, 146, 177
Validity coefficient, 48

Variables
  background, 3
  basic, 1
  minimum number for common
    factors, 68
  pure, 12
  reference, 1, 109, 199
  tie-in, 199
Variance
  basic sources of, 2
  common, 2, 45, 47
  common sources of, 3
  error, 3, 45
  maximization of desired, 205
  minimization of undesired, 205
  reliable, 47
  specific, 32 (footnote), 45, 47
  types of, 45
Vectors
  defined, 31
  extended, 167
  long, 123, 142
  null, 59
  orthogonal, 31, 34
  reference, 42, 107
  test, 107
Verbal ability, 2
Vernon, P. E., 77, 158

Washburne Social Adjustment
  Inventory, 165
Watson Scientific Computing Lab-
  oratory, 206
Welker, E. L., 206
Wherry, R. J., 159, 204, 219
Wolfle, D., 104, 221
Wrigley, C., 208

Zero loadings, maximizing by rotation, 118
Zimmerman, W. S., 115